Example	Common Name	IUPAC Name
$CH_3CH_2C(=O)-OH$	propionic acid	propanoic acid
$CH_3-C_6H_4-SO_3H$		n-toluenesulfonic acid
$CH_3CH_2-C(=O)-NH_2$	propionamide	propanamide
CH_3CH_2-CN	ethyl cyanide	propanenitrile
$CH_3CH_2-C(=O)-O-CH_3$	methyl propionate	methyl propanoate
$CH_3CH_2-C(=O)-Cl$	propionyl chloride	propanoyl chloride
CH_3CH_2CHO	propionaldehyde	propanal
$CH_3CH_2CH_2-C(=O)-CH_2CH_3$	ethyl n-propyl ketone	3-hexanone
$CH_3CH_2CH_2-NH_2$	n-propylamine	1-aminopropane
$CH_3CH_2CH_2-N(H)-CH_3$	methyl n-propyl-amine	N-methyl-1-aminopropane

FUNDAMENTAL
ORGANIC CHEMISTRY

Charles F. H. Allen *(American, 1895–). After receiving his doctorate from Harvard under one of the first important American organic chemists, E. P. Kohler, Allen taught at McGill University. It was there that he began to develop the most important carbonyl reagent yet known—2,4-dinitrophenyl-hydrazine. Of his numerous interests in synthetic organic chemistry two have occupied his attention over a long period of time: the synthesis of bridged carbonyl compounds, e.g.,*

and the products of the Michael reaction, e.g.,

After a lifetime of impressive contributions to synthetic organic chemistry from the Eastman Kodak Laboratories, Allen has now "retired" to continue his work, especially the development of qualitative organic reagents and studies of the thermal reversibility of the Michael reaction.

PRENTICE-HALL INTERNATIONAL, INC., *London*
PRENTICE-HALL OF AUSTRALIA, PTY. LTD., *Sydney*
PRENTICE-HALL OF CANADA, LTD., *Toronto*
PRENTICE-HALL OF INDIA PRIVATE LIMITED, *New Delhi*
PRENTICE-HALL OF JAPAN, INC., *Tokyo*

FUNDAMENTAL
ORGANIC CHEMISTRY

K. Thomas Finley

Senior Research Chemist, Eastman Kodak Company
Associate Lecturer, University of Rochester

James Wilson, Jr.

Associate Professor
Rochester Institute of Technology

PRENTICE-HALL, INC., ENGLEWOOD CLIFFS, NEW JERSEY

13-341412-4

Library of Congress Catalog Card Number: 75-112912

Printed in the United States of America

Current printing (last number):

10 9 8 7 6 5 4 3 2 1

This book is dedicated to

CHARLES F. H. ALLEN

whose example of hard and thoughtful work
has been an inspiration to the authors.

Preface

Fundamental Organic Chemistry was written to help students benefit from, and enjoy their brief contact with, this scientific discipline. We believe that this goal can best be reached if we try to impart a feeling of the way an organic chemist thinks and works. Naturally, a certain amount of factual knowledge must be mastered; but memorization will take second place to concepts and their application. Organic chemistry is so closely related to our everyday lives in this technical age that no truly educated person can afford to remain ignorant of it.

Inasmuch as the usual course for which this text is designed is two quarters or one semester in length, severe limits must be placed on the breadth and depth of the treatment. In general, we have favored a more detailed examination of a few topics. To accomplish this goal, it has been necessary to greatly reduce the number of reactions presented and to eliminate certain functional groups from consideration. Every effort has been made to include reactions which are actually used by today's organic chemist. However, we have tried to give a proper historical perspective. These considerations have been applied to the selection of ideas and concepts as well as compounds and reactions.

The bulk of the text is arranged along the traditional functional group lines. However, at the beginning we have presented chapters dealing with bonding, structure, stereochemistry, and reaction mechanisms. The subject of mechanisms, in both theory and experiment, is first treated in general terms, and then applied to specific examples as they are encountered.

The most distinctive feature of *Fundamental Organic Chemistry* is its emphasis on qualitative organic analysis. There is general agreement that analysis is a useful technique for the education of chemists, but it appears that its use in non-major courses is more limited. Our experience indicates that including a reasonable amount of wet organic analysis serves both to clarify the material and to stimulate the student's interest. In those courses which have a laboratory, the analytical approach takes on added importance. We have attempted to balance the classical analytical chemistry with an introduction to instrumental methods and a discussion of the synthetic aspects of organic chemistry.

In mastering this subject, there is no substitute for making use of the material. We have included a substantial number of problems which are widely varied both in style and difficulty. At the end of each chapter are problems arranged roughly in order af increasing difficulty. Many of these exercises are simply routine aids in the study of the topics treated in that chapter. However, there are also some problems which require understanding and thoughtful application of the material and in some cases further reading of later chapters and the Suggested Additional Readings. We use this technique to encourage independent study. If we are successful, the students will develop a habit which will be very useful to them in their professional lives.

In keeping with the analytical emphasis, we have included many "roadmap" problems. For the purpose of writing interesting problems of this type, without going to a heavily spectroscopic treatment, it has been necessary to slightly distort the present-day importance of certain tests and reactions as analytical methods. The modern organic chemist might take exception to classifying compounds by solubility and functional group reactions. We agree that infrared and nuclear magnetic resonance spectroscopy are much more frequently used; (see Appendix II) however, the gain is in terms of stressing the physical and chemical properties of the compounds.

As aids to the study of organic chemistry, we have included lists of Suggested Additional Readings with each chapter. These sources are subdivided by the major concepts treated in that chapter and include standard texts, advanced texts, and a limited amount of original and review literature. The complete book references are given in the bibliography. Important terms first appear in boldface. They are defined and illustrated at that point. For reference, a glossary is also included. Each chapter includes a very brief summary of significant concepts. The summaries are designed to assist the student, not to replace careful reading and individually prepared outlines. Other aids are given in appendices. There are worked examples of analytical and synthetic problems in Appendices I and III. Finally, we have provided the answers to the boldface problems so that the student may check his progress.

A number of people have made very significant contributions to *Fundamental Organic Chemistry*. We are especially indebted to Professors Norman J. Juster (Pasadena City College), Kenneth L. Marsi (California State College at Long Beach), and William H. Saunders, Jr. (University of Rochester) for their careful reading of the entire manuscript and for many thoughtful and stimulating comments. The Photographic Research Staff of the Eastman Kodak Research Laboratories have produced the photographs of molecular models and scientists. Mr. Albert A. Belskie and the Editorial Staff of Prentice-Hall have worked very hard in bringing this text to completion. Finally, we wish to express our very great appreciation to our wives and families. They have endured many long evenings and weekends of our struggles with writing and rewriting.

K. Thomas Finley
James Wilson, Jr.

Rochester, New York

Contents

1

The Carbon Atom

The fact that you are taking this course in chemistry indicates that your major field of professional interest is one which is either closely related to this science or else depends on it for a substantial portion of its methods and materials. If this subject is approached as one which a knowledgeable member of your field of endeavor should appreciate, you will find that it is a logical presentation of scientific fact and that you will gain not only from the specific information, but from the methods of attacking and solving problems. Later, as you enter your profession, you will be surprised to find how many problems, completely unrelated in detail, can be usefully approached by these same routes.

This introduction gives you some indication of why you should be taking this course and what you can expect to gain from it. Now, it is only fair to warn you about something you should not expect to obtain. Many excellent students with the best of intentions approach organic chemistry with the hope and desire of learning its special applications to their fields of interest.

There is nothing wrong with this approach in theory. However, in practice, it is analogous to wanting to read Homer in the original without having studied Greek grammar. No one would question the desirability of reading the original Homer or of understanding the organic chemistry of your special field of interest, but there is a prerequisite. For our purposes, this requirement is a sound knowledge of the fundamentals of the science of organic chemistry, which can and should be followed by the application and extension of this knowledge to related fields. This second step may take the form of additional courses, independent reading, practical experience, or most probably a combination of all three. Whatever the method, it will depend on a solid foundation, which is all that you should expect from this course.

1.2
ORGANIC CHEMISTRY BEGINS

You have studied general introductory chemistry, which was principally inorganic and ionic in nature. With this background the following problem should be no challenge to you. Suppose you were instructed to describe the products formed when an aqueous solution of ammonium chloride is mixed with an aqueous solution of silver cyanate. Your first thought would be to compare it with the textbook example of solutions of sodium chloride and silver nitrate and to write the double decomposition equations for each.

$$Na^+ + Cl^- + Ag^+ + NO_3^- \rightleftharpoons Na^+ + NO_3^- + AgCl(s)\downarrow$$

$$NH_4^+ + Cl^- + Ag^+ + CNO^- \rightleftharpoons NH_4^+ + CNO^- + AgCl(s)\downarrow$$

From this analysis it is easy to see that the very slightly soluble silver chloride would precipitate and an aqueous solution of ammonium cyanate would remain. So far, so good.

Now what would happen if after removing the silver chloride you evaporated the remaining solution to dryness? Just as you would find the solid salt sodium nitrate remaining in the first example, the second reaction should result in the formation of crystals of ammonium cyanate. This time you would be wrong—your analogy would have misled you. It is true that a white crystalline solid would be formed, and even that its formula would be CH_4N_2O, but it would not be a salt, and it would show none of the characteristics of ammonium cyanate. If you were persistent enough, you would discover that you had obtained urea, a well-known by-product of metabolic processes.

The synthesis of urea today is part of a multimillion dollar industry, producing a useful agricultural chemical and a starting material for a very important class of plastics. In 1828, Friedrich Wöhler, a young chemist, published the results of his attempt to carry out the experiment we have just discussed, expecting, as we did, the production of ammonium cyanate. He found just as we did—*urea*!

1.2A   Historical Difficulties

Your previous knowledge of chemistry has probably taught you that it is possible to have more than one compound of the same formula, and, furthermore, that under certain circumstances, it is possible to convert chemicals derived from minerals into chemicals derived from living matter.

Toward the end of the eighteenth century, chemists were beginning to learn quite a few things about matter that we would recognize as being very modern. One of the most interesting aspects was the apparent distinction between the chemistry of

Friedrich Wöhler (German, 1800–1882). Although Wöhler is best known for his synthesis of urea and its effect on the vital force theory, he also carried out important studies of inorganic compounds. He studied medicine at the University of Heidelberg and should be remembered for his fine teaching as well as his research.

Courtesy of the Edgar Fahs Smith Memorial Collection.

mineral and that of living matter. The feeling that there was a fundamental difference had been growing for a long time, but the need for pure materials presented a great difficulty for the study of living or "organic" chemistry. The materials available were complex mixtures and the individual compounds sometimes changed when removed from the living organism.

Despite the difficulties cited, by the early years of the nineteenth century, a large number of organic compounds had been isolated to a reasonable degree of purity. It was also true that the techniques of quantitative analysis had been improved to a point where it was possible to determine with some certainty the composition of pure substances. When this type of data was combined with the developing atomic theory of Dalton, a new and even more difficult problem arose. Unlike the mineral or inorganic compounds, organic materials were all composed of the same few elements. Consider the problem presented to the chemists of that time: the inorganic compounds were made up from a large number of elements in only a very limited number of combinations, whereas organic compounds were made up from apparently unlimited combinations of three or four elements.

1.2B   Vital Force Theory

Faced with the twin problems of the strange composition and handling difficulties of these compounds, it is not too surprising that many chemists despaired of making sense of the data and sought to explain away their difficulties. They did so by the simple expedient of postulating the "**vital force**" theory—that is, the requirement of a living organism for the preparation of organic compounds. Therefore, at the time of Wöhler, most chemists did not attempt to prepare organic compounds in the laboratory. Wöhler's discovery that the clearly organic compound urea could be prepared from the clearly inorganic salts ammonium chloride and silver cyanate was of great importance. The "vital force" theory avoided the main issue and, consequently, held up the development of organic chemistry for a number of years.

1.2C   Millions of Compounds

With evidence that it was possible to bridge the gap between inorganic and organic matter, it was clear that other methods would be found, and chemists began to attempt the preparation of numerous new compounds with outstanding success. So great was this success that Wöhler and his close friend, Justus Liebig, could claim in 1838 that sooner or later all organic compounds would be prepared. No one today knows exactly how many organic compounds have been prepared and/or isolated, but it has been estimated as greater than two million. Despite the size of the number of known compounds, it can and shortly will be shown that it represents only a tiny fraction of the compounds that are not only theoretically possible but also probably entirely stable. If a "vital force" is not the answer, what is it about organic compounds that allows them to exhibit such variation and number?

1.2D Dualistic Theory

To find the answer to this question, we must look at one of the perplexing problems facing the early nineteenth century chemist. Jöns Jacob Berzelius had proposed the theory that compounds were formed because of the attraction of opposite electrical charges. This **dualistic theory**, as it was called, fitted both the chemical and the electrical facts of inorganic chemistry remarkably. No less remarkable was the impossibility of making organic chemistry conform to this interpretation of natural behavior. The basic problem is that of understanding how hydrogen can form a large number of compounds with carbon. This and other characteristics of organic compounds require some explanation other than the simple attraction of electrical charge.

1.3
FUNDAMENTAL PARTICLES

Matter is made up of atoms composed of fundamental particles, especially protons, electrons, and neutrons. This fact constitutes a basis for our current explanation of the facts of organic chemistry. It will be helpful at this point to review certain basic facts of atomic structure and bond formation.

A concept useful to the chemist is that of the **atomic number**, which designates the position of a given atom in the periodic system. This number is obtained from, and, in turn, tells us the magnitude of the positive charge on, the nucleus of that atom. When the atom is electrically neutral, it is necessary that the atomic number also be equal to the number of extranuclear electrons. To a first approximation, the remaining weight of the atom is in the form of uncharged neutrons contained in the nucleus. This simple picture of atomic structure, although it does not begin to present the more subtle knowledge we now have, is quite useful for the present purpose of an introduction to organic chemistry.

The electrons found outside the nucleus are arranged in a definite manner depending on energy considerations. Table 1.1

TABLE 1.1

Atom	Symbol	Atomic number	Isolated atom ground-state electronic configuration
Hydrogen	H	1	$1s^1$
Helium	He	2	$1s^2$
Lithium	Li	3	$1s^2 2s^1$
Beryllium	Be	4	$1s^2 2s^2$
Boron	B	5	$1s^2 2s^2 2p_x^1$
Carbon	C	6	$1s^2 2s^2 2p_x^1 2p_y^1$
Nitrogen	N	7	$1s^2 2s^2 2p_x^1 2p_y^1 2p_z^1$
Oxygen	O	8	$1s^2 2s^2 2p_x^2 2p_y^1 2p_z^1$
Fluorine	F	9	$1s^2 2s^2 2p_x^2 2p_y^2 2p_z^1$
Neon	Ne	10	$1s^2 2s^2 2p_x^2 2p_y^2 2p_z^2$
Sodium	Na	11	$1s^2 2s^2 2p^6 3s^1$
Magnesium	Mg	12	$1s^2 2s^2 2p^6 3s^2$
Aluminum	Al	13	$1s^2 2s^2 2p^6 3s^2 3p_x^1$
Silicon	Si	14	$1s^2 2s^2 2p^6 3s^2 3p_x^1 3p_y^1$
Phosphorus	P	15	$1s^2 2s^2 2p^6 3s^2 3p_x^1 3p_y^1 3p_z^1$
Sulfur	S	16	$1s^2 2s^2 2p^6 3s^2 3p_x^2 3p_y^1 3p_z^1$
Chlorine	Cl	17	$1s^2 2s^2 2p^6 3s^2 3p_x^2 3p_y^2 3p_z^1$
Argon	A	18	$1s^2 2s^2 2p^6 3s^2 3p_x^2 3p_y^2 3p_z^2$

shows the complete atomic distribution of these electrons for the first three periods and includes all of the atoms commonly found in organic compounds; those italicized are most important and their electronic structure should be recalled.

It is the number and type of electrons in the outermost or valence shell (highest energy level) that usually governs the formation of bonds between the light atoms. Those atoms with complete valence shells (e.g., helium, neon, and argon) show very little tendency to react chemically; hence, the name inert gases. Atoms with nearly complete or nearly empty shells react by electron transfer, and the resulting bonds (and compounds) are called **ionic** or **electrovalent.** The symbolism used in this equation

$$Na \cdot + \cdot \ddot{\underset{..}{Cl}} : \rightarrow Na^+ + : \ddot{\underset{..}{Cl}} :^-$$

is very useful and widely employed, and it should be carefully noted. It employs the chemical symbol to represent the nucleus and all of the electrons below the valence shell and some simple unit (dots) to indicate the valence electrons. The notation was devised by G. N. Lewis and is usually referred to as the Lewis formula. Occasionally, different symbols are used to indicate the origin of the electrons in a reaction, and it is important to keep in mind that this variation is only for clarity and that it is quite impossible to distinguish among electrons.

Gilbert N. Lewis (American, 1875–1946). After obtaining his doctorate at Harvard, Lewis showed the great contribution a physical chemist could make to the understanding of organic chemistry. In addition to building a strong department of chemistry at the University of California, he made important studies in thermodynamics and the electronic theory of valence.

Courtesy of the Edgar Fahs Smith Memorial Collection.

In the intermediate cases, such as carbon, where a larger number of electrons would have to be transferred and a large charge built up, the stable electronic arrangement is obtained by sharing electron pairs between atoms. This mode of bond formation is known as **covalence** and represents the most common bond found in organic chemistry. The following equation illustrates the covalent bond, and, like the preceding equation, should not be taken as an actual method of preparation:

$$\cdot \overset{\cdot}{\underset{\cdot}{C}} \cdot \ + 4\,H \cdot \ \rightarrow \ H : \overset{\displaystyle H}{\underset{\displaystyle H}{\overset{\cdot\cdot}{\underset{\cdot\cdot}{C}}}} : H$$

methane

1.5
ATOMIC ORBITALS

As useful as the Lewis model of bonding was (and still is for many purposes), it left many questions unanswered and many observations unexplained. The specific shortcomings of this theory need not concern us here, but the more modern hypotheses advanced because of them are of great importance to our understanding of organic chemistry.

The early years of the twentieth century saw a great increase in our experimental understanding of nature. At the same time, it became apparent that **classical** or **Newtonian physics** was inadequate to explain the behavior of atoms and parts of atoms. The **quantum** or **wave mechanics** that was developed has shown that the earlier ideas were only approximately correct. The physical principles determining the energy, momentum, acceleration, and so forth, of objects with masses of grams or kilograms are the same as those governing atoms and electrons. The difference is in the precision needed in the measurements we wish to make.

From some rather complicated mathematics arises a basic and at first rather discouraging concept—the **Heisenberg Uncertainty Principle.** It tells us that what classical physics regarded as its task—that is, the exact description of a mass in terms of position and energy—is not possible. If we are to know one (position or energy) more exactly, it must be at the expense of how accurately we know the other. Thus, the subatomic physics must rely on **probability.** Specifically, we cannot calculate the exact location or exact energy of an electron at any given instant. We only obtain the probability of finding it in a given volume of space or of it having an energy within a certain range.

The probability of finding an electron, supposedly belonging to a particular atom, at a very great distance from that atom is still finite, so we cannot unequivocally assign electrons to particular atoms. In fact, we can no longer say anything implying that we have "pinned down" a specific electron. It might seem that this state of affairs would preclude any useful description of compounds or their chemistry. Such is not at all the case. The quantum mechanical picture of nature leads to a very nice qualitative model of natural systems, as well as to more exact quantitative predictions.

We can write a **wave equation** describing any given atom or molecule. Solutions of the wave equation are called **wave functions,** and they define the **orbitals** occupied by the electrons of the system. The orbital is simply that region of space in which the electron is most likely to be found; it can be represented graphically as a plot of probability (or electron density) versus position. Each orbital has a characteristic energy, and electrons can occupy only these energy levels. Because the electron can possess only discrete energies, its energy levels are said to be **quantized.** We do not need to understand the wave equation in detail, but the qualitative concepts of **orbitals** and of **quantization of energy** are extremely important.

A great number of very detailed studies have established the fact that a series of four **quantum numbers** are needed to describe a given electron. Furthermore, the **Pauli Exclusion Principle** states that these numbers, which deal with both the energy and the spatial position of the electron, must be different in at least one respect for every electron of a given atom. Thus, the hydrogen atom has one "s" electron written $1s^1$. Helium adds another electron and is designated $1s^2$. Table 1.1 shows the **electronic** arrangement or **configuration** of the first three periods.

There are a few questions raised by this table; for example, why are there three different "p" orbitals whereas there is only one "s" orbital? This problem is related to the solutions for the wave equations and results in an orbital that is spherical for "s" and dumbbell for "p," as shown in Figure 1.1. The "s" orbital of higher quantum number (i.e., $2s$ compared with $1s$) corre-

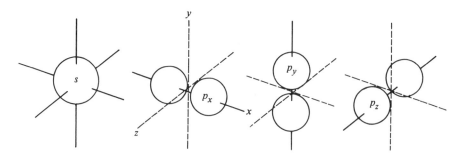

FIGURE 1.1.   Shapes of Atomic Orbitals.

sponds to a higher energy and a greater orbital diameter or probable average distance from the nucleus. The "p" orbitals, being dumbbell-shaped, can be related to each of the three mutually perpendicular coordinates.

The second question occurs with the carbon atom and asks why the second $2p$ electron is placed in a different $2p$ orbital ($2p_x^1 2p_y^1$ rather than $2p_x^2$). **Hund's Rule** states that when two orbitals of equal energy are being considered, the total energy of the system will be kept at a minimum if pairing—that is, placing electrons in the same orbital—is avoided. When oxygen is reached, it requires much more energy to place the eighth electron in the $3s$ orbital, and pairing in one of the $2p$ orbitals occurs (e.g., $2p_x^2$).

1.6
THE COVALENT BOND

Any basic understanding of chemistry requires an appreciation of the manner in which atoms are held together, that is, **bonding.** The most common bond in the carbon compounds is **covalent** in nature, and you should become familiar with the details of its structure.

Since the discovery of the electron by J. J. Thompson in 1897, and Lord Rutherford's description of the atom in 1911, ionic and covalent bonding have been understood in terms of the valence or outermost shell of electrons. In 1916, G. N. Lewis proposed the model for bonding that we have already described.

According to the Lewis concept, atoms form bonds in such a way as to attain an electronic structure resembling that of the practically unreactive "**rare**" or "**inert**" **gases** (e.g., helium, neon, argon, etc.). In most cases, where atoms have one or two loosely held electrons and where atoms have six or seven tightly held electrons, the so-called "**closed shell**" of eight electrons can be best achieved through a loss or gain of electrons. For example, in the formation of sodium chloride, the sodium atom has lost its single valence electron to become a positively charged sodium ion, whereas chlorine has gained this electron to become a negative chloride ion. The resulting bond is the **ionic** or **electrovalent** one so common in inorganic chemistry.

However, in the case of atoms such as carbon, where four electrons would have to be lost or gained, the resulting high charge (± 4) built up on a small atom leads to a very unfavorable situation. Lewis extended his picture to include compounds of this type by suggesting that these atoms form bonds by sharing pairs of electrons with other atoms. He thus defined an ordinary covalent bond as a bond in which two atoms each donate one electron in order to reach the stable octet.*

1.7
MOLECULAR ORBITALS

With the qualitative picture of atomic orbitals given in Section 1.5, it is now possible to extend the concept to a description of the manner in which atoms unite to form compounds—that is, bonding. Just as electrons could be thought of as combining to form bonds in the Lewis theory, we can visualize orbital electrons combining in a molecular orbital to hold atoms together. The quantum mechanical term for this process is **overlap.**

As was the case with atomic orbitals, the exact solution of the equation describing the overlapping of two atomic orbitals—that is, a molecular orbital—is beyond the range of our present mathematical equipment, except for the simplest molecules. Therefore, we must resort to approximation methods, the most common of which is simply to take a linear combination of the atomic orbitals involved (LCAO). Thus, to use this method in the case of the simple covalent molecule hydrogen, we can postulate that two $1s$ orbitals overlap to form a single molecular

---

*You should bear in mind that many molecules lie between these extremes. For example, HCl, H_2F_2, H_2O, and so on are ionic with a good deal of covalent character or vice versa (p. 15).

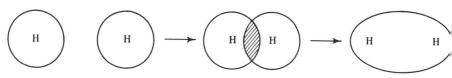

FIGURE 1.2.   Hydrogen Molecular Orbital (LCAO).

orbital that includes both nuclei (see Figure 1.2). This new orbital is no longer spherical in shape, but rather tends to have a higher electron density between the two protons or hydrogen nuclei. Such a picture includes the older and more approximate Lewis picture of a pair of dots or a dash joining the hydrogens and also illustrates the nonpolar character of the resulting bond. The bond described here is known as a **sigma (σ) bond.**

1.8
HYBRIDIZATION AND THE MOLECULAR ORBITALS OF CARBON

The study of a great many organic compounds has produced many facts about their structure and chemistry which can only be explained and understood as the result of a **tetracovalent** and **tetrahedral** (from the Greek, *tetra*, four, and *hedra*, base) **carbon** atom. When we attempt to apply the ideas of overlapping atomic orbitals to the simplest organic compound, a hydrocarbon or **alkane** called methane (see Figure 1.3), it appears that a different geometry results.

The two $2p$ electrons of carbon, which can be described as two half-filled $2p$ orbitals, should form two covalent bonds rather than the four observed. Furthermore, these bonds should be perpendicular to each other, that is, at 90° instead of the 109° 28' of a regular tetrahedron (Figure 1.4). The first of these difficulties can be overcome by placing one of the pair of $2s$ electrons in the vacant $2p$ orbital. With four unpaired electrons, the tetracovalence of carbon would be predicted; however, the question of the observed shape of methane remains. Operating with the $2s$ and three $2p$ orbitals, we should expect three bonds that are perpendicular to one another and a fourth bond, resulting from the $2s$ orbital, that shows no special direction because of the spherical shape of the $2s$ orbital (Figure 1.5).

One of the consequences of the quantum mechanical or

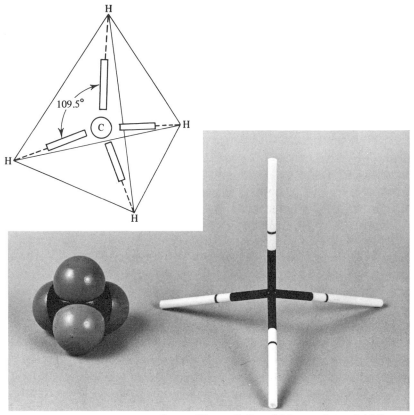

Courtesy of Photographic Research Laboratory, Eastman Kodak Company.

FIGURE 1.3.   Tetrahedral Geometry of Methane.

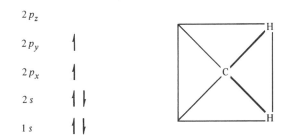

Electronic Ground State of   Expected Bonding of Ground State Carbon
Isolated Carbon Atoms*

FIGURE 1.4.

*Each arrow represents an electron and indicates the sign of its spin number.

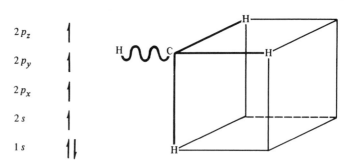

Electronic Excited State of Carbon   Expected Bonding of Excited State Carbon

FIGURE 1.5.

atomic orbital approach to bonding is the fact that as long as the total energy of a system remains the same we are allowed to subdivide this total in any manner we choose. It is therefore possible for us to suggest that the one $2s$ orbital and the three $2p$ orbitals are mixed or **hybridized** to form four identical sp^3 orbitals, each of which contains one sp^3 electron. The wave function resulting from this mathematical technique predicts a tetrahedral geometry for the carbon atoms of the alkanes. Figure 1.6 shows the electron density of an sp^3 orbital.

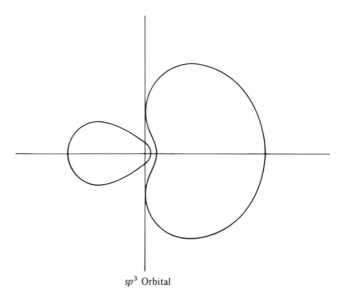

sp^3 Orbital

FIGURE 1.6.

Although energy must be put into the system to change the $2s$ electron to the $2p$ orbital, the net result of such an investment along with hybridization is a stronger carbon-hydrogen bond. This increase in strength is owing in part to the shape of the orbital, which allows the electrons to be located between the bonded atoms with greater ease and results in a decrease in the free energy of the system. Therefore, the methane molecule can be nicely described by using the hypotheses of atomic and molecular orbitals.

1.9
POLAR COVALENT BONDS

The sharing of electrons between atoms does not have to be equal and, in fact, never will be except in the case of two identical atoms (e.g., H_2 or Cl_2). For a number of reasons, different atoms will have a greater or smaller tendency to gain or lose electrons. We term the overall effect **electronegativity.** The more electronegative an element is, the greater will be its hold on an electron. Thus, the ionic bond is simply an extreme case of a covalent bond and occurs when the difference in electronegativities is so great that one atom gains nearly complete control of the electron in question.

Of greater concern to us in the study of organic compounds are those cases in which the difference is intermediate. In such a situation, the two shared electrons that make up the covalent bond will, on the average, be more associated with one atom than with the other. The result is that one atom (the more electronegative one) possesses some amount of negative charge and the other atom (the more electropositive one) possesses some amount of positive charge. Both will, of course, be less than the unit charges of monovalent ionic compounds.

$(Na^+ Cl^-)_x$ $H:H$ $H^{\delta+}:Cl^{\delta-}$

ionic bond   covalent bond   polar covalent bond

We signify a fractional charge on an atom by the lowercase Greek letter *delta* (δ). We shall have frequent use for this partial ionic charge in our forthcoming discussions of properties and reaction mechanisms.

If we examine the case of hydrogen chloride in terms of the approximate molecular orbital approach, we discover that the bond-forming orbital overlap must involve the $1s$ orbital of hydrogen and a half-filled (one electron) third-level orbital of chlorine. Because this chlorine orbital is not spherical, the bond formed has very unequal sharing and the center of electrical charge is shifted toward the chlorine end of the covalent bond. The net effect is the observed dipole of HCl, which may also be explained in terms of the difference in electronegativity of hydrogen and chlorine (see Figure 1.7).

FIGURE 1.7.   Hydrogen Chloride Molecular Orbital (LCAO).

1.10
COORDINATE COVALENT BONDS

One point that was implied but not explicitly stated in our discussion of the covalent bond was the requirement that each atom involved in the bonding contributes one of the electrons. Such will not always be the case, and a bond may also be formed when both of the bonding electrons were originally associated with a single atom. In this type of bonding, known as **coordinate covalence,** one of the atoms has donated both of the electrons involved in the bond and, therefore, has in a sense transferred one of them to the other atom. The nature of this bond can be seen qualitatively by considering two simple nitrogen acids. If we draw a Lewis structure for nitrous acid, we see that the nitrogen atom has a pair of electrons that are not involved in bonding:

$$H:\ddot{O}:\dot{N}::\ddot{O}$$

This nonbonding pair can form a covalent bond with oxygen to give the familiar compound nitric acid:

$$\overset{\ddots\ddots}{:\ddot{O}:} \qquad \overset{O}{\underset{\uparrow}{}} \qquad \overset{O^-}{\underset{|}{}}$$
$$H:\ddot{O}:\ddot{N}::\ddot{O} \qquad H-O-N=O \qquad H-O-N^+=O$$

Several different ways in which structural formulas are drawn have been illustrated for nitric acid. Our earlier discussion of atomic and molecular orbitals makes it clear that these are very approximate, and especially that they give a distorted view of the shape of the molecule and the electronic distribution in the bonds. Still, they are easily drawn and very useful as long as their imperfections are understood; therefore, they will be used often in this text just as they are by organic chemists in their daily work.

Nitric acid, as shown in the example, also provides an illustration of still another basic attribute of covalent bonds. Between the nitrogen atom and one of the oxygen atoms, two pairs of electrons are being shared. This behavior is well known in organic chemistry and will produce interesting chemical and physical differences among compounds that differ in the number of pairs of electrons shared by adjacent atoms. The following provides an example of each of the types of multiple bonds drawn in both the Lewis and the graphic manner:

$$H\!:\!\ddot{O}\!: \qquad \ddot{O}\!:\!:\!C\!:\!:\!\ddot{O} \qquad H\!:\!C\!:\!:\!N\!:$$
$$\ \ H$$

$$H\!-\!\ddot{O}\!: \qquad \ddot{O}\!=\!C\!=\!\ddot{O} \qquad H\!-\!C\!\equiv\!N\!:$$
$$\ \ |$$
$$\ \ H$$

| single | double | triple |
| (water) | (carbon dioxide) | (hydrocyanic acid) |

It is the ability of the carbon atom to form stable covalent bonds with other carbon atoms that makes it possible to obtain long chains of carbons which may be continuous or contain branches.

It is also possible to arrange these atoms in the form of rings

and combinations of both chains and rings. With this array of known and possible compounds, it should be no surprise that early chemists found organic chemistry a complex field.

SUGGESTED ADDITIONAL READINGS

In each chapter the authors will select the most important general topics and suggest a few more advanced sources that they and their students have found interesting and useful. None of these will be too difficult if you have read and understood the material presented in the chapter. Hopefully, these references will add to your understanding and enjoyment of organic chemistry. The complete citation for each book will be found in the Bibliography.

The History of Organic Chemistry

Benfey (History).
Ihde, Chapters 7–8, 12–13, and 23.

The Covalent Bond

Allinger and Allinger, Chapters 2 and 3.
Cason, Chapter 3.
Cram and Hammond, Chapter 8.
Herz, Chapters 2–4.
Morrison and Boyd, Chapter 1.
Roberts and Caserio, Chapter 5.

C. R. Noller, "A Physical Picture of Covalent Bonding and Resonance in Organic Chemistry," *J. Chem. Educ.*, **27**, 504 (1950).

R. J. Gillespie, "The Valence-Shell Electron-Pair Repulsion (VSEPR) Theory of Directed Valency," *J. Chem. Educ.*, **40**, 295 (1963).

W. F. Luder, "The Electron Repulsion Theory of the Chemical Bond. Part I," *J. Chem. Educ.*, **44**, 206 (1967); "Part II," *J. Chem. Educ.*, **44**, 269 (1967).

F. L. Lambert, "Atomic Orbitals from Wave Patterns. Part I," *Chemistry*, **41** (2), 10 (1968); "Part II," *Chemistry*, **41** (3), 8 (1968).

R. Ferreira, "Molecular Orbital Theory, An Introduction," *Chemistry*, **41** (6), 8 (1968).

Summary of Organic Chemistry

F. H. Westheimer, "A Summer Short Course in Carbon Chemistry. Part I," *Chemistry*, **38** (6), 12 (1965); "Part II," *Chemistry*, **38** (7), 10 (1965); "Part III," *Chemistry*, **38** (8), 18 (1965).

"A Summer Short Course in Carbon Chemistry.   IV," *Chemistry*,
    38 (9), 21 (1965).

SUMMARY

1. This text is designed to give you a brief, but fundamental background in organic chemistry.

2. The organic compounds contain carbon and relatively few other elements. There are a great number of carbon compounds, and many of them are found in natural material that either is or was living.

3. Among the numerous particles that make up atoms the protons, electrons, and neutrons are especially important.

4. The covalent bond formed by two atoms sharing a pair of electrons is of central importance in organic chemistry.

5. Orbitals (both atomic and molecular) are regions of space where a given electron is most likely to be found.

6. The four valence electrons of carbon can be mixed or hybridized in different ways. In the saturated compounds they form sp^3 orbitals.

7. The carbon atom is tetracovalent and in σ bonding it is tetrahedral.

8. Covalent bonds between unlike atoms will always be more or less polar.

9. Bonds with both electrons donated by one atom are called co-ordinate covalent.

10. Carbon atoms can form one or more bonds with another atom (including other carbon atoms). This fact allows organic compounds to exist in different oxidation states and structural arrangements.

PROBLEMS

The only way to master organic chemistry is to work problems. As you learn more chemistry the problems will become more varied and interesting. Many of the books listed in the Bibliography have large numbers of excellent problems. We especially recommend the two fine problem workbooks by Henderson *et al.* and Hansch and Helm-kamp.

1. Draw both the Lewis and the graphic structural formulas for each of the following compounds. The boldface letters and numbers indicate parts that are answered in the back of the text.

   a. C_2H_5OH d. $CHCl_3$ **g.** NaCN   j. $(CH_3)_3O^+$
   b. H_2SO_4 e. $AlCl_3$ h. $C_4H_{10}*$ **k.** CH_3O^-
   c. LiF   **f.** C_3H_6* i. NH_4Cl l. $(C_2H_5)_4N^+$

2. For each of the compounds in question 1, indicate the kind of bonding involved. Remember that a single compound may show more than one type.

3. Which of the molecular compounds in question 1 will show a dipole? Indicate the positive and negative ends.

---

*There are two forms of this compound.

2

The Structure
of Organic Molecules

The study of organic chemistry depends heavily upon the kind of atoms in a molecule and their arrangement in space. Therefore, it is vital that you begin your study by understanding some basic facts about the structure of molecules. Closely related to this subject are the questions of how the actual structures are represented in two-dimensional space and how they are named. If the pictures are neglected, you will not be able to visualize new compounds and reactions; if the names are neglected, you will not be able to communicate. Both of these abilities are serious matters in terms of your progress.

Generally speaking, the simplest compounds, the **saturated hydrocarbons** containing only σ bonds, are suitable for discussing the elements of organic structure and nomenclature. However, certain concepts and many good examples require the presence of a **functional group**. A group is a *part* of a molecule, and ordinarily it exists alone for only a very short time. We shall discuss these "free groups" along with reaction mechanisms (pp. 58–60). A functional group is a special arrangement of

21

atoms that shows certain reasonably well-defined chemical and physical properties. It is often useful to study the reactions of all organic compounds containing a given functional group together, inasmuch as their similarities are an aid in remembering. This text is arranged along functional group lines, but you should remember that all generalizations are somewhat imperfect and that the chemistry of a particular compound will *never* be exactly like that of any other, even if they both contain only one (identical) functional group.

We shall begin our study of structure and nomenclature by considering both the saturated hydrocarbons and the saturated alcohols. It will not be difficult because these two classes of compounds are simple and closely related. This approach will also allow us to move more rapidly from these important fundamentals to the chemistry of organic compounds.

2.2
STRUCTURAL FORMULAS OF ALCOHOLS

Alcohols are characterized by the presence of a **carbinol group** $\left(-\overset{\displaystyle |}{\underset{\displaystyle |}{C}}-\textbf{OH}\right)$. Using the facts learned in Chapter 1, you should be able to write a formula for methanol (see Figure 2.1), the simplest alcohol which is a derivative of methane. Keep in mind that each dash or bond represents a pair of shared electrons. You were told to remember that each carbon atom must have four bonds, and it does in this formula. Now, with the additional facts that each hydrogen will always have one bond, and, in alcohols (and most other oxygen-containing compounds), oxygen will have two, we can proceed to the next "higher" alcohol.

$$H-\overset{\overset{\displaystyle H}{|}}{\underset{\underset{\displaystyle H}{|}}{C}}-\overset{\overset{\displaystyle H}{|}}{\underset{\underset{\displaystyle H}{|}}{C}}-O-H$$

ethanol

We usually group atoms into segments of formulas. It is easier to visualize and simpler to write such **condensed formulas**.

$$CH_3-CH_2-OH \qquad or \qquad CH_3CH_2OH \qquad or \qquad C_2H_5OH$$

ethanol

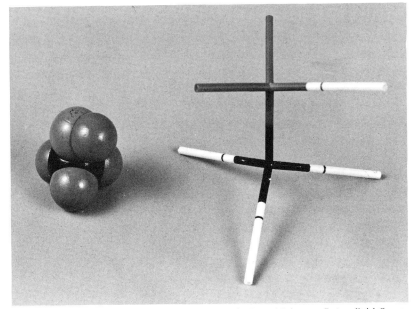

Courtesy of Photographic Research Laboratory, Eastman Kodak Company.

FIGURE 2.1.   Structure of Methanol.

The missing bonds (shared electrons) are *understood* to be present.

We can now proceed to write the higher members of this homologous series (from the Greek, *homos*, the same, and *logos*, proportion). **Homologs** are defined as members of a series of one type of compound, each adjacent member being increased by an increment of CH_2 (**methylene group**). Thus, we obtain

$$CH_3—CH_2—CH_2—OH \qquad \text{1-propanol}$$
$$CH_3—CH_2—CH_2—CH_2—OH \qquad \text{1-butanol}$$
$$CH_3—CH_2—CH_2—CH_2—CH_2—OH \qquad \text{1-pentanol}$$
$$CH_3—CH_2—CH_2—CH_2—CH_2—CH_2—OH \qquad \text{1-hexanol}$$

We must also consider other possible arrangements of atoms that still retain the molecular formula for alcohols. Keep in mind the "rules":

A. Each carbon has four bonds.
B. Each hydrogen has one bond.
C. Each oxygen has two bonds

D. Alcohols must have the carbinol group $\left(\begin{array}{c} | \\ -C-OH \\ | \end{array}\right)$ present.

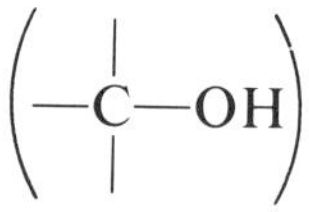

Now, let us look at the three-carbon alcohol, writing it first as we did previously, and second, in another arrangement.

$$CH_3-CH_2-CH_2-OH \qquad CH_3-\overset{\displaystyle |}{\underset{\displaystyle OH}{C}}H-CH_3$$

1-propanol   2-propanol

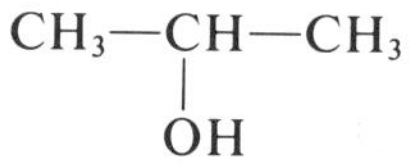

These two propanols are **isomers** (from the Greek, *isos*, equal, and *meros*, part). Isomers are defined as different compounds having the same molecular formula. When we proceed to the four-carbon alcohol, we find still more possible arrangements.

$$CH_3-CH_2-CH_2-CH_2-OH \qquad CH_3-CH_2-\overset{\displaystyle |}{\underset{\displaystyle OH}{C}}H-CH_3$$

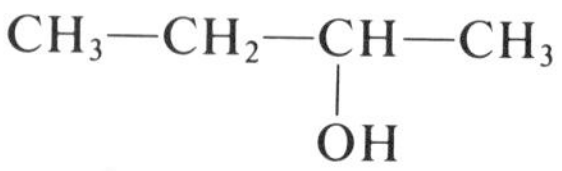

1-butanol   2-butanol

$$CH_3-\overset{\displaystyle |}{\underset{\displaystyle CH_3}{C}}H-CH_2-OH \qquad\qquad CH_3-\overset{\displaystyle CH_3}{\underset{\displaystyle OH}{\overset{|}{\underset{|}{C}}}}-CH_3$$

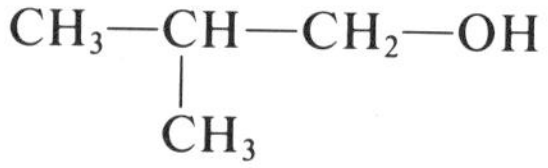

2-methyl-1-propanol 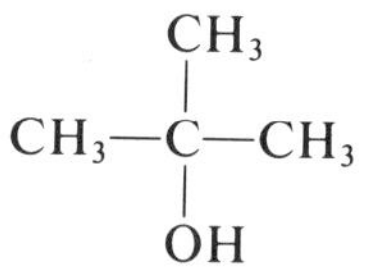   2-methyl-2-propanol

It is obvious that each of these compounds has a molecular formula of C_4H_9OH, but that the atoms are arranged in a different manner—that is, their structural formulas are not identical. They are truly different compounds with different properties.

2.3
NAMING SATURATED HYDROCARBONS AND ALCOHOLS

As we indicated in Chapter 1, a very large number of organic compounds are known and many of them are closely related, as is the case with isomers and homologs. During the early development of organic chemistry, naming compounds was no problem, but as the rate of discovery of new materials grew more rapid, it became increasingly clear that some agreement about what to call a given structure would have to be reached.

A group of chemists met at Geneva, Switzerland, in 1892, for the purpose of "establishing a single, systematic, official name for every organic compound." This goal was unrealistic, because it would require a very complicated set of rules, it would provide quite impossible names for some common compounds, and, finally, it would demand a high court to decide questions of application as they arose.

In 1930, a commission of the International Union of Chemistry met in Liège, Belgium, and, using much of the Geneva report along with usage of the time (e.g., that used by *Chemical Abstracts*), it established a system that, with many modifications, is in use today. The general rules of IUPAC (International Union of Pure and Applied Chemistry) follow. Additional rules will be discussed when they are first required.

1. The first step in naming any compound that does not contain a ring (and many that do) is to determine the longest continuous chain of carbon atoms. This chain must include the carbon atom involved in, or attached to, the functional group.

2. The stem name is derived from the corresponding saturated hydrocarbon, as shown in the following partial list:

Structure	*IUPAC name*	*Stem*
CH_4	methane	meth-
CH_3CH_3	ethane	eth-
$CH_3CH_2CH_3$	propane	prop-
$CH_3(CH_2)_2CH_3$	butane	but-
$CH_3(CH_2)_3CH_3$	pentane	pent-
$CH_3(CH_2)_4CH_3$	hexane	hex-
$CH_3(CH_2)_5CH_3$	heptane	hept-
$CH_3(CH_2)_6CH_3$	octane	oct-
$CH_3(CH_2)_7CH_3$	nonane	non-
$CH_3(CH_2)_8CH_3$	decane	dec-
$CH_3(CH_2)_9CH_3$	undecane	undec-

3. Each functional group and homologous series has a suffix, which is added to the stem. For the saturated hydrocarbons, the suffix is **-ane** and for the saturated alcohols it is **-anol**.

4. The longest continuous carbon atom chain is numbered from the end that will give the functional group the lowest number.

5. If the carbon chain is branched, the attached groups are named and numbered. The numbers and names precede the parent name in alphabetical order. When there is more than one group with the same structure, they are collected; *all* of the carbon numbers are used, and an appropriate prefix (di-, tri-, tetra-, etc.) is attached to the group name.

6. With a few exceptions, the name of the compound is written as a single word. The punctuation is shown in the
preceding and following examples.

2.4
ALKYL GROUPS

Before we can begin to apply these rules, it is necessary to ex-
pand upon rule 5. For the present time, we will limit the attached
groups to some **alkyl groups**, which consist only of carbon and
hydrogen. Table 2.1 shows the arrangement of the carbons and
the corresponding name of the group. The expression R- is often
used as a general representation of alkyl groups.

TABLE 2.1

Group formula	Group name	Group formula	Group name
CH_3-	methyl	$CH_3-CH_2-CH_2-CH_2-$	butyl
CH_3-CH_2- or (C_2H_5-)	ethyl	$CH_3-CH-CH_2-$	isobutyl
$CH_3-CH_2-CH_2-$	propyl	$\quad\quad\vert$	
CH_3-CH-	isopropyl	$\quad\quad CH_3$	
$\quad\vert$		CH_3-CH_2-CH-	sec-butyl
$\quad CH_3$		$\quad\quad\quad\quad\vert$	
		$\quad\quad\quad\quad CH_3$	
		$\quad\quad CH_3$	
		$\quad\quad\vert$	tert-butyl
		CH_3-C-	(or t-)
		$\quad\quad\vert$	
		$\quad\quad CH_3$	

Note that the total number of carbon atoms is consistent with
the parent name as given in rule 2. For alkyl groups, the **-ane** is
dropped from the parent hydrocarbon and **-yl** is added. Pay
special attention to the arrangement of carbon atoms and the
prefix that indicates that group—for example, *iso-*, *sec-*, and
tert-.

2.5
EXAMPLES OF NAMES OF ALCOHOLS

As is the case with much of organic chemistry, learning to name
compounds is accomplished only through practice. At the end of

this and later chapters, you will find typical compounds to name; these should be carefully studied. In addition to this minimal amount of practice, you should make it a habit to name properly every compound you come upon in this course. For a start, return to the butanols used earlier as examples of isomerism (p. 24). A careful study of the names will indicate that the preceding rules were applied in each case. For additional practice, apply the IUPAC system to the various isomers of some five carbon alcohols.

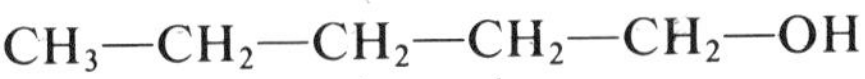

$CH_3-CH_2-CH_2-CH_2-CH_2-OH$
1-pentanol

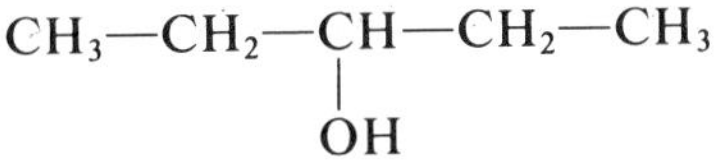

$CH_3-CH_2-\underset{\underset{OH}{|}}{CH}-CH_2-CH_3$
3-pentanol

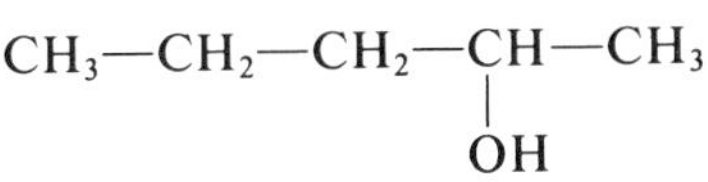

$CH_3-CH_2-CH_2-\underset{\underset{OH}{|}}{CH}-CH_3$
2-pentanol

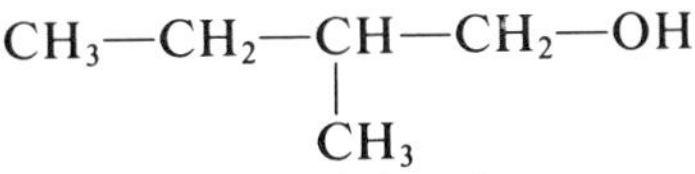

$CH_3-CH_2-\underset{\underset{CH_3}{|}}{CH}-CH_2-OH$
2-methyl-1-butanol

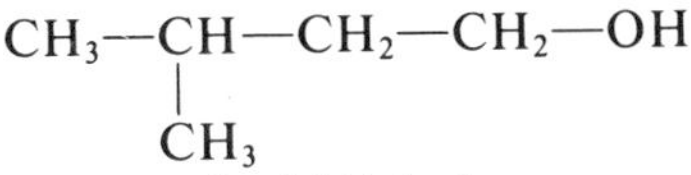

$CH_3-\underset{\underset{CH_3}{|}}{CH}-CH_2-CH_2-OH$
3-methyl-1-butanol

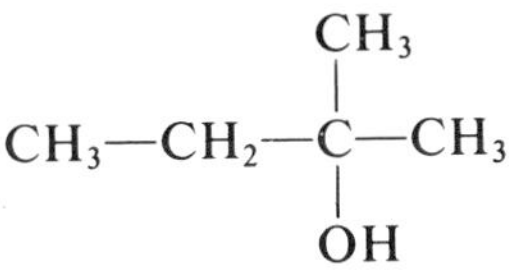

$CH_3-CH_2-\overset{\overset{CH_3}{|}}{\underset{\underset{OH}{|}}{C}}-CH_3$
2-methyl-2-butanol

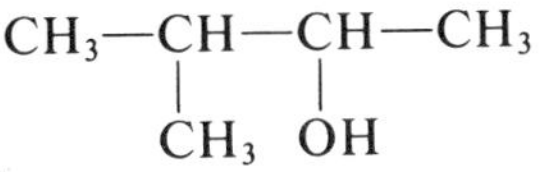

$CH_3-\underset{\underset{CH_3}{|}}{CH}-\underset{\underset{OH}{|}}{CH}-CH_3$
3-methyl-2-butanol

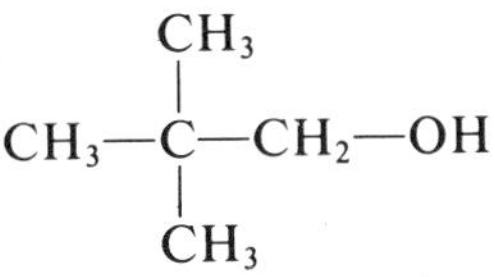

$CH_3-\overset{\overset{CH_3}{|}}{\underset{\underset{CH_3}{|}}{C}}-CH_2-OH$
2,2-dimethyl-1-propanol

Now look at the name of a more complicated compound:

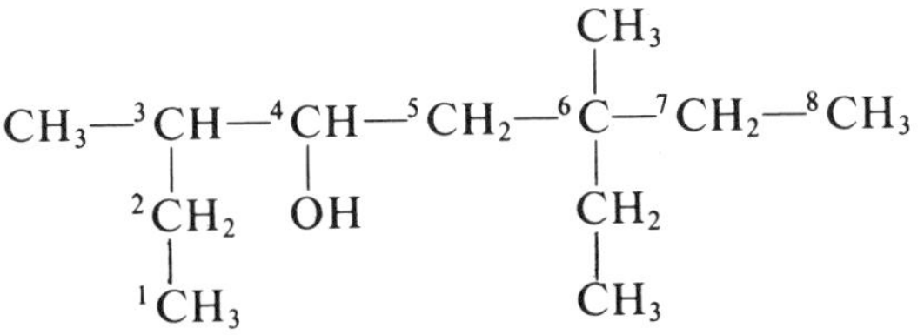

$CH_3-{}^3CH-{}^4CH-{}^5CH_2-{}^6\overset{\overset{CH_3}{|}}{C}-{}^7CH_2-{}^8CH_3$
with ${}^2CH_2$ and OH below ${}^3CH$ and ${}^4CH$, ${}^1CH_3$ below ${}^2CH_2$, and CH_2 / CH_3 below ${}^6C$

The first step is to select the longest continuous carbon chain. In numbering the chain, it is clear that left to right will allow the lower number to place the hydroxyl group. This process results in branches at the 3 and 6 carbons of the chain. There are three branches, and they are attached to an 8-carbon alcohol where the hydroxyl group is attached to carbon 4. It is only necessary now to collect identical branches and to write the correct name:

6-ethyl-3, 6-dimethyl-4-octanol

The names of the saturated hydrocarbons should present no difficulty at this point. Try the following examples:

$$CH_3CHCH_2CH_3$$
$$|$$
$$CH_3$$

2-methylbutane
(common: isopentane)

$$CH_3CH_2CHCHCH_2CH_2CH_3$$
$$| \quad |$$
$$H_3C \quad CH_2$$
$$|$$
$$CH_3$$

4-ethyl-3-methylheptane

$$CH_3CHCHCH_3$$
$$| \quad |$$
$$H_3C \quad CH_3$$

2,3-dimethylbutane

$$CH_3$$
$$|$$
$$CH_3CCH_2CHCH_2CH_3$$
$$| \quad |$$
$$CH_3 \quad CH_2$$
$$|$$
$$CH_3$$

4-ethyl-2,2-dimethylhexane

The **common name**, isopentane, raises a point of caution. Many organic compounds have more than one name, and it is often true that the IUPAC name is not the one most frequently used. The simple alcohols provide several examples; for example, ethanol is called ethyl alcohol and 1-butanol is called *n*-butyl alcohol. The prefix *n*- indicates a straight chain compound, and it is frequently used in the common names of all functional group classes. Be sure you know at least one acceptable name for every compound you encounter and *never* mix parts of common and IUPAC names—for example, *n*-butanol is incorrect.

2.6
FREE ROTATION AND CONFORMATION

It is a useful approximation of organic structural theory that σ bonds allow more or less free rotation of the atoms involved. Although many important exceptions exist, this concept does explain why carbon chains twist in space without producing new isomeric compounds. It has become clear in recent years that certain spatial arrangements or **conformations** of atoms in compounds are energetically preferred. The infinite number of such arrangements possible through rotation about any given bond all have a particular energy, but it is necessary only to examine those that represent the maximum and minimum energies to appreciate the principle involved.

The clearest pictures of these rotational isomers or conforma-95072 tions are those devised by Professor M. S. Newman, which represent the molecule as viewed along the σ bond in question. Let us consider the simple hydrocarbon, ethane. Its three-dimensional drawing and Newman projections would be as shown in Figure 2.2.

From these drawings, we see that in the staggered conformation, the hydrogens are as far apart as possible, and when ϕ (the angle between two hydrogens on opposite carbons) is plotted against the energy of the system, the curve shown in Figure 2.2 is obtained. The maxima of the curve (2.8 kcal/mole higher in energy) correspond to the eclipsed conformations, whereas the minima correspond to the staggered conformations. The reason for this condition is related to the interaction of opposite hydrogens, but there is no doubt that there are other effects involved. The situation becomes more complex, both in the experimental observations and their explanation, when higher homologs, carbon rings, or noncarbon substituents—such as the hydroxyl

Melvin S. Newman (*American, 1908–   ). Educated at Yale University and a professor of chemistry at Ohio State University, Newman is well known for his work with the polynuclear aromatic hydrocarbons. Studies conducted in his laboratory on the steric effect of groups in organic reactions were in part re-sponsible for the development of the very useful projections with which we indicate conformational forms. Perhaps his best known synthetic accomplishment is hexahelicene in which the 1 and 6 benzene rings

hexahelicene

overlap giving rise to a right and left handed configuration. Hexahelicene's optical activity is the result of molecular asymmetry.

Courtesy of Professor Newman.

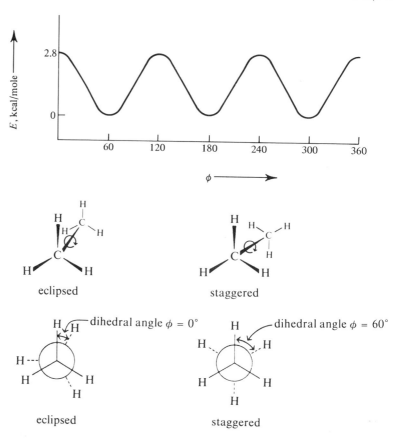

FIGURE 2.2.   Free Rotation and Conformation in Ethane.

group—are considered. Some of these will be discussed later as they become important for our understanding of the chemistry of certain compounds. If you wish more detail at this time, refer to the Suggested Additional Readings at the end of this chapter.

2.7
STEREOISOMERISM—THE OPTICAL PROPERTIES OF ORGANIC MOLECULES

You have already learned that organic molecules that are isomers of one another can exist (p. 24). The example of 1- and 2-propanol represents only one type, called **structural isomerism**; it depends on the component atoms being bonded together in a different sequence. The fundamental difference between the members of this or another set of isomers is that they are not **superimposable**. In the case of structural isomers, even two-dimensional drawings make it clear that the compounds are not identical. But now we must deal with a more subtle form of isomerism. In **stereoisomerism**, the atoms are all linked together in the same sequence but their spatial arrangement is different. There are two subdivisions of stereoisomers: **geometric** and **optical**. The former will be treated when we discuss compounds in which it is observed (pp. 76–79).

In 1848, the French chemist Louis Pasteur observed that sodium ammonium tartrate crystallized in two different forms (see Figure 2.3). After he had separated the crystals into two sets

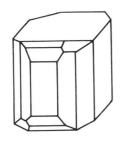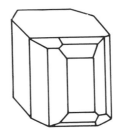

FIGURE 2.3.   Hemihedral Crystals of Sodium Ammonium Tartrate.

and converted the salts to the corresponding acids, Pasteur found that a solution of one acid rotated **plane-polarized light (ppl)** to the right. A solution of the other (at the same concentration) rotated it the same number of degrees to the left, and equal amounts of the two had no effect. This experiment is of great significance, because it shows that the observed effect is not a result of the crystal structure, a phenomenon that was already known, but can also be a property of molecules and observed in solution.

Just as the tartrate crystals are right and left handed or **asymmetric**, the tartaric acid molecule can be written in two different forms that show an **object-mirror image** relationship.

$$
\begin{array}{ccc}
CO_2H & \vdots & CO_2H \\
\mid & \vdots & \mid \\
H\!-\!\overset{\mid}{C}\!-\!OH & \vdots & HO\!-\!\overset{\mid}{C}\!-\!H \\
\mid & \vdots & \mid \\
HO\!-\!\overset{\mid}{C}\!-\!H & \vdots & H\!-\!\overset{\mid}{C}\!-\!OH \\
\mid & \vdots & \mid \\
CO_2H & \vdots & CO_2H \\
& \text{mirror} &
\end{array}
$$

These drawings are generally clearer than the usual flat projections, and you will encounter them in later discussions. The solid line represents a bond in the plane of the page, the wedges project above the plane, and the dashed lines project below the plane. The photograph of a molecular model of tartaric acid (shown in Figure 2.4) may help, but you should make models of

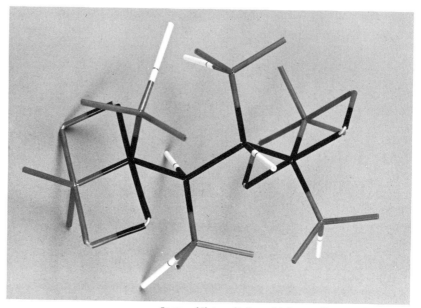

FIGURE 2.4.   Molecular Model of Tartaric Acid.

your own to be sure you understand how the stereoisomers (**stereomers**) are related and, especially, that they are not superimposable.

2.7A   Method of Observing Stereomers

The usual physical properties of the two isomeric tartaric acids (e.g., melting point, solubility, etc.) are identical. The only way to distinguish between such **enantiomers** or **optical isomers** is to use a tool that is itself asymmetric. Two methods often used are (1) the observed effect on ppl and (2) the reaction with another asymmetric compound. We shall describe the latter method when we discuss the separation or **resolution** of mixtures of enantiomers.

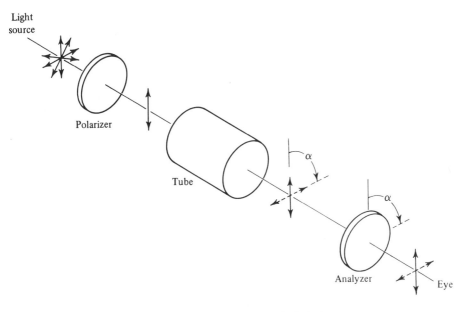

FIGURE 2.5.   Schematic Drawing of a Polarimeter.

The instrument that determines the effect asymmetric molecules have on ppl is called a **polarimeter** (see Figure 2.5). It consists of a source of monochromatic light (a single wavelength), a means of obtaining ppl, a sample tube, and an analyzer attached to a scale graduated in degrees. The light beam is passed through the polarizer, which can be of several different types— for example, a sheet of polaroid film; the net effect is to reflect the light waves vibrating in all planes except one. This light is transmitted or passes through. The ppl that is produced goes through an empty sample tube to a second polarizer, the analyzer, which is used to detect its presence. If the analyzer is rotated through 360°, relative to the polarizer, two points of maximum and two points of minimum light intensity are observed. The maxima occur when the polarizer and analyzer are parallel, and the minima occur when they are perpendicular. In practice, the instruments are provided with a means of splitting the beam into two segments, and these are matched for the minimum amount of light intensity. The eye can compare the two fields much more easily than it can estimate relative brightness or darkness.

The above procedure provides a zero setting for the instrument. The same reading would be obtained if the sample tube were filled with any optically inactive material—for example, the solvent in which the rotation of a substance is to be determined. If an optically active material like one of the tartaric acids is dissolved in a suitable solvent and placed in the sample tube, it will be found that the fields no longer match. By rotating the analyzer, the match can be restored and the angle of rotation (α) read from the graduated scale. The explanation must be that the substance in the tube has caused the ppl to change its vibration plane by that number of degrees. This rotation angle is a physical constant characteristic of the material. It is useful in identifying the compound when the solvent, temperature, concentration, sample tube length, and wavelength of light are known.

2.7B   The Cause of Optical Activity

The question of greatest interest to you at this time is the following: Why do certain organic molecules, otherwise identical, show this peculiar property? The answer lies in two of the basic facts of organic chemistry: (1) the tetrahedral structure of carbon atoms involved in σ bonding; and (2) the requirement that identical compounds be exactly superimposable.

Consider an organic compound containing a carbon atom bonded to four different groups, for example, 2-butanol.

$$CH_3-\overset{\displaystyle H}{\underset{\displaystyle CH_2CH_3}{C^*}}-OH$$

The carbon atom marked with an asterisk is bonded to four different groups: hydrogen, methyl, ethyl, and hydroxyl. Such an asymmetric atom is a common cause of asymmetric molecules and, hence, of optical isomers. The following drawings and photographs of models may help you see the enantiomeric relationship (see Figure 2.6).

We can also use the projection discussed earlier. In fact, it is often used, but even more often the wedges and dashes are replaced by the simple solid lines used in the first structure in this section. When this latter is done, you must remember the assumption that the top and bottom groups are below the plane of the paper and that the right and left groups are above it.

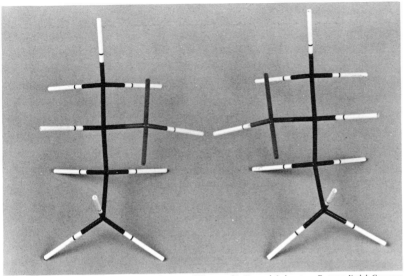

Courtesy of Photographic Research Laboratory, Eastman Kodak Company.

FIGURE 2.6.   Enantiomers of 2-Butanol.

$$\begin{array}{ccc}
\text{CH}_3 & \quad & \text{CH}_3 \\
| & \quad & | \\
\text{H}\!-\!\text{C}\!\rightarrow\!\text{OH} & \quad & \text{HO}\!\rightarrow\!\text{C}\!-\!\text{H} \\
| & \quad & | \\
\text{CH}_2\text{CH}_3 & \quad & \text{CH}_2\text{CH}_3 \\
[\alpha]_D^{20} + 13.8° & \quad & [\alpha]_D^{20} - 13.8°
\end{array}$$

There are other reasons for optical activity in organic molecules beside a carbon atom bonded to four different groups, but for the purpose of an introduction, this most common example will be sufficient.

When the two forms of 2-butanol are observed in a polarimeter, either pure or in solution, one rotates ppl in a clockwise direction and is designated the **dextro** or (+) isomer. The molecule with the opposite spatial arrangement—that is, the mirror image—will rotate light in a counterclockwise direction the same number of degrees, and it is called the **levo** or (−) isomer. A mixture of equal amounts of the two isomers is optically inactive. This **racemic mixture** or **racemate** contains as many molecules that rotate light in one direction as those that rotate it in the other; therefore, the net effect is no rotation at all.

2.7C Configuration

The problem of which of the two isomers has which arrangement of atoms and which direction of rotation is one that has concerned organic chemists for a long time. It has only been in recent years that a satisfactory answer has become available. It was found that x-ray diffraction experiments could provide the required data. The methods will not be discussed in this text, but certain of the results are instructive.

Prior to the determination of **absolute configuration**, a large number of very careful chemical transformations had been carried out in order to relate various optically active compounds to a standard of assumed configuration.* These **relative configurations** had shown that there was no simple relationship between the arrangement of atoms and the direction of rotation of ppl. Once the absolute configuration of a few compounds was known, it was possible to designate the configuration of all the other molecules of known relative configuration.

A number of terms used in the consideration of molecular structure unfortunately all have the same first letter and about the same length. This situation can lead to confusion, and it is important that you understand clearly both the meaning of these terms and where they apply.

1. *Composition.* The most basic information about the structure, it refers to the molecular formula—that is, the number and kind of atoms involved.

---

*The standard chosen was (+)-glyceraldehyde, which was assumed to have the following configuration designated D:

$$\begin{array}{ccc}
\text{CHO} & & \text{CHO} \\
| & & | \\
\text{H}\!-\!\text{C}\!-\!\text{OH} & \text{or} & \text{H}\!-\!\text{C}\!-\!\text{OH} \\
| & & | \\
\text{CH}_2\text{OH} & & \text{CH}_2\text{OH}
\end{array}$$

Any other optically active compound that could (by chemical means that do not affect the asymmetric carbon) be converted to D(+)-glyceraldehyde (or vice versa) was also assigned the D configuration. In the case of lactic acid, the (−) enantiomer corresponds to D(+)-glyceraldehyde.

$$\begin{array}{ccc}
\text{CHO} & & \text{CO}_2\text{H} \\
| & \xrightarrow[\text{steps}]{\text{several}} & | \\
\text{H}\!-\!\text{C}\!-\!\text{OH} & & \text{H}\!-\!\text{C}\!-\!\text{OH} \\
| & & | \\
\text{CH}_2\text{OH} & & \text{CH}_3 \\
\text{D(+)-glyceraldehyde} & & \text{D(−)-lactic acid}
\end{array}$$

The functional groups characteristic of aldehydes and acids (−CHO and −CO$_2$H) will be considered later and need not concern us at this time.

2. *Constitution.* The manner in which the atoms are bonded together, it deals with the subject of structural isomerism, including both positional and functional isomerism.

3. *Configuration.* The arrangement of atoms in space, this term is usually restricted to the discussion of the stereoisomers that can be separated—that is, they are interconverted only with difficulty, such as by breaking and reforming bonds. Optical and geometric isomers are said to have configuration.

4. *Conformation.* The arrangement of atoms in space is conformation. Unlike configuration, the term refers to isomers between which there is a low-energy barrier and which can be easily interconverted. The name **rotational isomers** is used.

The distinction between configuration and conformation is not very clear in some cases. In this elementary text, the examples of ethane (conformation) and the isomeric 2-butanols (configuration) will be adequate.

2.7D   Molecules Containing More Than One Asymmetric Center

The number of possible stereomers increases very rapidly as the number of carbon atoms bonded to four different groups increases. In fact, 2^n, where n equals the number of optical centers,

Jacobus H. van't Hoff (Dutch, 1852–1911). During the time van't Hoff was studying for his doctorate at Utrecht, he published a pamphlet that was not connected with the work he was doing for his degree. This little sideline set forth his concepts of the spatial arrangement of atoms and its relationship to optical activity. His work in these areas won him the first Nobel Prize in chemistry (1901).

Courtesy of the Edgar Fahs Smith Memorial Collection.

gives the maximum number of possible isomers.* Our discussion requires that we look at those compounds that contain two such centers and, therefore, exist in four stereoisomeric modifications. The compound 2,3-dihydroxybutanoic acid provides a useful example.

$$
\begin{array}{cccc}
CO_2H & CO_2H & CO_2H & CO_2H \\
H-C-OH & HO-C-H & H-C-OH & HO-C-H \\
H-C-OH & HO-C-H & HO-C-H & H-C-OH \\
CH_3 & CH_3 & CH_3 & CH_3
\end{array}
$$

You will notice that there are two pairs of enantiomers and that the members of each pair are not related as mirror images to the members of the other pair. Compounds having the same constitution but different configurations are either enantiomers or diastereomers. In other words, the **diastereomers** do *not* have a different configuration at *every* asymmetric atom. Inasmuch as diastereomers have different physical properties, they can be separated by the usual physical techniques; this topic will be discussed in greater detail later (pp. 330 and 401).

Another example of compounds with two asymmetric centers is the interesting case that results when they are both bonded to the same set of four different groups. Tartaric acid, studied by Pasteur, gives us a fine example.

$$
\begin{array}{cccc}
CO_2H & CO_2H & CO_2H & CO_2H \\
H-C-OH & HO-C-H & H-C-OH & HO-C-H \\
H-C-OH \equiv & HO-C-H & HO-C-H & H-C-OH \\
CO_2H & CO_2H & CO_2H & CO_2H
\end{array}
$$

*meso*tartaric acid   (+)-tartaric acid   (−)-tartaric acid

The right-hand pair of drawings represents two enantiomers, but those on the left are identical because the two ends are both carboxyl groups, permitting the structures to be superimposed by rotation of 180°. Such a *meso* **form** is optically inactive because it has a plane of symmetry between the two asymmetric carbon atoms. It is the same as saying that one end of the molecule is the mirror image of the other and that these two cancel one

---

*The van't Hoff Rule.

another in the same manner as equal amounts of enantiomers in a racemate.

2.7E   Absolute Nomenclature of Stereomers

In naming optical isomers or enantiomers, it is usual to indicate the direction of rotation—for example, (+)-2-butanol and (−)-2-butanol. In the light of our previous discussion, this fact still does not say anything about the actual arrangement of atoms. Experiment has shown that the following is the actual representation of the two isomers of 2-butanol.

$$
\begin{array}{cc}
CH_3 & CH_3 \\
| & | \\
H-\!\overset{\,}{C}\!-\!OH & HO-\!\overset{\,}{C}\!\rightarrow\!H \\
| & | \\
CH_2CH_3 & CH_2CH_3 \\
\text{(+)-2-butanol} & \text{(−)-2-butanol}
\end{array}
$$

A system of nomenclature has been developed to indicate which configuration is being discussed, and it can be applied to simple cases with considerable ease. The most important consideration for us is that it is necessary to arrange the groups attached to the asymmetric center in an order of atomic priority. The convention adopted is that the atom of highest atomic number has the highest priority and each bond is considered in the assignment. To illustrate with the two 2-butanols, the oxygen of the hydroxyl group (atomic number 8) is clearly 1 and the hydrogen (atomic number 1) is 4. Both the methyl and the methylene of the ethyl group are carbon atoms and therefore have the same priority, but the methyl is bonded to three hydrogens whereas the methylene is bonded to two hydrogens and a carbon. Therefore, the ethyl group has higher priority than the methyl group. In more complicated molecules, this same basic technique of following the chain until a difference is found can be applied. Thus, we have, in order of increasing priority, methyl, ethyl, propyl, *iso*propyl, *sec*-butyl, *tert*-butyl, and so on.

The next step in naming these stereomers is to visualize the molecule as it would appear if you were to look along the carbon bond from the asymmetric center toward the group of lowest priority (hydrogen, in the present case; see Figure 2.7).

The three remaining groups are arranged as the spokes of a wheel, and the order of decreasing priority is observed. In cases of a clockwise decrease, such as (−)-2-butanol, the assignment **R**,

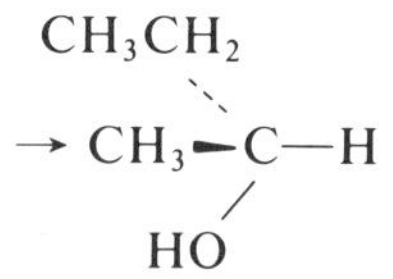

$$CH_3CH_2$$
$$\rightarrow CH_3 - C - H$$
$$HO$$

R-(−)-2-butanol

FIGURE 2.7.   Method of Observing R and S Convention.

from the Latin *rectus* or right, is made, and the complete name becomes R-(−)-2-butanol. When the decrease is in a counter-clockwise sense, it is designated **S** from the Latin *sinister* or left, yielding S-(+)-2-butanol.

SUGGESTED ADDITIONAL READINGS

Nomenclature

Benfey (Nomenclature).
Traynham.

C. D. Hurd, "The General Philosophy of Organic Nomenclature," *J. Chem. Educ.*, **38,** 43 (1961).

Conformation

Allinger and Allinger, Chapter 6.
Cram and Hammond, pp. 148–150.
Herz, pp. 38–39.
Morrison and Boyd, pp. 92–99.
Roberts and Caserio, pp. 11–13.

M. S. Newman, "A Notation for the Study of Certain Stereochemical Problems," *J. Chem. Educ.*, **32,** 344 (1955).

N. L. Allinger, "Conformational Analysis in the Elementary Organic Course," *J. Chem. Educ.*, **41,** 70 (1964).

J. P. Idoux, "Conformational Analysis and Chemical Reactivity," *J. Chem. Educ.*, **44,** 495 (1967).

Stereoisomerism

Allinger and Allinger, pp. 26–30.
Cason, Chapter 22.

Cram and Hammond, pp. 162–180.
Herz, Chapter 11.
Morrison and Boyd, pp. 70–90.
Roberts and Caserio, Chapter 17.

E. L. Eliel, "Teaching Organic Stereochemistry," *J. Chem. Educ.*, **41,** 73 (1964).

R. S. Cahn, "An Introduction to the Sequence Rule," *J. Chem. Educ.*, **41,** 116 (1964).

J. A. Schellman and C. Schellman, "Optical Rotation and the Shape of Molecules," *Chemistry*, **40** (5), 12 (1967).

B. S. Dodge, "Louis Pasteur's Looking Glass World," *Chemistry*, **41** (2), 16 (1968).

Models

E. J. Barrett and J. G. Harwell, "Molecular Framework Models. Part I," *Chemistry*, **39** (10), 14 (1966); "Part II," *Chemistry*, **40** (3), 16 (1967).

SUMMARY

1. A given functional group will generally impart certain characteristic properties to any molecule containing it.

2. The compounds containing a carbinol group are called alcohols.

3. Homologs are compounds containing a given functional group and differing from one another by a methylene group.

4. Isomers are compounds having the same molecular formula, but a different structural and/or spatial arrangement.

5. Atoms connected by σ bonds are usually free to rotate, and the various spatial arrangements of the molecule during such rotation are called conformations.

6. Stereoisomers are compounds which differ only in the arrangement of their atoms in space.

7. Enantiomers are related as an object and its mirror image. This difference is detected by its effect on plane-polarized light.

8. Many organic reactions leading to asymmetric atoms give racemic mixtures which contain equal numbers of the two possible enantiomers. Such mixtures can often be separated or resolved.

9. The configuration of an enantiomer is the arrangement of its atoms in space and can be expressed in either relative or absolute terms.

10. Stereomers which do not have the opposite configuration at every asymmetric atom are called diastereomers.

PROBLEMS

1. From the following list of compounds:
   a. Select a pair of isomers.
   b. Select two homologs.
   c. Indicate the functional group.
   d. Write the general molecular formula for the compounds listed.
   e. Write the structural formula of a *new* homolog.

   (1) CH_3 (2) CH_3

   CH_3—C—OH   CH—OH

            CH_3 CH_3

   (3) $CH_3CH_2CH_2CH_2$—OH

   (4) CH_3—OH   (5) CH_3CH_2—OH

2. a. Draw the structural formulas for all isomeric alcohols (diols) having the formula $C_4H_8(OH)_2$. Do not include simple diols with both hydroxyl groups on the same carbon.
   b. Draw the structural formula for one homolog of the preceding compounds.
   c. Draw an isomer, of this formula, which is no longer an alcohol.

3. Draw the most important conformations of the following compounds. Which conformation (in each case) would you expect to be most stable? Least stable?

   a. Cl_3CCCl_3 c. $CH_3CH_2CH_2CH_3$
   b. CH_3CH_2Cl d. $CHBr_2CH_2Br$

4. How many stereoisomers would you expect for each of the following compounds?

   a. CHFClBr
   b. $CH_3CHCHCH_2CH_3$
            $|$ $|$
            OHOH
   c. $CH_3CH_2CHCO_2H$
              $|$
              NH_2

d. CH_3CHO

e.  $CH_3CHCH_2CH_3$
      |
     NH_2

f. 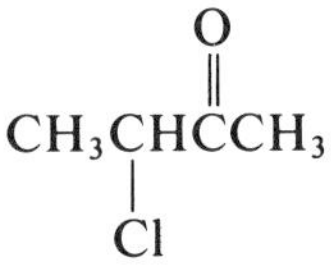   O
         ||
  CH_3CHCCH_3
     |
    Cl

g. 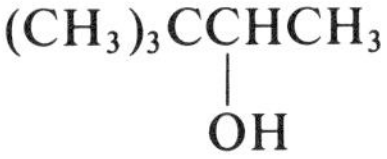 $(CH_3)_3CCHCH_3$
          |
        OH

h.  $CH_3CHCHCHCHO$
      | | |
    OHOHOH

i.  $HO_2CCHCHCO_2H$
       | |
     Cl Cl

j. 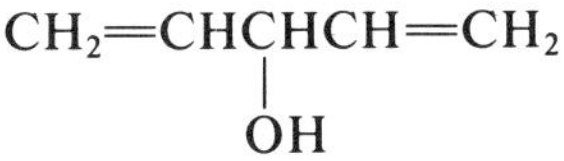 $CH_2{=}CHCHCH{=}CH_2$
         |
       OH

Draw three-dimensional figures for each enantiomer.

3

The Mechanism
of Organic Reactions

3.1
IONIC REACTIONS AND THE IMPORTANCE OF CHARGE

A reaction has occurred when one compound has been converted to another compound or changed in some other way so that it no longer shows its characteristic properties. The covalently bonded organic compounds can undergo reactions only by breaking some bonds and generally forming new ones. As you will see in this and later chapters, there is more than one way in which this can happen, but, regardless of the details, it must involve electrons. Because electrons are unit negative charges, it follows that the magnitude and distribution of charge are important considerations in the study of organic reactions.

Earlier, when we considered bonding, it was pointed out that covalent and ionic are simply the extremes with a continuum of intermediate polar covalent bonds between. Thus, although organic compounds may not usually show the full unit(s) of charge found in ionic structures, many of them are more or less charged in that there is an uneven distribution of electrons. As an example, consider chloromethane:

$$\overset{\longmapsto}{\underset{H_3C\text{---}Cl}{\overset{\delta+\qquad\quad\delta-}{}}}$$

In the same way as HCl, this molecule is a polar one by virtue of the different electronegativities of carbon, hydrogen, and chlorine.

In addition to the molecule undergoing reaction (the **substrate**), the **attacking reagent** of an organic reaction will often be ionic (or partly ionic) in nature. Numerous examples will be discussed in the subsequent chapters of this text: for example, H_3O^+, ^-OH, X^-, NH_3, HBr, and so forth.

From this brief discussion, which will be greatly extended in later chapters, we realize that the fact that charged and polar species are involved in organic reactions will be of great help in predicting the nature of the reaction observed. For example, if hydroxide ion were to attack chloromethane, it would be reasonable for the reaction to take place on the partially positive carbon rather than the partially negative chlorine.

$$^-OH + \overset{\delta+}{C}H_3 \overset{\delta-}{-}Cl \rightarrow HO \overset{\delta-}{-} \overset{\delta+}{C}H_3 + Cl^-$$

This prediction is exactly in accord with the reaction that is typical of alkyl halides, and it also offers us a reasonable explanation of the observation.

Still another example of the importance of charged collections of atoms in organic reactions can be found in various arrangements of atoms, which have a short life, between reactants and products. If an ion reacts with a neutral molecule, it is clear that the charge of the ion must be included in at least one of these arrangements. Returning to our example of the transformation of chloromethane to methanol, we see that

$$HO^- + \overset{\delta+}{C}H_3 \overset{\delta-}{-}Cl \rightarrow [HO \cdots \overset{\delta+}{C}H_3 \cdots \overset{\delta-}{Cl}] \rightarrow HO \overset{\delta-}{-} \overset{\delta+}{C}H_3 + Cl^-$$

Species like that shown in square brackets must be considered to understand many organic reactions. The arrow from the hydroxy anion to the methyl carbon is intended to indicate the shift of an electron pair and will be used often.

One final point to be appreciated in the matter of ionic organic reactions is the role played by the solvent. Ionic reactions are usually favored by solvents that are themselves ionizing —that is, those which are good solvents for ionic materials. The example we have been discussing is carried out most successfully in water, which is one of our best ionizing solvents.

3.2
WHAT IS A REACTION MECHANISM?

Perhaps the chief reason organic chemistry is so fascinating to both the experienced and the novice chemist, and even to the layman, is its complexity. How can so many compounds of such variety exist? How does it happen that it is possible to convert one arrangement of atoms into several others of such different properties? Questions of this kind have been explored in the last chapter in our discussion of the structure of organic compounds.

Once even the most limited laboratory experience has been gained, other more sophisticated questions arise. Why do small changes in reaction conditions produce such striking differences in the products? Why do compounds that are apparently very similar react so differently when treated with the same reagents? It is the purpose of this chapter to discuss the methods by which these questions are studied. In later chapters, you will see how these tools are applied.

Since the early twentieth century, organic research chemists have spent a great deal of effort in studies of questions such as those just raised. Their work, in the area known as **physical-**

Christopher K. Ingold *(English, 1893–   ). In a long and productive career Ingold has developed much of the foundation of physical-organic chemistry. From his D.Sc. thesis at Imperial College, London, through his over 400 papers he continues to show both imagination and remarkable versatility. Ingold's influence on the science of organic chemistry is difficult to overestimate. His classic book,* Structure and Mechanism in Organic Chemistry, *continues to be widely read and the second edition has appeared. Probably Ingold's most extensive and widely known studies were in collaboration with E. D. Hughes and dealt with the mechanism of substitution and elimination reactions.*

organic chemistry, has resulted in an improved understanding of the manner in which reactions occur. It has enabled scientists to predict the best conditions for carrying out both new and old reactions, and thereby it has made possible the synthesis of many new and useful organic compounds. Of perhaps greater scientific interest is the number of new questions the application of exact quantitative measurement to organic reactions has opened for study. Such always seems to be the consequence of scientific work—that is, that each new fact learned uncovers our ignorance of other interesting aspects of nature.

The general type of study that concerns us in this chapter is that of a **reaction mechanism**, and we should begin with a working definition. Any reaction involves the change of one molecule into another, which is made up of a different number and kind of atoms or, at least, a different arrangement of the atoms. The transformation of organic reactants into products does not usually happen so rapidly as inorganic reactions, but very often a substantial period of time is required. A series of changes takes place according to a very definite time schedule. The time difference is only one of degree; reactions between ions also require a sequence of events, but occur at a much more rapid rate.

The reaction mechanism is simply a detailed knowledge of what takes place as the reactant molecule is changed into the product(s). The amount of detail depends on a great many factors, the most important of which are the interest chemists have in the particular reaction and the techniques available to them for its study. Ideally, a reaction mechanism would be a motion picture of a reactant molecule becoming product and would include a complete knowledge of the position, energy, and motion of every atom and bond during the entire process. In practice, this ideal is rarely approached, and for most reactions we are satisfied with an understanding of certain points of special interest along the path of the reaction.

3.3
**POTENTIAL ENERGY DIAGRAMS AND
THE REACTION COORDINATE**

One of the most important considerations in the study of organic reaction mechanisms is that of energy. Of particular interest is that quantity known as the **activation energy**, the energy required for a given molecule to undergo a chemical change. We know from past observations in the laboratory that these energies can be substantial, because it is often necessary to heat organic reactants to cause them to react at a reasonable rate.

The consideration of energy as it affects organic reactions provides us with a very useful method of expressing and understanding a given reaction mechanism. The technique, usually referred to as an **energy diagram**, consists of plotting the progress of a reaction against energy. The progress of the reaction is called the **reaction coordinate** and may be thought of as the path (in terms of energy) by which a reactant molecule becomes product.* Figure 3.1 illustrates an energy diagram for a

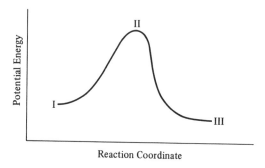

FIGURE 3.1.   Potential Energy Diagram for a Simple Displacement.

simple organic reaction. Numerals I and III represent the potential energy of reactant and product, respectively, and II is the maximum potential energy that the system reaches during the course of the reaction. We shall have a closer look at II in the following section. For now, we note that the energy of activation is the difference in energy between I and II. This fact is especially important, because energy differences can be measured much more accurately than individual energies.

3.4
INTERMEDIATE AND TRANSITION STATE

The point of maximum potential energy on the reaction coordinate in Figure 3.1, labeled II, is of special importance in the study

---

*The reaction coordinate is usually taken to illustrate in a general way the progress of the reaction, but it can be given exact quantitative significance.

of reaction mechanisms. The characteristics of this collection of atoms—for example, its geometry, charge distribution, and so on—have a great deal to do with the effect various changes in reaction conditions will have on the speed and outcome of the reaction. For this reason, often one of the goals of a mechanism study may be to learn something about the **transition state** or potential energy maximum.

Unfortunately, a species at such a potential energy maximum can never be isolated and cannot usually be studied directly. Therefore, everything known about such an important aspect of the mechanism generally must be learned by indirect methods. This fact often requires that we assume a **model** for the transition state and determine whether our observations are consistent with such a model. When they are not, it is necessary to modify that model or to design a new one that is in accord with all the known facts.

Figure 3.1 represents the energy diagram for the simplest possible reaction in which there is a single transition state and its accompanying energy barrier separating reactants and products. In more complicated cases, there will be additional transition states and intermediate energy minimum or minima [i.e., **chemical intermediate(s)**], as shown in Figure 3.2. As before, I and V

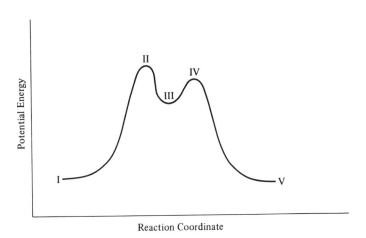

FIGURE 3.2.   Potential Energy Diagram for a Reactive Intermediate.

represent reactant and product; but in this reaction, there are two transition states (II and IV) with an intermediate III between. There are also two energies of activation—the difference between I and II and the difference between III and IV. In Figure 3.2, the former of these is much larger than the latter, and, therefore, this step of the overall reaction will proceed more slowly and control the rate at which the product is formed. It also follows from this energy consideration that III represents an **unstable intermediate**. This statement means that inasmuch as its activation energy is much lower for reaction (to form products) than for formation, it will be present in very low concentration and cannot usually be isolated.

3.5
THE SCIENTIFIC METHOD

The study of reaction mechanisms provides a good example of the proper application of the **scientific method**. The first step in any mechanistic study is to assemble all the available facts concerning the reaction, which would include the reaction conditions, the various reactants that have been used, the products obtained, the effect of changes of various kinds, what is known about related reactions, and so forth. From these accumulated data, it will be possible to construct an informed guess as to what the reaction mechanism might be—that is, to formulate a **hypothesis**.

The hypothesis must explain all the known facts concerning the reaction; it *may* be the correct reaction mechanism, but we have no assurance that it *is* the correct one. Therefore, it is necessary to design experiments to test the validity of this hypothetical reaction path. In other words, if it is the correct mechanism, it should lead to certain results with a given starting material and set of reaction conditions. By carrying out that reaction, we can test the correctness of the prediction. As was pointed out earlier, an important part of this hypothesis is the model selected for the transition state. The extent to which the observations and prediction agree will depend on this model and its appropriateness to the reaction under investigation.

As was the case in our discussion of transition state models, any disagreement between the predicted and observed results of an experiment designed to test a hypothesis must lead either to a modification of the hypothesis or to its abandonment in favor of a radically new hypothesis. Bear in mind that the mechanism must continue to be tested, even if it correctly predicted the outcome of the present test experiment.

This discussion brings us to our final point concerning the scientific method and reaction mechanisms—our uncertainty concerning the correctness of a hypothesis. It is a fundamental truth of the application of the scientific method to reaction mechanisms that one can never prove a hypothesis to be true, inasmuch as some key facts—for example, transition state structure—are not subject to direct observation. It is possible to prove it false, that is, that it is not consistent with the known facts; however, no matter how many correct predictions it has made, we never know that it will not fail on the next test. This aspect of scientific work is one that is poorly understood and leads to some misunderstanding. For example, it is usually believed that a scientific law is known to be true when in reality it simply means that the law has correctly predicted the outcome of a very great number of test experiments. We might recall the Laws of Conservation of Mass and Energy, which survived a great number of tests until Einstein showed that mass could be converted into energy and vice versa. Remember, we can say that a given mechanism is consistent with all known facts, but we can never say that it is proved unless the process has been completely observed at an informational level.

3.6
METHODS OF STUDYING MECHANISMS

The relatively new field of physical-organic chemistry has borrowed much from theoretical studies, yet it is basically an experimental science. The dependence on observation for data from which to formulate a hypothetical mechanism and the need to devise and execute experiments to test the validity of the hypothesis all require laboratory skill and a constant stream of new and more sophisticated instruments and techniques. An understanding of the mechanism of organic reactions requires a knowledge of the methods by which they are obtained. The following are among the most generally useful:

3.6A Product Analysis

This aspect of a mechanistic study may seem so obvious as not to be worth mentioning, yet it is sometimes neglected, which can greatly interfere with the progress of understanding. In formulating an initial hypothesis, we must isolate and identify (quantitatively, if possible) *all* components in the reaction mixture after the reaction. Nearly all organic reactions lead to more than one product, and much light can be shed on the possible mechanism if the minor products are found and identified.

3.6B   Isolation of Intermediates

The intermediates introduced earlier in our discussion of transition states were those of high energy; therefore, it was not possible to separate them from the reaction mixture. A great many organic reactions proceed through intermediates of sufficient stability that they can be obtained as pure, stable, organic molecules. Such a reaction might be described by an energy diagram shown in Figure 3.3. The various points on this graph

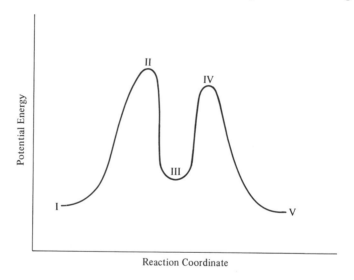

FIGURE 3.3.   Potential Energy Diagram for a Stable Intermediate.

have the same meaning as those in Figure 3.2, with the important difference that the intermediate III has such a high activation energy, to reach transition state IV or reverse to II, that it is stable enough to be isolated.

   In cases of this kind, important pieces of information can be obtained relative to the mechanism. The net effect is to break down a complex reaction into two or more simpler reactions, which certainly is of great help in eliminating unlikely mechanisms and rationalizing a pathway that is consistent with these additional facts. It is possible to prepare stable intermediates, and sometimes not so stable intermediates, by independent reactions and then subject the proposed intermediate to the conditions of the reaction under study. If the compound reacts to produce the same percentage and composition of products, it may be taken as evidence that it is indeed a probable intermediate.

Before leaving this specific method of studying reaction mechanisms, we should notice that although it is not always possible to isolate an intermediate, it is very often possible to demonstrate its presence in a reaction and to study it by using physical means. Thus, with infrared or ultraviolet spectroscopy, freezing point depression, and so on, information concerning intermediates (although not transition states) is available to the physical-organic chemist.

3.6C   Reaction Conditions and Substrates

A very potent tool for the study of reaction mechanisms is the systematic variation of various factors or parameters in the reaction. Among these would be solvent, temperature, catalysts, light, structure of the starting material, and the like. The application of this technique calls for all the skill, imagination, and experience at the researcher's command.

Any postulated mechanism will have certain predictable consequences as a result of changes, as previously suggested. For example, if the reaction in question is thought to involve the formation of ions, it would be expected to proceed more readily in good polar ionizing solvents than in nonpolar solvents, such as hydrocarbons. Numerous examples of these effects will be examined in our discussion of specific reaction mechanisms.

This technique is really a special case of the general scientific requirement of testing predictions made with a postulated mechanism. If the results of such a test are not in accord with the expected outcome, either the prediction was not based on sound reasoning or the postulated mechanism must be modified to accommodate these new observations.

3.6D   Kinetic Studies

The suggested variations of the preceding section can result in different products and yields of products, or they can be evaluated in other ways. However, the most important technique for this and other types of mechanistic study is that of determining the **velocity** or **rate** of a chemical reaction—that is, its **kinetics**. To appreciate the application of this method, we must introduce very briefly and in a very simplified manner the basic facts of kinetic studies.

If we consider the simple reaction,

$$A \rightarrow B$$

it is apparent that the rate can be considered the change of concentration of either A or B with respect to time. This change will be proportional to the concentration of the species present at any time and will be equal to it through a proportionality constant:

$$rate = k_1[A]*$$

This equation is known as a **rate law**, and k is called the **rate constant**. A more complicated reaction could lead to several different rate laws; for example, the reaction

$$A + B \rightarrow C + D$$

could have the following rate law:

$$rate = k_2[A][B]$$

These expressions have been justified by an analysis that will not be repeated here.

There are two further aspects of kinetics that we should understand at this point. The first is the **order of the reaction** and is defined as the sum of the exponents of the terms in the rate equation (excluding the rate constant). Thus, the preceding examples are first and second order, respectively. The second concept is that of the **rate determining step**. When a reaction goes through a series of steps or reactions between reactants and products, each of them will have its own rate. One of these individual steps will have the slowest rate, and when the overall rate of the reaction is determined, it will have to be the rate of this slowest step. Thus, the form of the rate equation will depend on those reactants that are involved during or prior to the rate determining step.

Important points in reaction mechanism studies are the fol-

*The brackets have the usual significance of concentration in moles per liter.

lowing: (1) the rate law required to describe a given reaction will usually show that some possible mechanisms are not acceptable; and (2) the change of rate constant with variation in reaction conditions is usually the best method of evaluating the effect of these changes. The required rate law will usually permit more than a single mechanism, and further evidence is required.

3.6E   Stereochemical Studies

The last tool to be considered in this brief outline of mechanism studies is the evidence that can be found by considering the change or lack of change in **stereochemistry** occurring during the course of a reaction. Data of this kind, coupled with kinetic study, are the most frequently used of all possible approaches in studying the problems of mechanism.

As was true in our other suggested methods, a postulated mechanism will frequently require a certain stereochemical outcome if the reaction is carried out at the asymmetric carbon of a particular enantiomer. Inasmuch as it is possible to obtain a sample of one isomer of a known configuration from natural materials or by resolution (pp. 330 and 401), the application of this technique is both practical and very informative.

The product(s) obtained from the reaction of an enantiomer under given conditions can show certain definite stereochemical characteristics. First, the product may show the same arrangement (configuration) at the asymmetric carbon atom. Such an outcome is referred to as **retention of configuration**. Second, the arrangement may be opposite to that of the starting material— **inversion products**. Third, the resulting compound may show no optical activity because there is an equal amount of retention and inversion. This last characteristic is known as **racemization,** inasmuch as a racemate or racemic mixture is found in the product (see Figure 3.4).

These three possibilities actually are points on a continuum, and mixtures of retention and inversion, other than 1:1, may result. Thus, there may be more retention than inversion, and the product may show a measurable, but decreased, optical activity. Such a situation would be described as a certain percentage of net retention with the balance racemization. On the other side of overall racemization would be a reaction in which inversion occurred more frequently than retention. This reaction

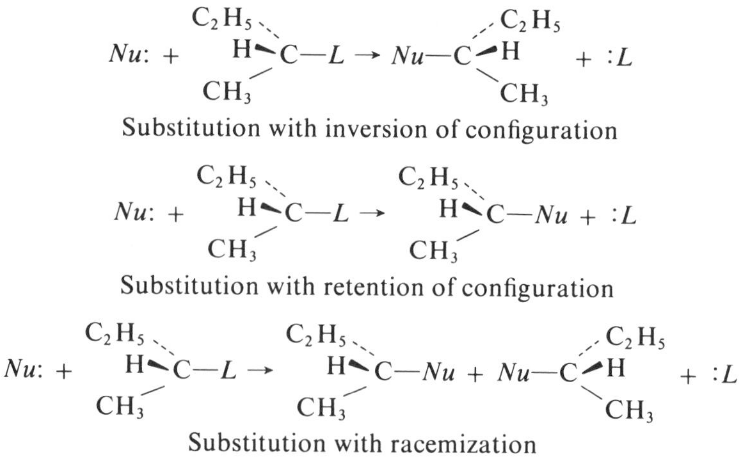

$$Nu: + \quad \underset{CH_3}{\overset{C_2H_5}{H{\smallsmile}C-L}} \rightarrow Nu-\underset{CH_3}{\overset{C_2H_5}{C{\smallsmile}H}} \quad + :L$$

Substitution with inversion of configuration

$$Nu: + \quad \underset{CH_3}{\overset{C_2H_5}{H{\smallsmile}C-L}} \rightarrow \quad \underset{CH_3}{\overset{C_2H_5}{H{\smallsmile}C-Nu}} + :L$$

Substitution with retention of configuration

$$Nu: + \quad \underset{CH_3}{\overset{C_2H_5}{H{\smallsmile}C-L}} \rightarrow \quad \underset{CH_3}{\overset{C_2H_5}{H{\smallsmile}C-Nu}} + Nu-\underset{CH_3}{\overset{C_2H_5}{C{\smallsmile}H}} \quad + :L$$

Substitution with racemization

FIGURE 3.4.   Stereochemical Results of Substitution

would be described as some percentage of net inversion. Whichever of these several possibilities is actually observed, it will cast doubt on some possible hypothetical mechanisms and remain consistent with others.

3.7
REACTION SITES AND REACTIVE INTERMEDIATES

Not only does the study of organic reaction mechanisms provide new and useful knowledge and understanding to the professional chemist, but it can also be helpful to the student. The chief reason is that even the little bit we know about these subtle details of nature helps us to organize and remember the huge number of organic reactions. In the past, the most useful method was to classify organic reactions on the basis of the functional groups involved. This process is certainly a very useful system, but it is not the only one.

It is becoming more common to associate reactions with their mechanistic types; this arrangement should become increasingly useful as we learn more about the mechanistic details. In this text, we shall use both the functional group and the mechanism approach to help us describe and remember reactions.

The following is a useful partial outline of reaction types:

1. ionic
2. radical

Each of these general classes may be further subdivided as follows:

(a) substitution (including esterification)
(b) elimination
(c) addition
(d) rearrangement

We should keep in mind that a given reaction may fall in more than one category, for example, substitution with rearrangement.

3.8
MAKING AND BREAKING COVALENT BONDS

All organic reactions, inasmuch as they result in one compound being transformed into another, must involve the breaking and forming of covalent bonds. The reaction mechanism as defined earlier is simply a detailed account of the sequence of these events. For these reasons, we are very concerned with the manner in which the bonds are broken, the nature of the resulting fragments, and the characteristics of these in forming new covalent bonds.

Inasmuch as a covalent bond is a pair of electrons shared by two atoms, there are two fundamentally different modes of cleavage:

$$A \overset{..}{.} B \rightarrow A^{\bullet} + B\bullet \qquad \text{homolytic}$$

$$A \vdots B \rightarrow A^{+} + \mathbf{:}B^{-} \quad \text{or} \quad A\mathbf{:}^{-} + B^{+} \qquad \text{heterolytic}$$

The symmetrical or **homolytic** breaking of a covalent bond produces two uncharged **radicals,** each having a single unpaired electron. The unsymmetrical or **heterolytic** cleavage produces two oppositely charged **ions.** Which of the two atoms or groups of atoms loses its electron and becomes positively charged depends on the electronegativity of that atom or group. For example, if B were much more electronegative than A, the reactant would, in the absence of other strong factors, cleave as follows:

$$A \mathbf{:} B \rightarrow A^{+} + \mathbf{:}B^{-}$$

We shall be concerned with ionic substitution, elimination, addition, and rearrangement reactions, and radical substitution and addition reactions.

When a covalent bond is broken and either a radical or an ion is formed, we are immediately concerned with two questions: (1) Which type of cleavage is observed and why? (2) If more than one radical or ion could be produced, which would be observed? These questions of ease of formation and stability will be answered generally now and with specific illustrations later.

The formation of radicals or ions depends chiefly on the nature of the covalent bond being broken and on reaction conditions. We shall be interested mostly in radicals and ions of carbon, with a few cases involving oxygen and nitrogen.

Reactions involving **carbanions** and **carbonium ions** are strongly favored by polar covalent bonds and solvents of high ionizing power—for example, water, alcohol, acetic acid, and so forth.

$$-\overset{|}{\underset{|}{C}}-Br \xrightarrow{\text{H}_2\text{O}} \left[-\overset{|}{\underset{|}{C}}^+ \right] + Br^-$$

a carbonium ion

In the preceding equations, the ions are meant only to represent the unstable intermediate through which the reactions are thought to proceed. These **reactive intermediates** are usually not isolated, but, from the nature of the reactants and products, they are thought to be reasonable.

Radical reactions are generally promoted by reactants that possess weak and nonpolar covalent bonds. Such a bond might be expected to break in a homolytic manner. Inasmuch as there are no charged species to be stabilized, radical reactions generally do not show the strong relationship to solvent polarity that is characteristic of ionic reactions. The energy required for homolytic cleavage of a covalent bond is frequently provided by radiant energy ($h\nu$). This process requires that the molecule be able to absorb visible or ultraviolet light and that there be bonds of low enough energy to dissociate into radicals. If the reaction is greatly retarded in the dark, there is some evidence that radicals are involved. These uncharged atoms or groups of atoms are usually very short lived and are included in the class of reactive intermediates.

The question of the relative stability of various ions and

radicals is of some importance and will be presented here with only the briefest justification.

Carbonium ions CH_3^+ $<$ $R{-}CH_2^+$ $<$ $\underset{R}{\overset{R}{>}}CH^+$ $<$ $R{-}\underset{R}{\overset{R}{C}}{}^+$

Radicals $CH_3^{\bullet}$ $<$ $R{-}CH_2^{\bullet}$ $<$ $\underset{R}{\overset{R}{>}}CH^{\bullet}$ $<$ $R{-}\underset{R}{\overset{R}{C}}{}^{\bullet}$

Carbanions $R{-}\underset{R}{\overset{R}{C}}{}^-$ $<$ $\underset{R}{\overset{R}{>}}CH^-$ $<$ $R{-}CH_2^-$ $<$ CH_3^-

increasing stability $\longrightarrow$

The slight electron-donating tendency (**inductive effect**) of alkyl groups would correctly predict the observed order of stability for ions. With groups other than alkyl, the inductive order is still followed; for example, the electron-withdrawing carbonyl group ($>C{=}O$):

$$CH_3{-}\overset{O}{\overset{\|}{C}}{-}CH_2^+ \; < \; H{-}\overset{O}{\overset{\|}{C}}{-}CH_2{-}CH_2^+ \; < \; CH_3{-}CH_2{-}CH_2^+$$

The reasons for the observed stability of aliphatic radicals are less well understood, but it is clear that they are electron deficient like the carbonium ion. Therefore, they might also be stabilized by electron-donating groups, and the order of relative stability would be as observed.

One further topic to be mentioned at this point, without proof,* is the geometry of these reactive fragments. The evidence strongly indicates that the carbonium ion is planar and the radical is either planar or is a very rapidly inverting pyramid. The carbanion is also a very rapidly inverting pyramid (see Figure 3.5). The inversion referred to here involves the odd electron (of the radical) or the electron pair (of the carbanion) and is similar to the situation of the ammonia molecule. The shape of

---

*For a very interesting discussion of the question of the shape of molecules and ions, see the Suggested Additional Readings.

$$\ddot{C} \rightleftharpoons \ddot{C} \rightleftharpoons \ddot{C}$$

FIGURE 3.5.   Rapidly Inverting Carbanion

these groups will be very useful in the task of explaining the observed results of mechanistic studies.

3.10
NUCLEOPHILE AND ELECTROPHILE

Our earlier classification of organic reactions was made on the basis of the type of process that the substrate underwent. We often ask which ion or molecule is the substrate and which is doing the reacting (the "reagent"), or, as it is referred to, "making the attack." Inasmuch as it is frequently possible for different species (e.g., anions or cations) to carry out reactions of the same general class (e.g., substitution), it is useful to have a further subdivision based on the reagent.

It is quite reasonable that a positively charged carbonium ion would carry out its attack at a position of high electron density. Such a group is known as an **electrophile** or "electron-seeking" species. In a similar manner, a carbanion should seek a site of low electron density and is referred to as a **nucleophile** or "nucleus-seeking" group.

Positively and negatively charged carbon atoms are clearly not the only possible electrophiles and nucleophiles; a large number of charged and uncharged groups are electron rich or electron poor; for example,

Nucleophiles ^-OH, ^-X, $\ddot{N}H_3$, ^-CN, $H_2\ddot{O}$, R—$\ddot{O}H$, etc.

Electrophiles ^+H, BF_3, $^+NO_2$, SO_3, ^+Br, $AlCl_3$, etc.

The reactions in which one or the other of these types of attacking reagents take part are distinguished by an indication of their electronic nature. For example, a substitution by hydroxide ion would be discussed as a nucleophilic substitution.

Reaction Mechanisms in General

Allinger and Allinger, Chapters 7–8.
Breslow, Chapter 2.
Cram and Hammond, Chapter 12.
Gould, Chapters 5–6, pp. 127–31.
Pryor, Chapters 1–2 and 12.
Saunders, pp. 1–9.
Stewart.

R. H. DeWolfe, "Kinetics in the Study of Organic Reaction Mechanisms," *J. Chem. Educ.,* **40,** 95 (1963).

M. C. Caserio, "Reaction Mechanisms in Organic Chemistry. Part I, The Experimental Approach," *J. Chem. Educ.,* **42,** 570 (1965); "Part II, The Reaction Intermediate," *J. Chem. Educ.,* **42,** 627 (1965).

L. P. Hammett, "Physical Organic Chemistry in Retrospect," *J. Chem. Educ.,* **43,** 464 (1966).

Scientific Method

Wilson, Chapter 3.

The Shape of Molecules and Ions

R. J. Gillespie, "The Valence-Shell Electron-Pair Repulsion (VSEPR) Theory of Directed Valency," *J. Chem. Educ.,* **40,** 295 (1963).

W. F. Luder, "The Electron Repulsion Theory of the Chemical Bond. Part I," *J. Chem. Educ.,* **44,** 206 (1967); "Part II," *J. Chem. Educ.,* **44,** 269 (1967).

SUMMARY

1. Organic reactions involve the breaking and making of bonds; usually covalent bonds.

2. The curved arrow (⌒↘) indicates the shift of a pair of electrons and does not necessarily have mechanistic significance.

3. The mechanism of a reaction is a more or less detailed description of the route from reactant to product.

4. The transition state is a point of maximum potential energy.

5. A point of minimum potential energy is called an intermediate. The stability of an intermediate depends on the activation energies associated with it.

6. The potential energy difference between a reactant or intermediate and transition state is the activation energy. The greatest difference of this kind will be associated with the slowest reaction step and will controi the overall observed rate of the reaction.

7. The study of reaction mechanisms requires the careful application of the scientific method including the selection of a model, the formation and testing of a suitable hypothesis, and its subsequent modification.

8. Numerous techniques are used in mechanistic studies including: product and intermediate isolation, kinetic studies, and stereochemical studies.

9. It is often useful to discuss organic reactions on the basis of the reaction mechanism involved.

10. Radicals, carbanions, and carbonium ions are the most common reactive species in organic reactions. These and other reagents are often classified as electrophiles and nucleophiles depending on their relative electron density.

PROBLEMS

1. One of the most important aspects of this introduction to organic mechanisms is the terminology. Give a brief definition of each of the following, using examples and drawings where possible:

   a. activation energy
   b. transition state
   c. reaction rate
   d. substrate
   e. nucleophile
   f. retention of configuration

   g. carbanion
   h. racemization
   i. electrophile
   j. radical
   k. intermediate
   l. carbonium ion

2. After you had determined that the following sets of characteristics were true of a reaction under investigation, sketch the potential energy diagram that would describe such a reaction.

   a. The reactants and products are of approximately equal potential energy, and the reaction passes through a single transition state.

   b. The products are of higher potential energy than the reactants and the reaction involves two steps with the first being rate determining. The intermediate is of high potential energy and cannot be isolated.

c. The reactants are of higher potential energy than the products, and a very stable intermediate is involved in the reaction. The conversion of the intermediate to product is the slow step of the overall reaction.

In each of sections (a) through (c), label all the important parts of the diagrams.

3. The example shown at the beginning of Chapter 3 is known to proceed in a single, nearly irreversible reaction to the products given:

$$HO^- + CH_3Cl \rightarrow [\overset{\delta-}{HO}\cdots\overset{\delta+}{CH_3}\cdots\overset{\delta-}{Cl}\ ] \rightarrow HOCH_3 + Cl^-$$

a. Draw and label the potential energy diagram for this reaction.
b. What kinetic expression (rate law) would you expect for this reaction?
c. Draw a three-dimensional sketch of how the transition state might look.
d. Identify the type of reaction taking place from the list on pp. 56–57.
e. What is the substrate and the nucleophile or electrophile in the reaction?

4. A reaction that appears to be very similar to that discussed in question 3 is the reaction of t-butyl chloride with hydroxide ion:

$$(CH_3)_3C\!-\!Cl \xrightarrow[slow]{} [(CH_3)_3C^+] + Cl^- \xrightarrow[fast]{OH^-} (CH_3)_3C\!-\!OH + Cl^-$$

a. Answer questions 3(a)–(e) in terms of this new reaction.
f. Is it reasonable that t-butyl chloride should follow this mechanism more easily than methyl chloride? Why?
g. What kinds of solvents should be best for this reaction? Would the same be true of the reaction in question 3?

5. Suppose we had a compound that could undergo reactions by both of the mechanisms in questions 3 and 4. Further suppose the chloride was optically active (a single enantiomer).

$$\underset{\underset{C_2H_5}{|}}{\overset{\overset{CH_3}{|}}{H\!-\!C}}\!-\!Cl + OH^- \rightarrow \underset{\underset{OH}{|}}{CH_3CH_2CHCH_3} + Cl^-$$

Considering each reaction (one step and two steps) separately, what would you expect the configuration(s) of the 2-butanol product to be? If 50% of the reaction takes place in one step and 50% takes place in two steps, what will the net stereochemical outcome be relative to the starting (optically pure) *sec*-butyl chloride?

4

Hydrocarbons: Unsaturated and Carbocyclic Compounds

In Chapter 2, you found that the alcohols could be thought of as a series of very similar compounds in which adjacent members differed by a CH_2 group. This concept of the homologous series allows you to write a general formula to describe the molecular formula—$C_nH_{2n+1}OH$, which is only one of such series. Now it is useful to look at a new general formula describing two quite different homologous series—$C_nH_{2n-1}OH$.

These new series of compounds contain two fewer hydrogen atoms than the alcohols with only σ bonds. There are a number of ways in which these two atoms can be removed; however, at this point we shall be concerned only with those that involve a change in the carbon structure of the molecule. Recall that rings and multiple bonds are both possible arrangements in organic compounds. Examples of these new series are on p. 66.

One of the greatest advantages of the IUPAC system of nomenclature is that once the basic rules have been mastered, it is

$$CH_2{-}CHOH$$
$$CH_2{-}CH_2$$

cyclobutanol

$$\overset{OH}{\underset{|}{}} $$
$$CH_2 \quad \overset{CH}{} \quad CHCH_2CH_3$$
$$CH_2{-}CH_2$$

2-ethylcyclopentanol

$$\overset{OH}{\underset{|}{}}$$
CH
$$CH_2 \quad CH_2$$
$$CH_2 \quad C \quad CH_3$$
$$CH_2 \quad CH_3$$

3,3-dimethylcyclohexanol

$$CH_2{=}CHCH_2OH$$

2-propen-1-ol

$$CH_2{=}CCH_2CH_2OH$$
$$\underset{CH_3}{|}$$

3-methyl-3-buten-1-ol

$$CH_3CH{=}CHCH_2OH$$

2-buten-1-ol

necessary to make only minor adjustments to add any new series of compounds. For example, the cyclic compounds have names that are exactly like the alcohols of Chapter 2, with the prefix **cyclo-** added to indicate the ring nature of the parent structure. The numbering of the ring always begins at the carbon associated with the functional group.

Alcohols containing a carbon-to-carbon double bond require other modifications. The suffix **-enol** is used in place of **-anol**, and the positions of the double bond and the hydroxyl group are indicated. The location of the double bond is given by the lower-numbered of the two carbon atoms connected by it. Thus, in the first compound that has a double bond between the second and third carbon, we use the number 2. The number locating the hydroxyl group is placed between the -en- and the -ol.

The hydrocarbons corresponding to these two new homologous series are equally easy to name correctly. The prefix **cyclo-** continues to apply and the suffix **-ene** replaces **-ane** for the open-chain hydrocarbons.

$$CH_2{-}CH_2$$
$$CH_2{-}CH_2$$

or □

cyclobutane

$$\overset{CH_2}{} $$
$$CH_2 \quad CHCH_3$$
$$CH_2{-}CH_2$$

or

$$CH_3$$

methylcyclopentane

$$CH_3CH=CH_2$$

$$\underset{\underset{\underset{CH_3}{|}}{\overset{\overset{CH_3}{|}}{CH_2}}}{CH_3C=CHCHCH_3}$$

propene   2,4-dimethyl-3-hexene

You should study all these examples because they illustrate
several new ideas. First, note the highly simplified notation for
the cyclic compounds. All the ring hydrogens are omitted; thus,
each angle represents a methylene group, unless there is another
substituent. Second, inasmuch as all the ring carbons of an
unsubstituted ring are identical, the first group attached must be
at the 1 position. This number is usually assumed—for example,
methylcyclopentane and 2-ethylcyclopentanol. The straight-
chain alcohols discussed earlier (p. 23) would also not have the 1
written as part of the name—that is, *n*-hexyl alcohol would be
simply hexanol.

The third point deals with the question of naming compounds
in which there is more than one functional group. In general, the
question is to decide which is the principal functional group.
There is no IUPAC rule as yet, but the system developed by
Chemical Abstracts is followed by a great many chemists. Some
functional groups can be indicated only by a suffix, others only
by a prefix, and still others by either. We shall discuss this topic
in more detail as we encounter additional functional groups, but
the basic rule is to use only one suffix (that of the principal functional group) and indicate all others by prefixes. Our present
example appears to be an exception, because the alcohol group
can be either hydroxy- or -ol. The explanation lies in the fact that
the hydrocarbon suffix -ene can *only* be a suffix and the alcohol
must be the principal functional group. This requirement is illustrated by the example of 3-methyl-3-buten-1-ol. If the alcohol
function were not present, the hydrocarbon double bond would
require the lower number and the numbering would be from the
other end of the chain:

$$\underset{\underset{CH_3}{|}}{CH_2=CCH_2CH_3}$$

2-methyl-1-butene

You should try naming the compounds given in the problems at the end of the chapter and also write structures for the names given. A table summarizing much of the information on nomenclature makes up the endpapers of this book. It is arranged in decreasing order of precedence for those groups that can be indicated by either a prefix or a suffix. In addition to these aids, two excellent programmed nomenclature books are listed in the Suggested Additional Readings.

4.3
THE HYDROCARBONS

When we discussed nomenclature, it was necessary to look at the simplest compounds composed only of carbon and hydrogen. In the case of molecular structure, we also looked at conformation in terms of these unsubstituted compounds. Now that we are ready to think about the properties of organic molecules, we shall once again start with the hydrocarbons.

4.3A Alkanes

1. Physical Properties (Table 4.1). It might be thought that the chemist is interested only in the chemical properties of molecules; however, you will find that such physical properties as melting point, boiling point, and solubility are important for the identification of organic structures; they even help predict chemical properties. For these reasons, we shall briefly outline the trends in physical properties for each of the functional group classes. With respect to these data, two points should be kept in mind: (1) the treatment will be qualitative in nature, and, despite the fact that specific figures are used to illustrate the point, you are responsible only for generalizations; (2) as will be shown, the concept of the homologous series is useful in remembering physical properties.

The low molecular weight alkanes are gases (C_1 to C_4), the medium chain lengths are liquids (C_5 to C_{18}), and the higher molecular weight compounds are waxlike or plastic solids. In general, the boiling and melting points increase with increasing molecular weight. Of great interest to the chemist is the matter of solubility. The question involved here is that of molecular

TABLE 4.1   PHYSICAL PROPERTIES OF SOME COMMON HYDROCARBONS

Name	Formula	Boiling point, °C	Melting point, °C	Density (liquid), g/ml
Alkanes				
Methane	CH_4	−162	−183	0.424
Ethane	CH_3CH_3	−89	−172	0.546
Propane	$CH_3CH_2CH_3$	−42	−187	0.582
Butane	$CH_3(CH_2)_2CH_3$	0	−138	0.579
Isobutane	$(CH_3)_2CHCH_3$	−12	−159	0.603
Pentane	$CH_3(CH_2)_3CH_3$	36	−130	0.626
Isopentane	$(CH_3)_2CHCH_2CH_3$	28	−160	0.620
Neopentane	$(CH_3)_4C$	10	−17	0.613
Heptadecane	$CH_3(CH_2)_{15}CH_3$	302	22	0.777
Octadecane	$CH_3(CH_2)_{16}CH_3$	316	28	0.777
Nonadecane	$CH_3(CH_2)_{17}CH_3$	330	32	0.778
Cycloalkanes				
Cyclopentane	$(CH_2)_5$	49	−94	0.746
Cyclohexane	$(CH_2)_6$	81	6	0.778
Cycloheptane	$(CH_2)_7$	118	−12	0.810
Alkenes				
Ethene	$CH_2{=}CH_2$	−102	−169	0.610
Propene	$CH_3CH{=}CH_2$	−48	−185	0.610
Cycloalkenes				
Cyclopentene	$(CH_2)_3CH{=}CH$	46	−93	0.774
1,3-Cyclopentadiene	$CH{=}CHCH_2CH{=}CH$	42	−85	0.798
Alkynes				
Ethyne	$CH{\equiv}CH$	−75	−82	0.618
Propyne	$CH_3C{\equiv}CH$	−23	−102	0.671

polarity or dipole moment, and, as would be expected for carbon-hydrogen bonds, the magnitude of this polarity is close to zero. The old axiom "like dissolves like" applies very well here, and the alkanes are almost completely insoluble in water and other very polar liquids, whereas the lower molecular weight ones are quite soluble in nonpolar organic liquids, such as ether and other hydrocarbons.

2. Chemical Properties. The first compounds in Table 4.1 are known as the **saturated hydrocarbons**, which is somewhat more descriptive than the present-day term alkane, because it indicates both their composition (carbon and hydrogen) and the fact that each carbon has four single covalent bonds (is saturated). Little can be said about the alkanes except that they are very unreactive. It is for this reason they were once called paraffins (from the Latin *parum*, little, and *affinis*, responsive). Thus, the alkanes, the paraffins, and the saturated hydrocarbons are all the same series of compounds, and although you should use the modern name, it is instructive to have learned and understood the historical names as well.

If, as in this section, we wish to limit still further the scope of our study to the open-chain compounds and to leave the ring compounds for later, we apply another new term, **aliphatic**. Like paraffin, this word has a classic derivation; it comes from the Greek *aleiphatos* meaning fat and describes the early source of many compounds of this type.

It is appropriate at this point to recognize a difference in this matter of reactivity between industry and laboratory. In many cases, a reaction that will be of great value in the commercial preparation of chemicals will be all but useless in the laboratory and vice versa. There are many reasons for this fact, including cost, equipment available, use intended, purity required, quantity involved, and the like. When a limitation of this type is involved, it will be pointed out; in solving problems, you should indicate what you know about the conditions required to bring about the desired reaction.

Although you need to distinguish between industrial and laboratory preparations, be careful not to feel that the chemistry of industrial processes is unimportant to the research chemist. There are three compelling reasons for its great importance: (1) it is frequently possible to study and therefore understand reactions involving high pressures and temperatures as well as many other factors that would be very inconvenient in the laboratory; (2) industrial chemistry is the source of many useful starting materials for further synthetic studies; and (3) an industrial application is frequently the objective of the research.

One of the few useful reactions of the alkanes is **halogenation** (mostly chlorination and bromination although fluorination is becoming increasingly important). The reaction falls in a general class of reactions, of which there are many more examples, known as **substitution reactions**. With hydrocarbons, this substitution involves the replacement of a hydrogen atom by some new atom, and, in the specific case under consideration, it would be accompanied by the production of a molecule of a simple hydrogen halide (i.e., HCl or HBr).

$$CH_4 + Cl_2 \xrightarrow{\text{heat and/or } h\nu} CH_3Cl + HCl$$

$$h\nu = \text{radiant energy}$$

The equation shown is a specific one involving methane as starting material and producing chloromethane; to show that a reaction is more general, we often write

$$RH + X_2 \xrightarrow[\text{heat}]{h\nu} RX + HX$$

$$X = Cl \text{ or } Br$$

The R simply stands for an alkyl group (p. 26)—methyl in the case of the specific equation.* In effect, it is a symbolic way of stating the concept of the homologous series, and it will be extensively used in this text where such generalization is justified. We shall be concerned with general reactions, but keep in mind that there will be exceptions to any equation in which the symbol R is used.

The halogenation of alkanes is a radical substitution; now is a good opportunity to examine the mechanism of the process and some of the evidence for it. Generally speaking, there are three distinct stages in an organic reaction having a radical mechanism:

1. **initiation**
2. **propagation**
3. **termination**

The chlorination of alkanes is frequently carried out in the gas phase, but it can also be observed in solution. When a reaction shows little sensitivity to solvent effects and will occur in the gas phase, the evidence is good that a radical mechanism may be involved. The initiation step may be formulated as the homolytic cleavage of the chlorine molecule.

$$:\ddot{C}l\!:\!\ddot{C}l\!: \xrightarrow[\substack{\text{energy} \\ (h\nu)}]{\text{radiant}} 2 :\ddot{C}l\cdot$$

---

*Any C—H bond in an alkane is a possible site for halogenation, and a complex mixture of products, consisting mostly of polyhalogenated hydrocarbons, is obtained unless special care is taken.

The radiant energy required for this dissociation is usually ultraviolet light, but it may also include heat. In later examples, you will see that other chemical initiators can be used successfully.

The propagation stage of a radical reaction always consists of at least two separate reactions, in which one of the products of the last reaction is one of the reactants of the first reaction.

$$:\ddot{C}l\cdot + H_3C:H \rightarrow H_3C\cdot + HCl$$

$$H_3C\cdot + :\ddot{C}l:\ddot{C}l: \rightarrow CH_3Cl + :\ddot{C}l\cdot$$

The chlorine atom—or radical—produced is now free to attack another methane molecule and continue this **chain reaction**. If the energy factors are right, it is possible for a single initiation reaction to start a chain of hundreds of reactions. The relationship between the yield of product and the number of photons of energy used is known as the **quantum yield**. Large values indicate that long chains are involved.

The methyl chloride formed in this reaction is also available for reaction with chlorine atoms, which leads to a serious limitation of the reaction.

$$:\ddot{C}l\cdot + H_2\overset{\overset{\displaystyle H}{\displaystyle |}}{C}Cl \rightarrow H_2\dot{C}Cl + HCl$$

$$H_2\dot{C}Cl + :\ddot{C}l:\ddot{C}l: \rightarrow H_2CCl_2 + :\ddot{C}l\cdot$$

This type of side reaction can continue, and it leads to the formation of all possible chlorinated products. As the complexity of the starting alkane increases, the product mixture becomes very complicated. The result is that except in special cases this type of reaction is not of great use as a laboratory method. In industrial applications it has been used to great advantage for the production of useful mixtures of chlorinated hydrocarbons. Also, relatively pure chlorocarbons can be separated by distillation techniques.

The final, or chain termination, step is generally the combination of pairs of radicals with the result that no new radical is produced to continue the chain.

$$2 : \ddot{\underset{..}{C}}l \cdot \rightarrow : \ddot{\underset{..}{C}}l : \ddot{\underset{..}{C}}l :$$

$$2 \, H_3C \cdot \rightarrow CH_3 : CH_3$$

$$H_3C \cdot + : \ddot{\underset{..}{C}}l \cdot \rightarrow CH_3 : \ddot{\underset{..}{C}}l :$$

4.3B   Alkenes and Alkynes

In Chapter 1 and in the introduction to this chapter, we showed that it is possible to have more than one bond joining two carbon atoms. Two homologous series of hydrocarbons having general molecular formulas C_nH_{2n} and C_nH_{2n-2} result from the introduction of a double and triple bond, respectively. There are several

Courtesy of Photographic Research Laboratory, Eastman Kodak Company.

FIGURE 4.1.   Structure of Ethene.

other structural arrangements with the same general formulas, and we shall come to them in later chapters; for now, you might try drawing some reasonable examples.

The nomenclature of the **alkenes** (containing a double bond) has already been presented, and it was found that only a slight change from the alkanes was required. The triple bond of the **alkynes** also should present no difficulty. The suffix **-ane** is simply replaced by the suffix **-yne** and a number locating the triple bond added.

Courtesy of Photographic Research Laboratory, Eastman Kodak Company.

FIGURE 4.2.   Structure of Ethyne.

$$CH_3C\equiv CH \qquad CH_3CH_2\underset{\underset{CH_3}{|}}{C}HC\equiv C\underset{\underset{CH_3}{|}}{C}HCH_3$$

propyne   2,5-dimethyl-3-heptyne

Obviously, the 1- is understood in the case of propyne. When more than one multiple bond (or other functional group) is present in a compound, the parent chain is selected so as to include the greatest number of them, even if a longer chain is possible.

$$CH_3CH_2CH_2\underset{\underset{\underset{\underset{CH_2}{\|}}{CH}}{|}}{C}HCHCH_2C\equiv CCH=CH_2$$

with CH_3 branch above

6-methyl-7-propyl-1,8-nonadien-3-yne

4.4
MOLECULAR ORBITAL DESCRIPTION
OF UNSATURATED HYDROCARBONS

The approach that has proved so useful in understanding the alkanes can be applied directly to the unsaturated alkenes and alkynes. The modification that must be introduced is simply that of a new state of hybridization for the carbon atoms involved in the unsaturated linkage. Remember, from our earlier discussion, that we are quite free to carry out this operation, which simply amounts to a different subdivision of the same total energy.

To construct a picture of alkenes, we may consider the hybridization of one 2*s* and two 2*p* orbitals into three *sp*² orbitals. Thus, the simplest alkene, ethene, results from the overlap of four 1*s* hydrogen orbitals with four *sp*² orbitals of carbon and the overlap of two *sp*² orbitals between the carbon atoms to form the carbon-carbon bond (see Figure 4.3). At this point, there must

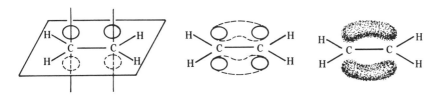

FIGURE 4.3.   Molecular Orbital Description of Ethene.

be one 2*p* electron in its dumbbell-shaped orbital on each of the carbon atoms. It must also be true that when these orbitals are parallel to one another, they can interact by overlap and form the required second carbon-carbon bond (see Figure 4.3). It might seem that two *sp*³ orbitals might bend and overlap to form the double bond, but the geometry of the bond (p. 76) is not in agreement.

The new type of bond formed by the overlap of two parallel orbitals lacks the cylindrical symmetry of linear overlap we have used until now. It is, therefore, a weaker bond, as is shown by experimental heats of formation indicating that carbon-carbon double bonds are not twice as strong as single bonds (CH_3—CH_3, −77.7 kcal/mole; CH_2=CH_2, −140.0 kcal/mole). Such a bond, called a **pi** (π) bond in contrast to the normal **sigma** (σ) bond we have been dealing with, is also much more reactive. This fact, too, is quite consistent with the reactions of the alkenes. It might be pointed out that any orbital containing *s* character can overlap to form a *sigma* bond—that is, *sp*³, *sp*², and *sp*.

The formation of the carbon-carbon triple bond of alkynes involves the simple and logical extension of the preceding reasoning to an *sp* hybridization for the two carbon atoms. This factor requires that two *p* orbitals which are mutually perpendicular

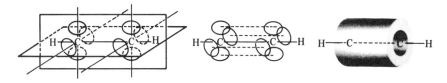

FIGURE 4.4.   Molecular Orbital Description of Ethyne.

remain on each carbon atom.   These two pairs of half-filled orbitals can overlap to form two π bonds (see Figure 4.4).

4.5
MOLECULAR GEOMETRY AND GEOMETRIC ISOMERISM

Just as the sp^3 hybridization of the saturated hydrocarbons required a particular geometry, the new modes of hybridization found in the alkenes and alkynes has its spatial arrangement (see Figures 4.3 and 4.4).   The sp^2 orbitals of the alkene are arranged in a planar, trigonal manner, with the π bond above and below the plane of the σ bonds.   For most effective overlap of two p orbitals, the sp hybridized orbitals of alkynes require a linear geometry with two π orbitals partially surrounding the carbon-carbon σ orbital.

The presence of a π bond in an alkene and its requirement that the p orbitals remain nearly parallel lead to a very interesting new kind of isomerism known as **geometric isomerism**.   The combination of a π and a σ bond in the alkene does not permit free rotation, because to do so would require the p orbitals to become perpendicular at one point, in which position they would cease to overlap—that is, the π bond must be broken.

Alkenes in which each carbon atom involved in the double bond is bonded to two groups that are not identical can, by virtue of this restricted rotation, exist in two nonsuperimposable forms or isomers.   These isomers are named *cis-* and *trans-*, depending on the location of similar groups.   It is clear that the

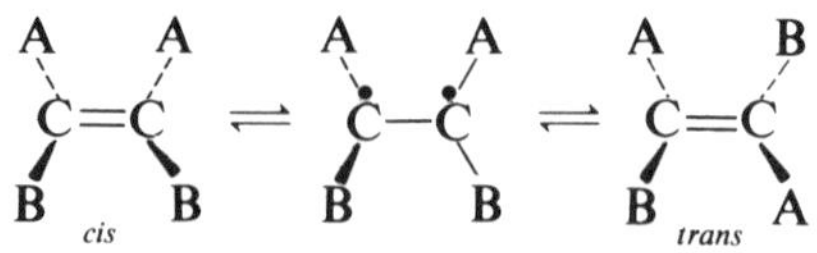

$$
\begin{array}{ccc}
\text{A}\quad\text{A} & \text{A}\quad\text{A} & \text{A}\quad\text{B} \\
\text{C=C} \rightleftharpoons & \text{C--C} \rightleftharpoons & \text{C=C} \\
\text{B}\quad\text{B} & \text{B}\quad\text{B} & \text{B}\quad\text{A} \\
\quad cis & & \quad trans
\end{array}
$$

FIGURE 4.5.   Geometric Isomerism.

A's and B's used in Figure 4.5 do not have to be the same to cause geometric isomerism.

$$CH_3 \diagdown \atop H \diagup C{=}C \diagup CO_2H \atop \diagdown H$$

cis-2-butenoic acid

$$H \diagdown \atop CH_3 \diagup C{=}C \diagup CO_2H \atop \diagdown H$$

trans-2-butenoic acid

$$CH_3 \diagdown \atop H \diagup C{=}C \diagup CO_2H \atop \diagdown Br$$

cis-2-bromo-2-butenoic acid

$$H \diagdown \atop CH_3 \diagup C{=}C \diagup CO_2H \atop \diagdown Br$$

trans-2-bromo-2-butenoic acid

4.6
CYCLOHEXANE—CONFORMATIONS AND GEOMETRIC ISOMERS

It has been known for a long time that cyclohexane does not exist as a planar ring, but rather in a "puckered" chair form and, in

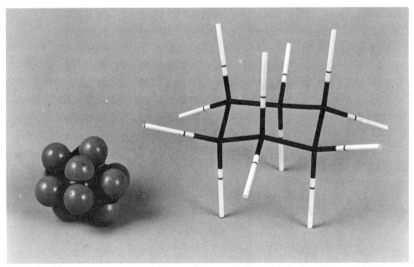

Courtesy of Photographic Research Laboratory, Eastman Kodak Company.
FIGURE 4.6.   Structure of Cyclohexane.

certain special cases, as a less stable boat conformation. These two spatial arrangements, plus a second chair form, are the most important conformations (see Figure 4.7).

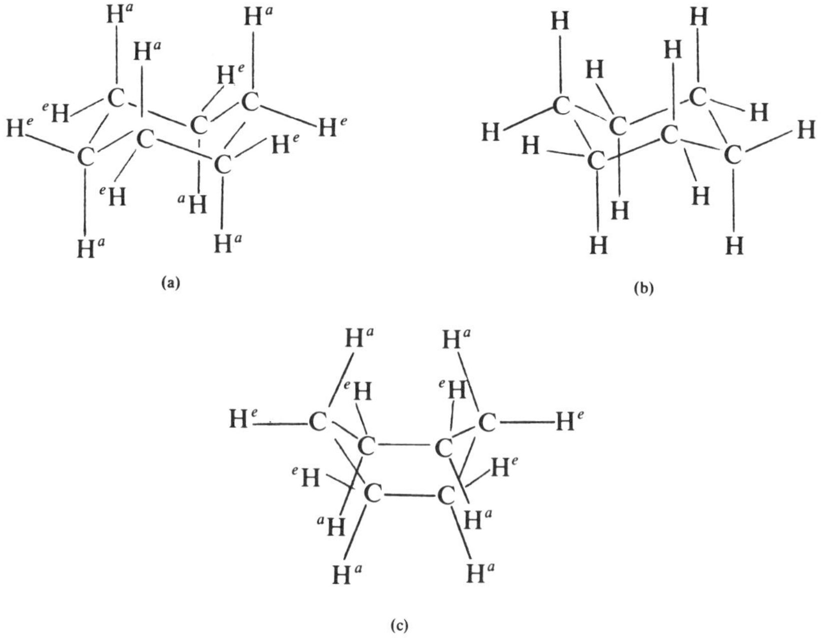

FIGURE 4.7. Cyclohexane Conformations.

The boat form (c), because of serious eclipsing of both adjacent and 1,4-hydrogens having bonds nearly perpendicular to the average ring "plane," is of much higher energy than the chair forms, and therefore represents only a very small percentage of cyclohexane molecules in an equilibrium mixture at room temperature. This fact greatly simplifies the conformational study of the cyclohexane system. Because of the symmetry of the ring, the 12 hydrogens compose two groups of 6 each. At each carbon, one hydrogen is nearly perpendicular to the average "plane" of the ring; they are called the **axial** (a) hydrogens. Other groups occupying a similar location are also identified as axial. The second set of hydrogen atoms, one at each carbon, extend outward in a belt slightly above and below the ring plane. These hydrogens and the position they occupy are known as **equatorial** (e).

Two points about these conformations are of interest: (1) at room temperature, one chair form easily converts (flips) to the other chair; and (2) bulky groups greatly prefer to be in the equatorial position because of interactions between the 1,3 and 1,5 axial hydrogens (see Figure 4.8). A direct consequence of

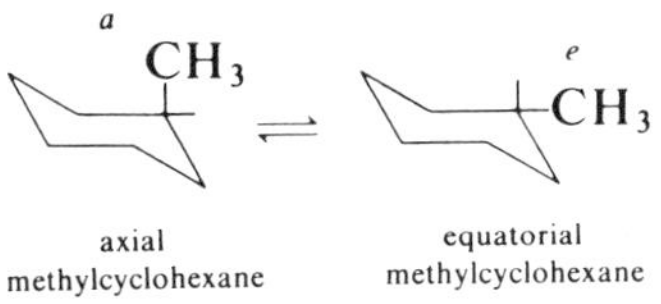

axial
methylcyclohexane

equatorial
methylcyclohexane

FIGURE 4.8.   Substituted Cyclohexane.

these facts is that any group introduced into the cyclohexane ring will shift the conformational equilibrium toward the chair that allows the group to occupy the equatorial position.   An alternative way of understanding this fact is that the inter-conversion of chair forms shifts all axial groups to equatorial and vice versa. If the group is sufficiently large, it may shift the equilibrium so far to one side that the ring can be considered "locked" in that conformation because it must pass through a high-energy boat conformation.   This tool is useful in the study of organic mechanisms because it allows some control over the geometry of the intermediates and transition states (pp. 48–50).

The final point to be considered about the cyclohexane ring is its ability to show geometric isomerism (see Figure 4.9). The easiest way to see the *cis-trans* relationship of groups in rings is to draw or think of the rings as planar. Clearly, then, *cis* groups would be found on the same side, whereas *trans* groups would reside one above and one below the ring's average plane. The chief difficulty comes in trying to understand the relationship

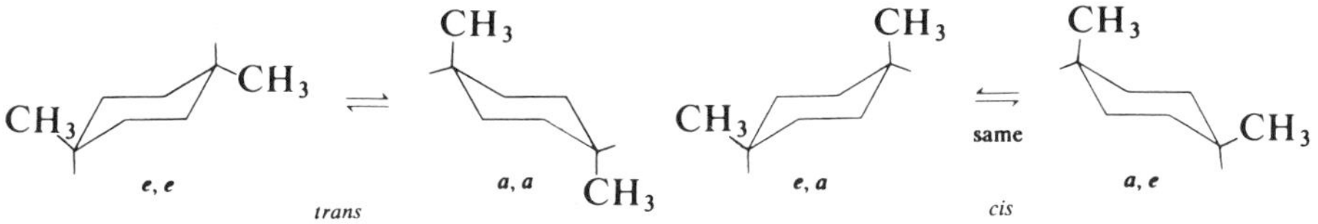

FIGURE 4.9.   Geometric Isomerism in 1,4-Dimethylcyclohexane.

of *cis-trans* to axial-equatorial. You should convince yourself that 1,2 groups are *cis* if one is axial and one is equatorial, and *trans* if both are either axial or equatorial; that 1,3 groups are *cis* if both are either axial or equatorial, and *trans* if one is axial and one equatorial; and that 1,4 groups follow the 1,2 arrangement. You can use drawings, but models are strongly recommended.

The term **unsaturated** appears first in the work of E. Erlenmeyer in 1862, and is intended to convey the marked tendency of these compounds to revert to the corresponding saturated form. The reversal is accomplished by the very simple process of adding some small molecule to the carbon atoms involved in the multiple bond. Thus, the disappearance of the color of bromine solutions is caused by the bromine being taken up by the unsaturation.

$$CH_2{=}CH_2 + Br_2 \rightarrow \underset{\underset{Br}{|}}{CH_2}\underset{\underset{Br}{|}}{CH_2}$$

$$CH_3C{\equiv}CH + 2\,Br_2 \rightarrow \quad \underset{\underset{Br}{|}}{\overset{\overset{Br}{|}}{CH_3C}}{-}\underset{\underset{Br}{|}}{\overset{\overset{Br}{|}}{CH}}$$

The second equation shows the very closely related reaction of the alkynes. Although it is possible in some cases to stop the addition after one molar equivalent, leaving a double bond in the

VLADIMIR V. MARKOWNIKOFF *(Russian, 1838–1904). He made numerous studies of organic compounds including the naphthenes found in Caucasian petroleum. These studies contributed greatly to our understanding of structural organic chemistry. His doctoral thesis at the University of Kazan contained the first statement of his rule concerning the direction of addition of acids to double bonds.*

Courtesy of the Edgar Fahs Smith Memorial Collection.

product, there is only one such case of very great importance. The partial reduction of alkynes requires a special catalyst and is frequently useful.

$$CH_3C\equiv CCH_3 + H_2 \xrightarrow[\text{catalyst}]{\text{Lindlar's}^*} CH_3CH=CHCH_3$$

In addition to the reagents mentioned, chlorine adds to multiple bonds in a similar manner.

4.7A   Markownikoff Addition

So far we have been considering the addition of symmetrical reagents (H_2, Cl_2, and Br_2), but, also of great importance is the addition of unsymmetrical molecules, such as hydrogen halide, HX (X = Cl, Br, or I), water (HOH), and sulfuric acid (HOSO$_3$H). When such additions are made to multiple bonds that are also unsymmetrically located, it is clear that two different products may be formed.

$$CH_3CH=CH_2 + HCl \left\{ \begin{array}{l} \rightarrow CH_3CH_2CH_2Cl \\ \\ \rightarrow \underset{\underset{Cl}{|}}{CH_3CHCH_3} \end{array} \right.$$

In 1875, the Russian chemist Markownikoff formulated an empirical rule for predicting the principal product of additions to hydrocarbons. After studying a large number of acid additions, he stated: "*The hydrogen of the acid adds to the carbon which has the greater number of hydrogens.*" The result of this rule is that the reaction shown in the preceding equation leads chiefly to 2-chloropropane (isopropyl chloride). Further illustrations of this normal mode of addition are given in the following equations:

$$CH_3C\equiv CH \xrightarrow{\text{HCl}} \left[\underset{\underset{Cl}{|}}{CH_3C}=CH_2 \right] \xrightarrow{\text{HCl}} \underset{\underset{Cl}{|}}{\overset{\overset{Cl}{|}}{CH_3CCH_3}}$$

---

*A mixture of finely divided palladium on calcium carbonate with lead acetate.

$$CH_3CH = CHCH_2CH_3 + HI \rightarrow$$

$$\underset{\underset{I}{|}}{CH_3CHCH_2CH_2CH_3} + \underset{\underset{I}{|}}{CH_3CH_2CHCH_2CH_3}$$

$$CH_3CH = CH_2 + HOSO_3H \rightarrow \underset{\underset{OSO_3H}{|}}{CH_3CHCH_3}$$

The reaction in the first equation simply requires the application of Markownikoff's Rule twice. The intermediate in square brackets is unstable under the reaction conditions and adds a second mole of HCl. The next equation produces an *approximately* equimolar mixture of the two possible products, because the number of hydrogen atoms attached to each carbon is the same. The addition of sulfuric acid (the third equation) is of some added importance, inasmuch as the product—isopropyl hydrogen sulfate or isopropyl sulfuric acid—reacts with water to give an alcohol.

$$\underset{\underset{OSO_3H}{|}}{CH_3CHCH_3} + HOH \rightarrow \underset{\underset{OH}{|}}{CH_3CHCH_3} + HOSO_3H$$

4.7B   Anti-Markownikoff Addition

There are two cases of interest in this chapter in which this rule is not followed. The American chemist M. S. Kharasch, in a truly brilliant study, found that HBr added to alkenes produced the opposite isomer if peroxides were present. A peroxide is a compound containing an oxygen-oxygen bond—for example, HO—OH.

$$RCH = CH_2 + HBr \xrightarrow{\text{peroxides}} RCH_2CH_2Br$$

The extensive use of alkyl bromides makes this reaction of great synthetic importance. Keep in mind that this reaction only takes place with HBr. The mechanism of this reaction is presented in Chapter 12.

The second example of anti-Markownikoff addition is one which has developed into a general synthetic tool of great versatility. As you will see in later chapters, the alcohols are very important compounds in the preparation of a wide variety of other organic molecules. Although there are many reactions available for the synthesis of alcohols—for example, the addition of H_2SO_4 shown—methods giving high yields and not affecting other substituents are always required. Professor H. C. Brown and his coworkers have studied at great length the addition of borane (in the form of the dimer B_2H_6, in most cases) to alkenes. The addition is anti-Markownikoff, and except in certain sterically unfavorable cases, involves three alkenes.

$$3\,CH_3\overset{\overset{\displaystyle CH_3}{|}}{C}\!=\!CHCH_3 + (BH_3) \xrightarrow{\text{ether}} (CH_3\overset{\overset{\displaystyle CH_3}{|}}{C}H\underset{\underset{\displaystyle CH_3}{|}}{C}H\!-\!)_3B$$

The higher molecular weight alkyl boranes can be isolated, but more often they are used in the solution in which they are prepared for further syntheses. The following scheme shows a few

HERBERT C. BROWN (*English-American, 1912–*). *He is almost certainly one of the most widely known chemists of our day. His research efforts at Purdue University have strongly influenced both mechanistic and preparative organic chemistry. There was a time when steric effects were used to explain anything that could not be understood; Brown made the concept acceptable again by a series of elegant studies of molecule addition compounds. For a number of years he has made important experimental contributions to our understanding of the detailed mechanism of carbonium ion reactions. Without any doubt, Brown's most significant work has been the development of the hydroboration reaction. In a virtual flood of publications, he and his students have created the method of choice for the preparation of compounds containing a wide variety of functional groups and having known stereochemistry.*

Courtesy of Professor Brown.

of the possible reactions of the alkyl boranes:

$$
(CH_3\underset{\underset{CH_3}{|}}{\overset{\overset{CH_3}{|}}{CHCH}}-)_3\,B
\begin{cases}
\xrightarrow[OH^-]{H_2O_2} & 3\,CH_3\underset{\underset{CH_3}{|}}{\overset{\overset{CH_3}{|}}{CH}}CHOH \\[2em]
\xrightarrow{RCO_2H} & 3\,CH_3\underset{\underset{CH_3}{|}}{\overset{\overset{CH_3}{|}}{CH}}CH_2 \\[2em]
\xrightarrow{CrO_3} & 3\,CH_3\underset{\underset{CH_3}{|}}{\overset{\overset{CH_3}{|}}{CH}}CH{=}O \\[2em]
\xrightarrow{AgNO_3} & CH_3\underset{\underset{CH_3}{|}}{\overset{\overset{CH_3}{|}}{CH}}CH-\underset{\underset{CH_3}{|}}{CH}CHCH_3 \\[2em]
\xrightarrow{heat} & (CH_3\underset{\underset{CH_3}{|}}{CH}CH_2CH_2-)_3\,B
\end{cases}
$$

These and numerous other reactions of the alkyl boranes have made possible the preparation of many useful and interesting organic compounds in high yield and under very mild conditions. It is especially important to note that a number of other functional groups may be present in the alkene and be unaffected by **hydroboration** (e.g., $-NO_2$, $-OCH_3$, $-Cl$, $-Br$, and $-CO_2R$).

The usual procedure is to generate the diborane by the reaction of sodium borohydride with boron trifluoride etherate.

$$3\,NaBH_4 + 4\,BF_3 \cdot (C_2H_5)_2O \rightarrow 2\,B_2H_6 + 3\,NaBF_4 + 4\,(C_2H_5)_2O$$

This process can be done in the reaction vessel itself or in a separate flask and the diborane gas passed through a solution of the alkene. More common solvents than ethyl ether are diglyme ($CH_3OCH_2CH_2OCH_2CH_2OCH_3$) or triglyme

$$[CH_3O(CH_2CH_2O)_3CH_3].$$

Tetrahydrofuran (THF), which is a five-membered cyclic ether, is also frequently used.

$$\text{furan} \xrightarrow[\text{Ni}]{2\,H_2} \text{THF}$$

furan   THF

ELECTROPHILIC ADDITION AT UNSATURATED CARBON

Unlike the relatively low electron density of saturated carbon atoms, the π bond of an alkene or alkyne is a region of high electron density. Thus, you should expect attack there by electrophilic reagents. One of the most thoroughly studied of the addition reactions is that of acids in which the proton represents a very efficient electrophile.

$$\underset{/}{\overset{\backslash}{C}}=\underset{\backslash}{\overset{/}{C}} + H^+X^- \rightarrow -\overset{|}{\underset{H}{C}}-\overset{|}{\underset{X}{C}}-$$

As in many of the other organic reactions for which we write a single overall equation, this addition actually takes place in two distinct steps.

$$\underset{/}{\overset{\backslash}{C}}=\underset{\backslash}{\overset{/}{C}} + H^+ \rightarrow -\overset{|}{\underset{H}{C}}-\overset{|}{\underset{+}{C}}- + X^- \rightarrow -\overset{|}{\underset{H}{C}}-\overset{|}{\underset{X}{C}}-$$

The second reaction, between the intermediate carbonium ion and halide, takes place very rapidly. One piece of evidence for this pathway comes from the simple case of bromine addition. If the addition of bromine is carried out in the presence of other anions, mixed products are formed that can best be explained by the mechanism suggested previously.

$$\underset{/}{\overset{\backslash}{C}}=\underset{\backslash}{\overset{/}{C}} + Br_2 \xrightarrow{Na^+Cl^-} -\overset{|}{\underset{Br}{C}}-\overset{|}{\underset{+}{C}}-$$

$$\begin{array}{c} \xrightarrow{Cl^-} -\overset{|}{\underset{Br}{C}}-\overset{|}{\underset{Cl}{C}}- \\ \\ \xrightarrow{Br^-} -\overset{|}{\underset{Br}{C}}-\overset{|}{\underset{Br}{C}}- \end{array}$$

Inasmuch as it is known that the bromine molecule has a slight tendency to ionize,

$$Br_2 \rightleftharpoons Br^+ + Br^-$$

it is reasonable to suggest the partial positively charged bromine ($Br^{\delta+}$) as the attacking electrophile. The electron-rich double bond can polarize the nonpolar bromine molecule; therefore, it is not necessary to have a free Br^+ ion.

$$\overset{\displaystyle \underset{\diagdown \diagup}{\overset{\diagup \diagdown}{C}}}{\underset{C}{\|}} \quad Br^{\delta+} \rightarrow Br^{\delta-}$$

Later we shall find a case where Lewis acids* form complexes with bromine to provide an electrophilic specie (pp. 122, 124).

$$Cl_3Al \cdots Br^{\delta+} \rightarrow Br^{\delta-}$$

Consideration of the carbonium ion intermediate enables us to understand the prediction of Markownikoff's Rule. You will recall from our earlier discussion of such additions that this empirical observation requires that when an acid is added to an unsymmetrical alkene, the hydrogen will add to that carbon which has the greater number of hydrogens; for example,

$$CH_3CH{=}CH_2 + HBr \begin{cases} \longrightarrow CH_3\underset{\textstyle Br}{CH}CH_3 \\ \\ \nmid\!\!\longrightarrow CH_3CH_2CH_2Br \end{cases}$$

The two carbonium ions possible from the initial reaction with the proton are:

$$CH_3\underset{+}{CH}CH_3 \quad \text{or} \quad CH_3CH_2CH_2^+$$

In the absence of other considerations, the secondary carbonium ion, being the more stable, would be expected to be the most frequently formed. There is, however, another factor contributing to the observed product.

One important reason for the observed order of carbonium ion stability was explained earlier by the inductive effect of electron donation by alkyl groups. When the π bond of alkenes

---

*A **Lewis acid** is defined as an atom, molecule, or ion having an empty orbital; a **Lewis base** has an unshared pair of electrons.

is considered, this effect becomes of even greater importance, inasmuch as the electrons of this bond are easily shifted or polarized.

$$CH_3 \longrightarrow CH \longrightarrow CH \longleftarrow CH_3 \qquad \text{symmetrical } \pi \text{ bond}$$

$$CH_3 \xrightarrow{\;\overset{\delta+}{}\;} CH \longrightarrow CH \overset{\delta-}{\longrightarrow} H \qquad \text{polarized } \pi \text{ bond}$$

This effect, although much less important than the one just described, also makes the attack of the electrophilic proton at the carbon bearing fewer alkyl groups reasonable in terms of its higher electron density.

An effect that is important in the case of the alkyne intermediate (a vinyl halogen compound) is the resonance stabilization of the carbonium ion.

$$CH_3C{=}CH_2 \underset{Cl}{\Big|} \xrightarrow{\;H^+\;} \left[CH_3\overset{+}{C}{-}CH_3 \underset{:\ddot{Cl}:}{\Big|} \leftrightarrow \right.$$

$$\left. CH_3C{-}CH_3 \underset{:\ddot{Cl}^+}{\Big\|} \right] \xrightarrow{\;Cl^-\;} CH_3\overset{\textstyle Cl}{\underset{\textstyle Cl}{\overset{|}{\underset{|}{C}}}}CH_3$$

4.9
THE OXIDATION OF ALKENES

The loss of color by dilute potassium permanganate solution is often used as a test of unsaturation and indicates the second chief reaction of these linkages—oxidation. This **Baeyer test**, as it is usually called, is carried out under rather mild conditions and produces compounds of intermediate oxidation state.

$$3\,CH_2{=}CH_2 + 2\,KMnO_4 + 4\,H_2O \rightarrow$$

$$3\,CH_2{-}CH_2 + 2\,MnO_2 + 2\,KOH$$
$$\underset{OH \quad\; OH}{\big|\qquad\big|}$$

The hydroxylation of double bonds by permanganate and similar reagents always leads to *cis*-glycols. This reaction can be demonstrated by using a cycloalkene, such as cyclopentene, and it strongly suggests that the following intermediate is involved:

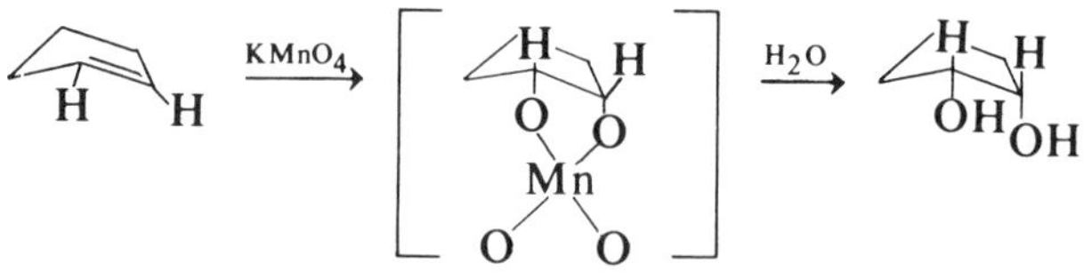

In the case of osmium tetroxide (OsO_4), such an intermediate has been shown to be stable. This 1,2-diol (or **glycol***) is easily oxidized further, and when the original alkene is treated with hot, concentrated potassium permanganate, it is not isolated at all.

When stronger oxidizing agents (or more drastic conditions) are used, the products obtained are determined by the nature of the double bond. When the oxidation takes place, the double bond is often completely broken and two new compounds are formed.

$$CH_3CH{=}CH_2 \xrightarrow{[O]\dagger} CH_3CO_2H + CO_2 + H_2O$$

$$\underset{\underset{CH_3}{|}}{CH_3C}{=}CH_2 \xrightarrow{[O]} \underset{\underset{CH_3}{|}}{CH_3C}{=}O + CO_2 + H_2O$$

These reactions are of general applicability; therefore, we should write them using general symbolism.

$$RCH{=}CH_2 \xrightarrow{[O]} RCO_2H + CO_2$$

$$\underset{\underset{R''}{|}}{RCH}{=}CR' \xrightarrow{[O]} RCO_2H + \underset{\underset{R''}{|}}{R'C}{=}O$$

Table 4.2 summarizes the stable oxidation products of various alkene arrangements. By selecting the proper combination of

---

*Glycols are defined as compounds having two adjacent carbinol groups, that is, dihydricalcohols. Some exceptions exist: $HO(CH_2)_3OH$ is called trimethylene glycol.

†A wide variety of oxidizing agents are useful in this and other such reactions and the general symbol [O] is often used. It should not be thought that this represents O_2, except in a few cases. A similar situation exists for [H], a general symbol for reduction.

TABLE 4.2

Number of hydrogens	Stable oxidation product
0 $(R-\overset{\overset{\displaystyle R'}{\displaystyle |}}{C}=)$	ketone $(R-\overset{\overset{\displaystyle R'}{\displaystyle |}}{C}=O)$
1 $(RCH=)$	acid (RCO_2H)
2 $(CH_2=)$	carbon dioxide (CO_2)

any two of them, it is possible either to predict the oxidation products or, given the products, to reconstruct the original alkene. The following example will serve to illustrate.

The products of the oxidation of an alkene are found to be 4-heptanone and 3-methylhexanoic acid. What was the structure of the alkene? The first step is to draw the structure of each of the oxidation products.

$$
\begin{array}{cc}
\begin{array}{c}
CH_3CH_2CH_2 \\
\diagdown \\
\qquad C=O \\
\diagup \\
CH_3CH_2CH_2
\end{array} &
\begin{array}{c}
HO_2CCH_2CHCH_2CH_2CH_3 \\
| \\
CH_3
\end{array}
\end{array}
$$

4-heptanone   3-methylhexanoic acid

The carbon atoms in the products that now are linked to oxygen must be those carbon atoms that were originally involved in the double bond. From Table 4.2, the number of hydrogen atoms that were attached to each carbon can readily be seen. Finally, remember that the R groups do not usually change either their nature or their position during the reaction. All that has to be done to write the answer is to connect the proper carbon atoms by a double bond.

$$
\begin{array}{c}
CH_3CH_2CH_2 \\
\diagdown \\
\qquad C=CHCH_2CHCH_2CH_2CH_3 \\
\diagup \qquad\qquad\quad | \\
CH_3CH_2CH_2 \qquad\qquad CH_3
\end{array}
$$

7-methyl-4-propyl-4-decene

Some confusion arises in the case of symmetrical alkenes and polyenes. There is no need for concern if the rules given are applied. A symmetrical alkene will yield two new molecules on strong oxidation—it just happens that they will be identical.

$$CH_3CH=CHCH_3 \xrightarrow{\text{[O]}} CH_3CO_2H + CH_3CO_2H$$

With polyenes, all double bonds will be affected; consequently, more fragments will result.

$$\underset{CH_3}{\overset{CH_3}{\diagdown}} C = CHCH_2CH_2CH = CH_2$$

$$\xrightarrow{[O]} \underset{CH_3}{\overset{CH_3}{\diagdown}} C = O \ + \ HO_2CCH_2CH_2CO_2H \ + \ CO_2$$

succinic acid
(a dicarboxylic acid)

The alkynes are also attacked by oxidizing agents and produce acids as the only organic product.

$$RC \equiv CH \xrightarrow{[O]} RCO_2H + CO_2$$

$$RC \equiv CR' \xrightarrow{[O]} RCO_2H + R'CO_2H$$

4.10
THE MEANING OF OXIDATION AND REDUCTION

For some organic reactions, a less complete view of oxidation and reduction can be used as an aid to learning. As hydrogens attached to carbon are replaced by oxygen atoms, that carbon (and, of course, the molecule as a whole) becomes more highly oxidized. The reverse process (the addition and/or substitution of hydrogen) is reduction. Thus, methane (or any saturated hydrocarbon) is the most reduced form of carbon, and carbon dioxide is the most highly oxidized. With the exception of formic acid, the carboxyl group is a very stable, high-oxidation state, because the production of CO_2 requires breaking carbon-carbon bonds.

—— more oxidized state ⟶

$$CH_4 \quad CH_3OH \quad H_2C = O \quad HCO_2H \quad CO_2$$

⟵ more reduced state ——

These definitions are not inconsistent with the more general definition of oxidation reduction as the loss and gain of electrons. It simply represents a more restricted special case.

As was stated earlier, the double and triple bonds have much in common. They also have some important points of difference. The hydration of alkenes is difficult in the laboratory because of the high pressures required.* The addition of water to a triple bond is easier and is of commercial value and theoretical importance.

$$HC\equiv CH + HOH \xrightarrow[\text{HgSO}_4{}^\dagger]{\text{H}_2\text{SO}_4} H_2C=CH \underset{\substack{|\\ \text{OH}}}{\rightleftharpoons} CH_3\overset{\overset{\textstyle H}{\textstyle |}}{C}=O$$

less stable   more stable

The less stable first product is known as an **enol** (-en for the double bond and -ol for the alcohol), and, with certain exceptions, it readily converts or **tautomerizes** to the carbonyl or **keto** form (carbon-oxygen double bond, as in a ketone). In addition to the example shown, which is used to produce huge quantities of acetaldehyde, the reaction can be carried out with terminal triple bonds to produce methyl ketones, as is required by Markownikoff's Rule.

$$CH_3C\equiv CH + HOH \xrightarrow[\text{HgSO}_4]{\text{H}_2\text{SO}_4} CH_3\underset{\substack{|\\ \text{OH}}}{C}=CH_2 \rightleftharpoons CH_3\overset{\overset{\textstyle O}{\textstyle ||}}{C}CH_3$$

Addition of water to nonterminal unsymmetrical alkynes results in an approximately equimolar mixture of two ketones, again predictable from our earlier discussions.

Hydrocarbons are, at most, very slightly polar in character, and the hydrogen atoms attached to carbon have little ionic

---

*An important industrial application is the production of low molecular weight alcohols by the acid-catalyzed hydration of alkenes.

†The mercuric sulfate is another Lewis acid catalyst that polarizes the triple bond by forming a π **complex** (see p. 86)

$$\delta+ \underset{\substack{|\\ C}}{\overset{\substack{|\\ C}}{|||}} \overset{\delta-}{\longrightarrow} HgSO_4$$

and facilitates addition of $H_2\ddot{O}$ as a nucleophile.

nature. However, in the case of hydrogen attached to carbons involved in triple bonds, a weak acidity can be shown—for example, reactions with very strong bases such as sodamide.

$$RC\equiv CH + Na^+NH_2^- \rightarrow RC\equiv C^-Na^+ + NH_3$$

This behavior forms the basis of a very sensitive test for distinguishing terminal alkynes. Silver ion [as $Ag(NH_3)_2^+$] forms a white precipitate whereas cuprous ion (which reacts similarly) produces a red precipitate. The reaction does not occur with nonterminal alkynes or with any of the alkenes.

$$
\left.
\begin{array}{l}
RC\equiv CR' \\
2\,RC\equiv CH \\
RCH\!=\!CHR' \\
RCH\!=\!CH_2
\end{array}
\right\}
+\; \xrightarrow{\;Cu(NH_3)_2^+\;}
\left\{
\begin{array}{l}
\rightarrow \text{no reaction} \\
\rightarrow 2\,RC\equiv C^-Cu^+ + 2\,H_2O + 2\,NH_4Cl \\
\rightarrow \text{no reaction} \\
\rightarrow \text{no reaction}
\end{array}
\right.
$$

4.12
PREPARATION OF ALKENES

In a formal way, the alkenes are thought of as alkanes from which a molecule of hydrogen has been removed. This concept is all right for the purpose of writing structures and names for these compounds, but you must be careful to avoid thinking that this method actually makes the desired molecule. In fact, only in certain cases and with quite different compounds can the actual removal of hydrogen be achieved. There are two principal methods of preparation that we shall consider. Both involve the removal of a small molecule from adjacent carbons and the formation of the double bond. They are known collectively as **elimination reactions**, and their names are very descriptive— **dehydration** and **dehydrohalogenation**.

4.12A   Dehydration

When alcohols are heated with a strong Lewis acid catalyst—for example, alumina, sulfuric acid, or phosphoric acid—a molecule of water is removed and a double bond is introduced.

$$CH_3CH_2OH \xrightarrow{H_2SO_4} CH_2{=}CH_2 + H_2O$$

In those cases in which more than one alkene is possible, depending on from which adjacent carbon the hydrogen is removed, both products will be formed with the more highly substituted* one being obtained in higher yield. Where this event occurs, the method of preparation should be avoided if another process is available, because the difference in yield will often be small.

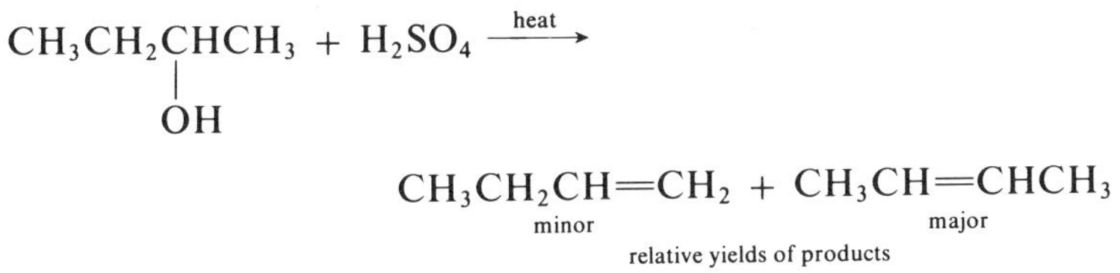

$$CH_3CH_2\underset{\underset{\displaystyle OH}{|}}{CH}CH_3 + H_2SO_4 \xrightarrow{heat}$$

$$CH_3CH_2CH{=}CH_2 + CH_3CH{=}CHCH_3$$

minor   major

relative yields of products

4.12B Dehydrohalogenation

The reaction, dehydrohalogenation, which is the reverse of the addition of HX to an alkene, may be accomplished by treating an alkyl halide (having a hydrogen on a carbon adjacent to the one with halogen) with a strong base dissolved in alcohol. Just as with the dehydration reaction, the more highly substituted alkene will predominate in cases where more than one is possible.

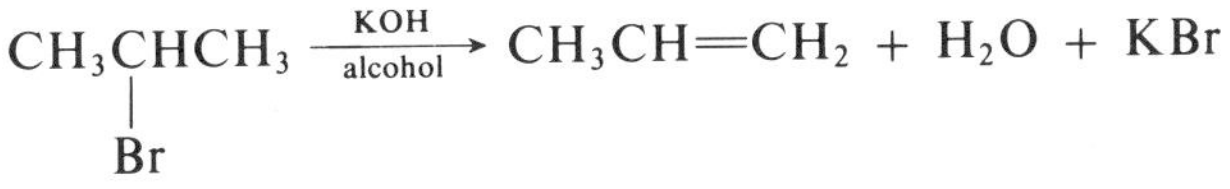

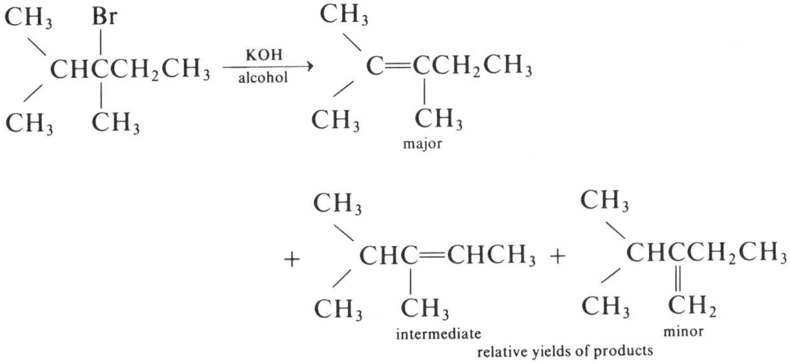

$$CH_3\underset{\underset{\displaystyle Br}{|}}{CH}CH_3 \xrightarrow[alcohol]{KOH} CH_3CH{=}CH_2 + H_2O + KBr$$

major

intermediate   minor

relative yields of products

---

*Fewer hydrogens attached to the carbons involved in the double bond.

4.13
ELIMINATION MECHANISMS

The processes by which carbon-carbon multiple bonds are formed have received a great deal of study. This section will review the details of the two types of elimination reactions already presented.

When an alcohol is heated with a strong mineral acid, one of the products frequently obtained is an alkene. The kinetics of this process are first order in the conjugate acid of the alcohol (ROH_2^+):

$$R-\overset{\frown}{\ddot{O}}H + H^+ \overset{\text{fast}}{\rightleftharpoons} R-^+OH_2$$
$$R\overset{\frown}{-^+OH_2} \overset{\text{slow}}{\rightleftharpoons} R^+ + H_2O$$

The carbonium ion produced, if it has a hydrogen on an adjacent carbon, can rapidly lose a proton and produce an alkene:

$$R'CH_2CH_2^+ \rightarrow R'CH=CH_2 + H^+$$

Courtesy of Mr. H. E. Whitmore

FRANK C. WHITMORE (American, 1887–1947). A superb teacher and administrator, Whitmore was also respected for his extensive and meaningful research. He was interested in the carbonium ion and especially its subsequent reactions. In Whitmore's laboratory at Penn. State the ideas of Meerwein were generalized to simple aliphatic systems. Whitmore wrote an influential organic chemistry text and was very active in the American Chemical Society, serving as its president in 1938. During World War II he was involved in the task of seeing that scientists were placed in positions where they could be of greatest service.

Some of the best evidence for this carbonium ion intermediate is found in the product analysis studies. Frequently, the products obtained are not at all what would be expected on the basis of the simple scheme just outlined; for example,

$$CH_3CHCHCH_3 + H^+ \rightarrow CH_3CHCH{=}CH_2 +$$
$$\quad\; | \quad\; | \qquad\qquad\qquad | $$
$$\quad H_3C \;\; OH \qquad\qquad\quad CH_3$$

$$CH_3C{=}CHCH_3 +$$
$$\quad\quad\; | $$
$$\quad\quad CH_3$$

$$CH_2{=}CCH_2CH_3$$
$$\quad\quad\;\; | $$
$$\quad\quad\;\; CH_3$$

plus other nonalkene products

The first two products would be expected and would depend on the direction of elimination. The third product, however, would not be predicted, and it results from a fundamental change in the hydrocarbon skeleton of the molecule—a **rearrangement**. Let us

HANS MEERWEIN (German, 1879–1965). Meerwein was one of the early physical-organic chemists. In the 1920's he used kinetic measurements to understand the mechanism of organic reactions. One of his major contributions was the concept of the carbonium ion as a reactive intermediate. The 1,2-hydride shifts often associated with carbonium ions were studied in his laboratory at Marburg as were the effects of solvent and metal ion catalysts. The name Wagner-Meerwein rearrangements is often used for hydride and alkyl group shifts in recognition of his contribution. Meerwein's work as a textbook editor and as an inspiring teacher also had a marked influence on the development of organic chemistry early in this century.

Courtesy of Professor G. A. Olah.

consider the change in structure of the intermediate carbonium ion:

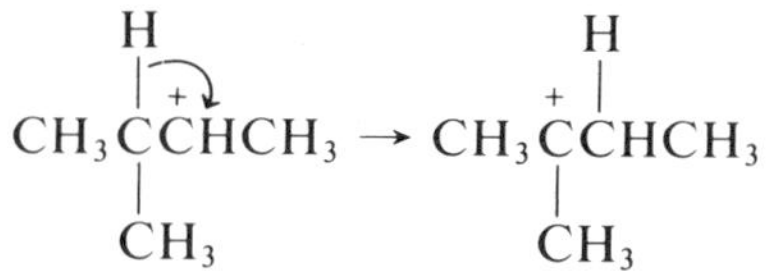

It is clear that by the migration of the hydrogen with its pair of electrons to the positively charged carbon, a new and more stable tertiary carbonium ion is formed. Such a **1,2-hydride shift** will occur in those cases where improved stability will result. It is also possible for carbanionlike methyl groups to migrate; for example,

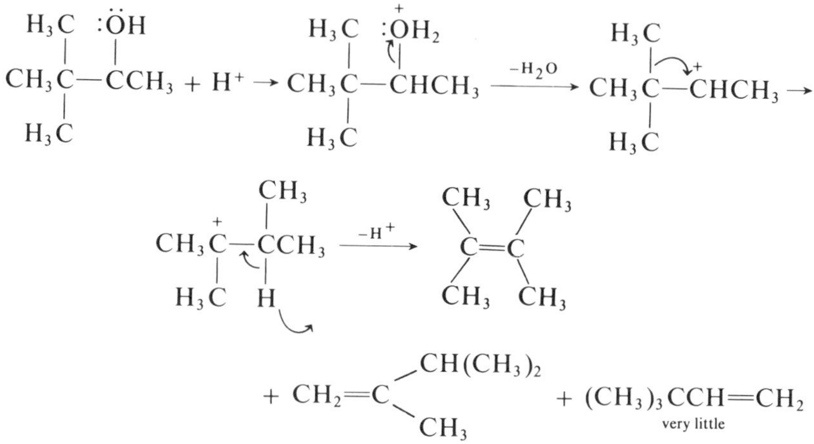

If the slow or rate-determining step of the elimination involves only the decomposition of the protonated alcohol, we should expect first order kinetics for the species ROH_2^+:

$$\text{rate} = k_1[\text{R—OH}_2^+]$$

Such a reaction would be called a **unimolecular elimination** and is often referred to as an **E1** reaction. Further evidence for this mechanistic pathway is found in the fact that the reaction occurs most readily with tertiary alcohols that would produce a more stable carbonium ion.

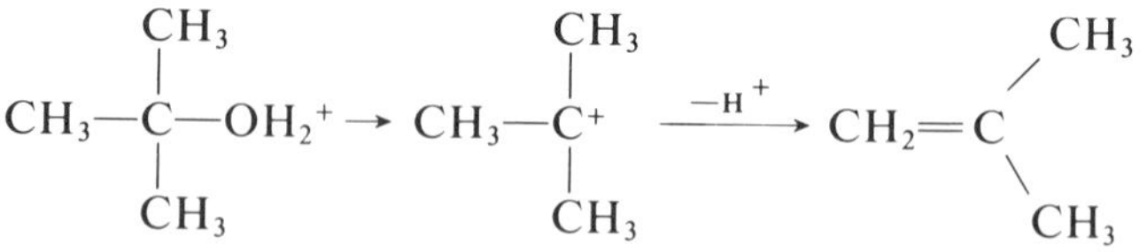

The tertiary alkyl halides will also show elimination when dissolved in strong ionizing solvents, such as water or acetic acid.

The base-catalyzed loss of HX from primary and secondary alkyl halides follows quite a different mechanism. Both the halide and the base are involved in the rate expression:

$$\text{rate} = k_2 \, [\text{R—X}][\text{base}]$$

A very large number of substrates and bases have been studied in **E2** or **bimolecular eliminations**; for example,

$$\underset{\text{CH}_3}{\overset{\text{CH}_3}{\diagdown\diagup}}\text{CH—X} + \text{Na}^{+ -}\text{OR} \rightarrow \text{CH}_3\text{CH}{=}\text{CH}_2 + \text{NaX} + \text{ROH}$$

This picture of elimination is true but very much simplified. There are a number of complications making it difficult and interesting to study the chemistry of such reactions. Keep this fact in mind; when you study the substitution reactions, additional details will be added.

The kinetics and the lack of rearrangement (along with much other experimental data) found in E2 reactions require a transition state involving both substrate and base.

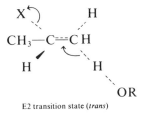

E2 transition state (*trans*)

A reaction of this kind is called **concerted**, for both the β hydrogen and the halogen bonds are being broken at the same time that the π bond is being formed. This situation leads to a variety of possible transition states, depending on the specific systems being studied and the relative amounts of bond breaking and forming that have taken place by the time the energy maximum has been reached. These details need not concern us here, but are pointed out with the hope that the richness and great complexity of reaction mechanisms will not be lost in our simplified picture.

4.14
PREPARATION OF ALKYNES

A very special reaction representing a valuable direct link between organic and inorganic chemistry is the preparation of ethyne (acetylene).

$$CaC_2 + 2 H_2O \rightarrow HC\equiv CH + Ca(OH)_2$$

This reaction, coupled with ethyne's ability to react with soda-mide, makes possible the most general synthesis of higher homo-logs in the alkyne series.

$$RC\equiv C^- Na^+ + R'X \rightarrow RC\equiv CR' + NaX$$

The R groups may be the same or different, and inasmuch as only the monosodium salt of ethyne is formed, the reaction may be carried out step-by-step to produce a variety of alkynes.

Dehydrohalogenation may be used in a manner similar to that for the formation of alkenes.

$$\underset{\underset{X}{|}\ \underset{X}{|}}{RCHCHR'} + 2 KOH \xrightarrow{\text{alcohol}} RC\equiv CR' + 2 KX + 2 H_2O$$

Gem*-dihalo compounds can also be used. The reactions are limited to the preparation of 1-alkynes, because the strong base required causes the triple bond to isomerize.

$$\underset{\underset{X}{|}}{\overset{\overset{X}{|}}{RCH_2CH}} + 2 KOH \xrightarrow{\text{alcohol}} RC\equiv CH + 2 KX + 2 H_2O$$

4.15
THE CHEMISTRY OF THE CYCLOALKANES

The saturated and unsaturated cyclic hydrocarbons show chem-ical reactions that are very similar to the alkanes and alkenes if only the 5,6 and greater than 12 carbon rings are considered.

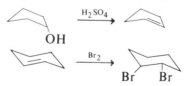

The diequatorial 1,2-dibromocyclohexane is the result of *trans* addition, which is typical of such addition reactions and illus-

---

**Gem-* (from the Latin *geminus*, twin) refers to systems having two identical groups attached to the same carbon atom. The compounds with halogens on adjacent carbons are often called *vic-* dihalides (from the Latin *vicinalis*, neighboring).

trates one way in which the geometry of the cyclic hydrocarbons has been of use in the study of organic reaction mechanisms.

Early in the history of organic chemistry, such 5- and 6-membered rings were known, but both smaller and larger sizes were not (at least not recognized; e.g., suberone, which was later shown to be cycloheptanone, was prepared in 1836). These observations led German chemist Adolf von Baeyer to propose

$$\text{suberone} = O$$

suberone

his famous **ring strain theory**. He suggested that the carbon rings were planar and then calculated the difference between their carbon-carbon bond angles and those of a tetrahedron. The fact is that a pentagon and a hexagon come quite close to 109°28′ or the "normal" bond angle. Both smaller and larger rings would be strained if they were planar. It was later pointed out by H. Sachse and E. Mohr that rings do not have to be planar but can exist in a "puckered" form. In time, this discovery has led to the study of alicyclic conformations, such as we have presented in this chapter.

At first, however, von Baeyer's theory seemed to fit the ex-

ADOLF VON BAEYER (German, 1835–1917). Baeyer is infrequently but properly known as Johann Friedrich Wilhelm Adolf von Baeyer. He was a truly brilliant experimentalist, and from his laboratory came many of the early synthetic accomplishments in organic chemistry. Baeyer's most important work was in the synthesis of natural products, especially those containing heterocyclic rings such as indigo. Unfortunately, Baeyer is most widely known for his imperfect Ring Strain Theory; we might well remember that experimental facts endure while theories are generally short lived.

Courtesy of the Edgar Fahs Smith Memorial Collection.

perimental facts very well. When small rings were prepared, at about the time he was developing the theory, they proved to be very reactive.

$$\triangle \xrightarrow[\text{Pt}]{\text{H}_2} CH_3CH_2CH_3$$

$$\triangle \xrightarrow{\text{Br}_2} \underset{\underset{\text{Br}}{|}}{CH_2}CH_2\underset{\underset{\text{Br}}{|}}{CH_2}$$

Cyclobutane reacts with hydrogen to give ring opening under slightly more vigorous conditions. In these cases, von Baeyer's theory is still considered to offer an essentially correct explanation, although it is recognized that cyclobutane is not completely planar.

It is with the rings larger than six carbons that von Baeyer was least correct and Sachse and Mohr offered the better model. The problem with large rings is not their reactivity; in fact, they are completely unstrained and behave much like alkanes. The difficulty is that they are not easy to prepare, inasmuch as the probability of getting the two ends of a carbon chain close enough to react is low. The methods by which this process was achieved represent an especially interesting chapter in synthetic organic chemistry, which is treated in Chapter 12.

SUGGESTED ADDITIONAL READINGS

Historical

A. J. Ihde, "The Development of Strain Theory," *Advances in Chemistry Series No. 61*, American Chemical Society, Washington, D.C.: 1966, Chapter 9.

Cyclohexane Conformation

Cason, pp. 89–99.
Cram and Hammond, pp. 155–60.
Herz, pp. 39–41.
Morrison and Boyd, pp. 282–90.
Roberts and Caserio, pp. 103–109.

N. L. Allinger, "Conformational Analysis in the Elementary Organic Course," *J. Chem. Educ.*, **41,** 70 (1964).

Geometric Isomerism

Morrison and Boyd, pp. 149–51 and 294–98.
Roberts and Caserio, pp. 115–18 and 158–62.

Radical Reactions

Breslow, Chapter 7.
Cram and Hammond, Chapter 22.
Gould, Chapter 16.
Morrison and Boyd, pp. 38–64 and 386–98.
Pryor, Chapters 7–8.
Roberts and Caserio, pp. 80–95.

Electrophilic Addition at Unsaturated Carbon

Breslow, Chapter 4–2.
Cram and Hammond, Chapter 18.
Gould, Chapter 13.
Morrison and Boyd, pp. 183–204.
Roberts and Caserio, pp. 175–91.
Saunders, Chapter 2.

Elimination Reactions

Breslow, Chapter 4–1.
Cram and Hammond, Chapter 16.
Gould, Chapter 12.
Morrison and Boyd, pp. 157–72 and 483–91.
Roberts and Caserio, pp. 306–19.
Saunders, Chapters 4–5.

Industrial Methods

Stille, Chapters 2–3 (Sections 3.1 and 3.4), and 4 (Sections 4.1
and 4.2).

SUMMARY

1. $R-H + X_2 \xrightarrow{h\nu} R-X + HX$
$X_2 = Cl_2$ or Br_2

2. The unsaturated alkenes and alkynes involve carbon hybridized as sp^2 and sp along with one or two π bonds.

3. Cyclohexane and alkenes with certain kinds of substitution can show geometric isomerism.

4. The most stable conformations of cyclohexane place the substituents in either the axial or equatorial position.

5. $\underset{\displaystyle}{>}C=C\underset{\displaystyle}{<} + X-Y \rightarrow -\overset{|}{\underset{|}{C}}-\overset{|}{\underset{|}{C}}- $
   $\phantom{>C=C< + X-Y \rightarrow -C}X\ \ Y$

$X-Y=X_2,\ HX,\ H_2,\ H_2O,\ H_2SO_4$

6. Markownikoff's Rule states that the HX acids add to unsymmetrical double bonds so that the hydrogen is attached to the carbon with the most hydrogens (that is, the least substituted carbon). The rule can be understood and extended by thinking in mechanistic terms.

7. An outstanding example of anti-Markownikoff addition is hydroboration.

$$3\,RCH{=}CH_2 + (BH_3) \xrightarrow{\text{ether}} (RCH_2CH_2)_3\,B$$

The alkyl boranes can be used in a variety of synthetic reactions, for example,

$$(RCH_2CH_2)_3\,B \xrightarrow[^-OH]{H_2O_2} 3\,RCH_2CH_2OH$$

8. Radical addition to alkenes takes place; with HBr it is anti-Markownikoff.

$$\underset{H}{\overset{\displaystyle}{>}}C{=}C\underset{\displaystyle}{<} + HBr \xrightarrow{h\nu} -\overset{|}{\underset{|}{C}}-\overset{|}{\underset{|}{C}}-H$$
$$\phantom{>C=C< + HBr \xrightarrow{h\nu} -C}H\ \ Br$$

9. The ionic addition mechanism involves an attack of an electrophile on the electron-rich multiple bond with the formation of some electron deficient species.

10. The oxidation of multiple bonds is a useful synthetic method and can provide structural information about the unsaturated compound.

$$>C{=}C< \xrightarrow{[O]} -\overset{|}{\underset{|}{C}}-\overset{|}{\underset{|}{C}}- \xrightarrow{[O]} \left. \begin{array}{c} CO_2 \\ -CO_2H \\ \overset{O}{\underset{\|}{}} \\ -C- \end{array} \right\} \text{possible products}$$

with $OH\ OH$ under the middle carbons.

11. Isomeric compounds with different structure but existing in equilibrium with each other are called tautomers. An example is found in the hydration of alkynes.

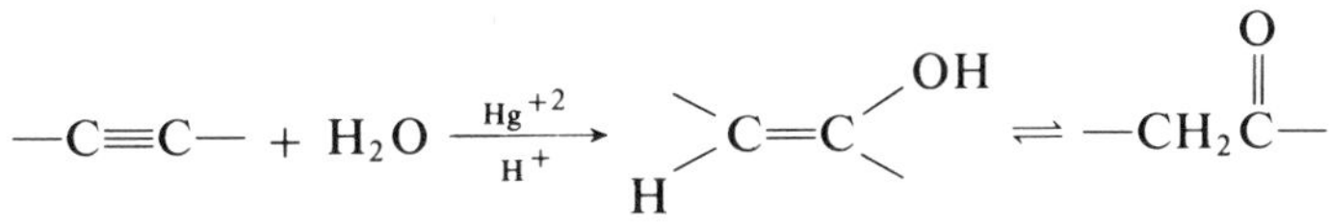

$$-C{\equiv}C- + H_2O \xrightarrow[H^+]{Hg^{+2}} \underset{H}{\overset{OH}{>}}C{=}C{<} \rightleftharpoons -CH_2\overset{\overset{\displaystyle O}{\parallel}}{C}-$$

12. Terminal alkynes show a slight acidity.

$$RC{\equiv}CH + Na^+NH_2^- \rightarrow RC{\equiv}C^-Na^+ + NH_3$$

The resulting sodium acetylides are useful in the preparation of other alkynes.

$$RC{\equiv}C^-Na^+ + R'X \rightarrow RC{\equiv}CR' + Na^+X^-$$

13. Two common methods for the preparation of alkenes are dehydration and dehydrohalogenation.

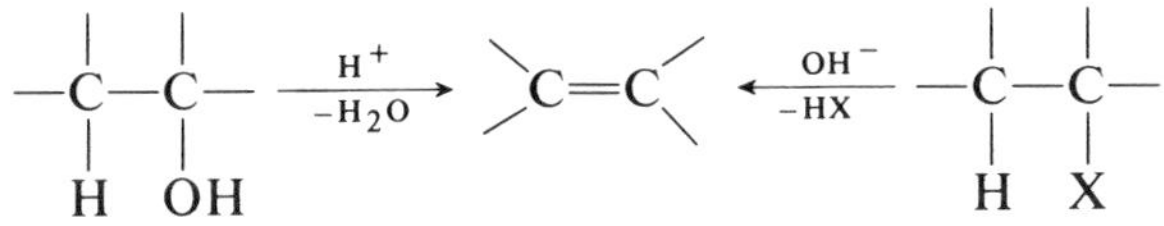

$$-\overset{|}{\underset{H}{C}}-\overset{|}{\underset{OH}{C}}- \xrightarrow[-H_2O]{H^+} \,>C{=}C<\, \xleftarrow[-HX]{OH^-} -\overset{|}{\underset{H}{C}}-\overset{|}{\underset{X}{C}}-$$

14. The formation of unsaturated compounds is called elimination, and the mechanism can involve either a charged intermediate (often a carbonium ion) or a single, concerted reaction. Substitution reactions often compete with elimination reactions.

15. During the course of a reaction it is sometimes possible for an intermediate to change its structure or rearrange before going on to product.

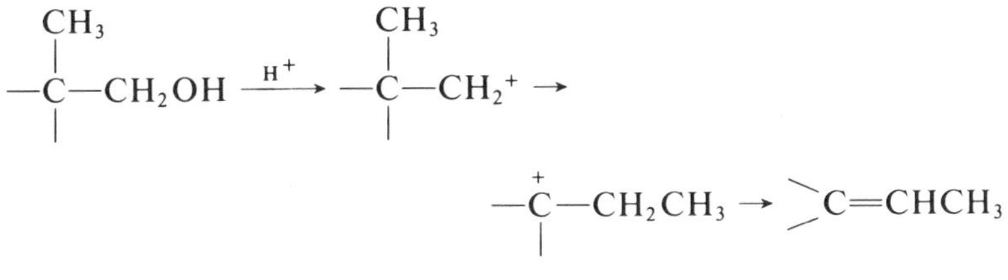

$$-\overset{\overset{\displaystyle CH_3}{|}}{\underset{|}{C}}-CH_2OH \xrightarrow{H^+} -\overset{\overset{\displaystyle CH_3}{|}}{\underset{|}{C}}-CH_2^+ \rightarrow$$

$$-\overset{|}{\underset{|}{\overset{+}{C}}}-CH_2CH_3 \rightarrow \,>C{=}CHCH_3$$

PROBLEMS

1. Complete the following reactions if any occurs under the conditions given (if no reaction takes place, write NR). Name all organic compounds.

   a. 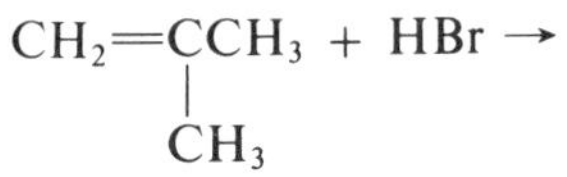 $CH_2{=}\underset{\underset{\displaystyle CH_3}{|}}{C}CH_3 + HBr \rightarrow$

b. $CH_3CHCH_2CH_3 \xrightarrow[\text{alcohol}]{\text{KOH}}$
    |
    Br

c. $CH_3C{\equiv}CCH_3 + 2\,HCl \rightarrow$

d. $CH{\equiv}CH + Na \xrightarrow{NH_3}$

e. $CH_3CH{=}CH_2 + Na \xrightarrow{NH_3}$

f. $CH_3CH{=}CHCH_2CH_3 + KMnO_4 \xrightarrow[\text{heat}]{^-OH}$

g. $CH{\equiv}C^-\,Na^+ + CH_3CH_2I \rightarrow$

h. $CH{\equiv}CCH_2CHCH_3 + H_2O \xrightarrow[\text{HgSO}_4]{H^+}$
                  |
                  CH_3

i. $\xrightarrow[\text{alcohol}]{\text{KOH}}$

j. 2-methyl-2-butene + $Br_2 \rightarrow$

k. 3-methyl-2-pentene + $HCl \rightarrow$

l. 2-propanol + $H_2SO_4 \rightarrow$

m. $\xrightarrow{Br_2}$

n. $\xrightarrow[\text{anhydrous}]{\text{HBr}}$

2. Give the structural formulas and names of the isomeric pentenes. Compare with the number of isomeric pentanes.

3. Draw structures for and name (IUPAC) all the isomers of
    a. C_6H_{12} b. C_4H_6 c. C_4H_4

4. Label each of the following molecules to show the types of carbon hybridization that can be identified. In each case, indicate the electrons that make up the bond.

    a. CH_3CH_3 f. $HC{\equiv}CCH_2CH_3$
    b. C_6H_{12} (2 isomers)   g. $(CH_3)_2CHNH_2$
    c. CH_3CH_2OH h. $C_2H_5O^-\,Na^+$
    d. $CH_2{=}CHCH_3$ i. CH_3OCH_3
    e. CH_3Br j. $CH_3COCH_2CH_3$

5. If any of the compounds listed can show geometric isomerism, draw and label both the *cis* and the *trans* forms.

a. 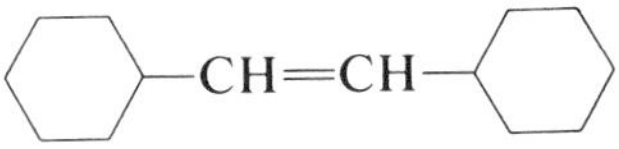 ⬡—CH=CH—⬡   f. $CH_3COCH=CHCH_3$

b. $CH_2=C(CH_3)_2$ g. 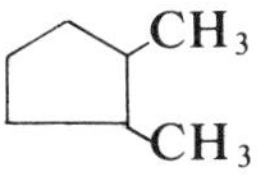 ⬡$\begin{smallmatrix}CH_3\\CH_3\end{smallmatrix}$

c. $CH_3CH=CHCH_3$ h. $BrCH=CHCl$
d. $CH_3C\equiv CCH_3$ i. $(C_2H_5)_2CHCH=C(C_2H_5)_2$

e. 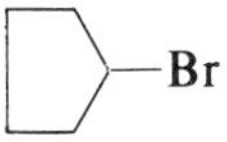 ⬠—Br   j. 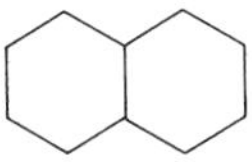 ⬡⬡

6. In each of the following cyclohexanes, draw all geometric and conformational arrangements and give the complete name of each (*cis*, *trans*, axial, equatorial). Which would you expect to be most stable? Least stable?

a. 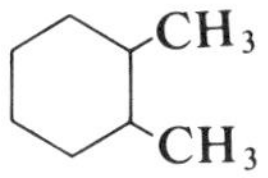 ⬡$\begin{smallmatrix}CH_3\\CH_3\end{smallmatrix}$ b. 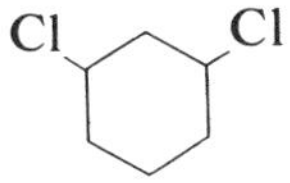 Cl⬡Cl   c. 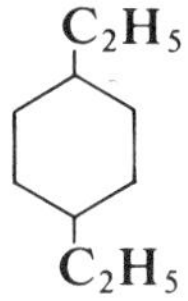 $\begin{smallmatrix}C_2H_5\\ \\C_2H_5\end{smallmatrix}$⬡

7. Complete the following reactions, name all organic compounds, and indicate the general mechanistic type involved.

a. $CH_3CH_3 + Br_2 \xrightarrow{h\nu}$

b. $CH_3CH_2CHCH_2OH + H_3PO_4 \rightarrow$
                $|$
               CH_3

c. $CH_3I + HC\equiv C^-Na^+ \rightarrow$

d. $HC\equiv CCH_2CH_2CH_3 + H_2O \xrightarrow[H^+]{HgSO_4}$

e. 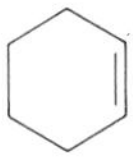 ⬡ $+ HCl \rightarrow$

8. For each of the overall reactions in problem 7, clearly draw the most significant arrangement(s) of atoms that occurs between reactants and products—that is, the intermediate(s) or, in the case of one-step reactions, the transition state.

9. Which of the reactions in problem 7 would be expected to show significant side reactions? Draw the structure(s) of all such products.

10. A substance contained 85.7% C and 14.5% hydrogen. One gram of the substance decolorized 38.0 g of 5% solution of bromine in CCl_4. Write a possible structure and give the name.

11. Two isomeric compounds, C_5H_8, react with bromine by addition at room temperature. Compound (A) reacts with one molar equivalent, whereas compound (B) reacts with two molar equivalents. Draw structures for and name each of the original compounds and their bromination products. Is there any other compound that fits all of these data? If yes, draw a structure and give a name for it and its bromination product.

12. Alcohol (A) has a molecular formula of $C_7H_{14}O$ and dehydrates smoothly to produce two isomeric hydrocarbons (B) and (C). Now, (B) adds HCl to produce (D) and (E), whereas (C) adds HCl to produce (E) and (F). Give structures and names for all organic compounds.

13. An organic compound containing only carbon and hydrogen fits the general formula C_nH_{2n-2}. It reacts by addition with one equivalent of HBr to yield an approximately equimolar mixture of two different brominated alkanes. Strong oxidation of the original compound produces two neutral compounds of formulas $C_6H_{10}O$ and C_3H_6O. Write structural formulas for each of the compounds described and indicate whether these are the only compounds consistent with the data.

14. An unknown compound (A) C_5H_8O is treated with H_2SO_4 to give (B) C_5H_6. When (B) is brominated, (C) $C_5H_6Br_4$ is produced. When (B) is reacted with HBr, (D) $C_5H_8Br_2$ is formed. Deduce possible structural formulas for all compounds and name each.

15. Using ethyne, cyclohexene, and any inorganic materials needed, outline a series of reactions that would allow the preparation of each of the following compounds. In most cases, several steps will be needed.

a. CH_3CH_2Br (bromoethane)   e. 1-bromobutane
b. 2-butanone (methyl ethyl ketone)   f. 1,3-cyclohexadiene
c. cyclohexylethyne   g. 3,3-dichlorohexane
d. 2-butyne   h. 1,4-hexadiene

16. A hydrocarbon containing five carbon atoms (A) reacts with cold, dilute potassium permanganate solution to give a new compound

(B), which reacts further with hot, concentrated permanganate to give two compounds. One of these (C) is acidic to litmus and has the formula $C_2H_4O_2$; the other (D) is neutral and has the formula C_3H_6O. Compound (A) reacts with Cl_2 to give (E), which has the formula $C_5H_{10}Cl_2$. Finally, (E) reacts with alcoholic KOH to give (F) C_5H_8. Draw structures for all of these lettered compounds that are consistent with the chemical data given. Name (IUPAC) compounds (A), (E), and (F).

5

Aromatic Compounds, Character, and Reactivity

5.1
STILL MORE UNSATURATION

Now a question arises. What about still more exotic combinations of the structural features discussed in Chapters 2 and 4? For example, are unsaturated, cyclic alcohols known? The answer is that many of them, along with polyunsaturated cyclic alcohols, have been studied.

2-cyclohexen-1-ol   2,4-cyclohexandien-1-ol   1,3,5-cyclohexatrien-1-ol
(unstable)

The first two examples show certain similarities to the saturated alcohols, except that there is a great increase in their ability to undergo addition reactions.* This factor is exactly what you would expect—as you increase the number of functional groups, you should find a corresponding increase in reactivity. Then a

---

*The alcohol 2,4-cyclohexandien-1-ol is unusual in that dehydration to form benzene takes place with great ease, the reasons for which will be discussed when we treat aromatic compounds.

most amazing change occurs when the very unsaturated compound 1,3,5-cyclohexatrien-1-ol (incorrect for a stable molecule; the proper name is phenol) is studied. First of all, the tendency toward addition reactions (except under special conditions) disappears. Also, this new compound is much more acidic than the alcohols, and, in several cases (oxidation, reduction, halogenation, dehydration, etc.), it is very different from the saturated or partially unsaturated alcohols. We shall return to these differences.

5.2
THE AROMATIC NUCLEUS

Early in the development of organic chemistry it was found that not only phenol, but also any one of a large number of compounds that contained the C_6H_5-group showed these "unusual" or, at least, unexpected properties. Let us begin by looking at the parent hydrocarbon—benzene (—OH replaced by —H).

In the early part of the nineteenth century, Michael Faraday (1825) isolated a new hydrocarbon with a very low hydrogen-to-carbon ratio. On the basis of the organic chemistry you have

Friedrich A. Kekulé (German, 1829–1896). One of the great German textbook (Lehrbuch) writers, Kekulé studied with Liebig and several other noted chemists in Europe. It was Liebig who made him turn from architecture to chemistry. His contributions to experimental organic chemistry were of minor importance, but his great imagination gave us such priceless concepts as the tetravalence of carbon and the structure of benzene.

Courtesy of Photographic Research Laboratory, Eastman Kodak Company.

FIGURE 5.1.   Structure of Benzene.

studied, you should expect, as did the chemists of 150 years ago, that this new molecule would be very reactive, especially in addition reactions.

The experimental facts, however, did not fit this picture. For example, benzene does not react rapidly with bromine or hydrogen bromide, as do simple unsaturated compounds. Bromine does add to benzene under special conditions to yield $C_6H_6Br_6$, but the usual reaction is of the **substitution** type.

$$C_6H_6 \ + \ Br_2 \ \xrightarrow[\text{FeBr}_3]{\text{Fe or}} \ C_6H_5Br \ + \ HBr$$

Friedrich Kekulé, an architect turned organic chemist, developed a structure for benzene in a rather unusual way. While dozing before his fire, he saw atoms in long snakelike chains twisting and twining in rapid motion. Then, as the vision became more acute, he saw one of the snakes seize hold of its own tail. This suggested the solution to the problem of benzene's structure and Kekulé tells us he spent the rest of the night working out the details of his hypothesis.

To provide the required tetracovalence for carbon in this structure, we must have alternating double and single bonds (which is known as a **conjugated** system).

Kekulé's structure for benzene was also consistent with the fact that all of its hydrogens are equivalent—that is, only one *mono*bromobenzene was obtained. However, when the dibromobenzenes are considered, only a single 1,2-isomer is found. It would be supposed that there should be two: the two bromine atoms located on either side of the single bond in one case and, in the other case, the bromine atoms on each side of the double bond.

This difficulty was "taken care of" by postulating rapid equilibrium between two forms as shown.

5.3
ELEMENTS OF RESONANCE THEORY

In introductory chemistry you discovered that there are times when it is possible to write more than one Lewis structure for a given group of atoms. The carbonate ion is a good example.

Whenever it is possible to draw more than one structure that differs only in the arrangement of electrons, we say that the true structure is represented by a **hybrid** composed of all the possible contributing structures. In other words, the molecule (or ion) is capable of **resonance**, and its properties will be explained only by considering all its possible forms. We can draw each structure and indicate by means of a doubleheaded arrow (↔) that they are resonance contributors to the hybrid form.

5.4
MORE RESONANCE

Benzene is now considered to be best represented as a single structure blended (on paper) from Kekulé and other forms.

To represent these resonance forms we shall use the following symbol:

This picture of benzene helps to keep us from being misled into thinking that there are double bonds and that they are jumping back and forth in the "real" structure of benzene. John D. Roberts, a contemporary American chemist, has suggested an analogy that may help in your understanding of benzene, and resonance in general. A medieval traveler returning to his home wished to tell his friends about a wonderful animal he had seen— the rhinoceros. He described it as being something like a unicorn and something like a dragon. As you well know, neither of these animals really exist, just as the Kekulé structures do not exist, but the rhinoceros (i.e., benzene) does exist, and, to some extent, it resembles each of them.

The term **aromatic** originally referred to the sweet odor of the compounds that later were found to contain a benzene ring. The term was thus applied to any compound containing such a ring. Today, the term has even broader meaning. It includes any planar cyclic molecule that shows resonance by virtue of continuous conjugation or other aspects of its structure.

One of the consequences of resonance is that it imparts added stability to a system capable of showing it. This fact is especially true of certain cyclic cases, of which benzene is the prototype. So great is this added stability factor that the aromatic ring is, with rare exceptions, retained during the course of a chemical reaction.

This tendency to retain the aromatic nucleus, plus the fact that the electrons are not localized as individual double bonds, helps to account for the general absence of addition reactions. When a substitution reaction is carried out, it is possible for both the reactant and the product to possess aromatic character, resulting in greater stability.

$$\text{benzene} + Br_2 \xrightarrow{Fe} \text{bromobenzene} + HBr$$

$$\text{phenol} + 3\,Br_2 \longrightarrow \text{tribromophenol} + 3\,HBr$$

In both cases, the type of reaction is substitution; however, phenol is much more reactive than benzene, and, in the absence of special indirect methods, only the tribromo product is obtained (p. 157).

Many kinds of evidence show the stability of aromatic systems, but one of special interest is the effect of such a structure on unstable intermediates. You will recall in Chapter 3 we found that primary (RCH_2^+) carbonium ions were on the lower end of the relative stability scale, whereas the primary carbanions were on the upper end. We said this effect could be understood as the result of electron donation or release by the alkyl groups. Now if you look at the stability of these ions when R is an aromatic ring (Ar), you find that they are comparatively stable. In fact, they will be more stable than tertiary carbonium ions or the methyl carbanion, but still of only fleeting existence. The great stability of both benzyl ions can be attributed to resonance with the aromatic ring:

This application of resonance will be of great interest later in our study of the properties and reactions of many organic compounds.

One interesting example of the importance of resonance is the greater acidity of the phenols as compared to the alcohols. The experimental fact is that the alcohols ionize, but are much weaker acids than water.

$$CH_3CH_2OH \xrightarrow{H_2O} CH_3CH_2O^- + H^+(aq)$$

Phenols, on the other hand, are stronger acids than water but not usually as acidic as the carboxylic acids. Their acidic nature is reflected in the common name of phenol, "carbolic acid," the antiseptic substance in disinfectants such as "Lysol." The increased acidity is owing to the resonance structures possible for the phenoxide ion. The loss of a proton (H^+) to a base is facilitated because the negative character of the oxygen is decreased by this resonance.

Several resonance forms may be pictured as follows:

The overall idea may be simply expressed in the following equation:

(stabilized by
resonance)

5.5
CONJUGATED AND AROMATIC MOLECULES

One of the greatest successes of the molecular orbital concept is its ability to provide us with a useful description of conjugated systems. When we consider the simplest conjugated hydrocarbon, 1,3-butadiene (see Figure 5.2), there is no obvious reason why the p orbitals should overlap only to form two isolated π bonds. The results of a large number of experiments indicate that such is not the actual situation, and, in fact, a single ("de-

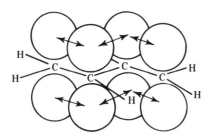

FIGURE 5.2.   First Molecular Orbital of 1,3-Butadiene.

localized" or spread-out) molecular orbital is formed involving two of the four *p* electrons and a slightly higher-energy orbital for the other two.

In a similar manner, the six *p* electrons of a benzene ring are found to overlap in a π electron cloud of three low-energy, de-

George W. Wheland (American, 1907–   ). *After receiving his Ph.D. degree at Harvard in 1932, Wheland held several fellowships at leading uni-*

versities until 1937 when he joined the faculty of the University of Chicago. His very productive career has centered on the application of resonance theory to organic chemistry. In addition to making important contributions to the development and application of resonance theory he also wrote a very influential book on the subject. Through Resonance in Organic Chemistry a large number of organic chemists have become more aware of the possible usefulness and limitations of this powerful concept. Wheland is also the author of a highly regarded textbook of advanced organic chemistry. This latter book is interesting in that it seeks to discuss those aspects of organic chemistry which are often treated inadequately or not at all.

Courtesy of Professor Wheland.

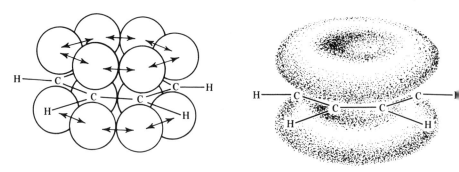

FIGURE 5.3.   First Molecular Orbital of Benzene.

localized orbitals covering the entire aromatic molecule (see Figure 5.3).

5.6
THE MEANING OF RESONANCE ENERGY

When we first encountered the aromatic compound benzene, we said that it was more stable than one would expect for a cyclic triene. In fact, organic chemists have stopped using the old Kekulé formula except for certain special kinds of descriptions, such as the resonance delocalization of ionic charge or unshared pairs of electrons. The entire idea was presented in only the most qualitative terms. At the present state of our development, we are able to have a more detailed look at these interesting cyclic compounds.

Much of the recent research with benzene, and a large number of compounds related to it, has been aimed at the problem of understanding the meaning of aromaticity. You should recall that the early relationship to odor has long since been replaced by a definition of cyclic conjugation leading to increased stability. It is the magnitude of this increased stability that we refer to as the **resonance energy**.

As a practical matter, the resonance energy of a system is the **difference between its actual energy and the energy of an identical system that does not show resonance**. For example, if we were to measure the energy of benzene and subtract the energy of 1,3,5-cyclohexatriene, we should obtain the resonance energy of benzene.

$$E \bigcirc - E \bigcirc = \text{R.E.} \bigcirc$$

It is at this point that we come face-to-face with the great difficulty and source of uncertainty in the estimation of this important quantity. The completely localized 1,3,5-cyclohexatriene does not have more than a transitory existence under ordinary conditions. Inasmuch as the energy of the system cannot easily be measured directly,* one can select a **model compound**—that is, a substance which is available and which we have reason to believe approximates the required compound, at least in the particular way we wish to study it. This approach is very similar to our earlier discussion of the scientific method. The model, like the hypothesis, will be more or less imperfect, and, as new knowledge becomes available, it will be necessary to modify or abandon the model (pp. 49–51).

Erich Hückel (German, 1896–). *Hückel represents a fine example of the close relationship which exists among the sciences. His training and interests*

are properly labeled physics and mathematics; yet he has had an important effect on organic chemistry. To the organic chemist he is best known for the Hückel Rule which, on the basis of molecular orbital calculations, predicts that monocyclic systems containing $4n + 2\pi$ electrons will show aromatic properties. The physical chemist is indebted to Hückel for his contribution to the Debye-Hückel theory of electrolytes. The importance of this latter work is now beginning to be more appreciated by the organic chemist interested in reaction kinetics and mechanisms.

Courtesy of Professor Hückel.

*Except by means of spectrographic analysis, which yields *differences* in electronic energy states.

The reasoning just described allows us to place our study of aromatic character on at least a semiquantitative basis. However, in addition to the difficulty of selecting a suitable model compound, there is the question of the method of evaluating the total energy of a given organic compound. As you will see, the two most widely used techniques lead to the same general conclusions but differ significantly in the magnitude of the resonance energy obtained.

One of the most commonly used model compounds for determining the resonance energy of benzene is cyclohexene. A frequently employed method of evaluating the energy of unsaturated systems is hydrogenation. Thus, if cyclohexene is catalytically reduced, the heat of hydrogenation is equal to -28.6 kcal/mole.*

$$\bigcirc\!\!| + H_2 \rightarrow \bigcirc \qquad \Delta H° = -28.6 \text{ kcal/mole}$$

In a similar manner, if benzene is reduced, its heat of hydrogenation is -49.8 kcal/mole.

$$\bigcirc\!\!\!\bigcirc + 3 H_2 \rightarrow \bigcirc \qquad \Delta H° = -49.8 \text{ kcal/mole}$$

Inasmuch as there are three times as many bonds broken and formed in the second reaction, it would seem reasonable that the change in energy should be three times as much.

$$3 \times -28.6 \text{ kcal/mole} = -85.8 \text{ kcal/mole}$$

The only reasonable explanation of the 36 kcal/mole discrepancy between the values predicted and those observed lies in the fact that benzene is already 36 kcal/mole more stable than expected. We therefore have estimated the value of the resonance energy of benzene (see Figure 5.4).

An alternative method of evaluating resonance energies is to compare the observed heat of combustion with that calculated.

---

*The negative sign indicates that the reaction is **exothermic**—that is, heat is given off.

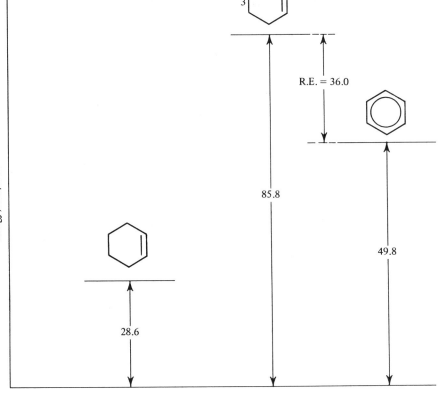

FIGURE 5.4.   Benzene Resonance Energy.

Such a calculated value can be obtained by using the individual bond contributions that give satisfactory agreement for nonaromatic molecules:

$$
\begin{aligned}
(6\ \text{C—H bonds})(54.0\ \text{kcal}) &= 324.0\ \text{kcal} \\
(3\ \text{C—C bonds})(49.3\ \text{kcal}) &= 147.9\ \text{kcal} \\
(3\ \text{C=C bonds})(117.4\ \text{kcal}) &= \underline{352.2\ \text{kcal}} \\
& \quad\ \ 824.1\ \text{kcal}
\end{aligned}
$$

The observed value of 789.1 kcal for benzene gives a resonance energy of 35.0 kcal, in good agreement with that obtained by hydrogenation.

Before leaving the subject of resonance energy, we note that the tendency of aromatic molecules to undergo substitution reactions rather than addition reactions is a direct consequence of their natural reluctance to forfeit this energy. Therefore, a very useful qualitative indication of aromatic character in hydrocarbons is the ease of substitution reactions under suitable conditions.

5.8
AROMATIC NOMENCLATURE

It is tempting to look at a Kekulé structure for benzene and to name it 1,3,5-cyclohexatriene. After reading the introduction to this chapter, you should have no doubt that such a name would be completely inappropriate. Benzene is obviously unlike any triene ever made. For this reason, aromatic compounds (containing a benzene ring) are named as derivatives of benzene (or other simple aromatic compounds) in the IUPAC system.

5.8A.   Monosubstituted Benzene

Inasmuch as all positions on the benzene ring are identical, there can never be more than one monosubstituted derivative of it, as illustrated.

ethylbenzene   bromobenzene   nitrobenzene

It is frequently useful to have a name for the C_6H_5— as a substituent in some other molecule. This **phenyl group** is an **aryl group** analogous to the alkyl groups encountered earlier. Like them, it is incomplete and requires another part of a molecule to be a proper compound. The expression Ar- is used as a general representation of aryl groups.

phenyl (Ph-)

Because of the great stability and wide natural occurrence of aromatic compounds, many of them have been known since the early days of organic chemistry. For this reason, they have common names which are in such wide use that they are retained both for the compound itself and as parent names for more highly substituted derivatives. A few of the best known of these should be memorized:

	toluene
$-CH_3$	toluene
$-OH$	phenol
plus $-CO_2H$	benzoic acid
$-NH_2$	aniline
$-CHO$	benzaldehyde
$-SO_3H$	benzenesulfonic acid

5.8B. Disubstituted Benzene

When a second group is introduced on the benzene ring, it may occupy three possible positions; hence, there are three isomeric forms for any such benzene system. It would be possible to number the ring starting with the substituent chosen as the parent compound. It is, in fact, done, but another method is in such common use that it must be learned. As shown, the three isomers have been given the names *ortho* (*o*-), *meta* (*m*-), and *para* (*p*-).

| ortho | meta | para |

In this text, we shall use the latter system rather than numbering.

| *o*-nitrotoluene | *m*-bromobenzoic acid | *p*-phenylphenol |

With more highly substituted benzene rings, it is common practice to number the ring and to assign the lowest possible number to each group.

| 3,5-dibromobenzaldehyde | 2,4,6-trinitrotoluene (TNT) |

5.9
THE REACTIVE AROMATIC NUCLEUS

In contrast to the substitution reactions of the alkanes, the benzene ring provides a favorable site for a variety of very specific and useful reactions. We shall begin with the simple case of introducing a single substituent because it is quite possible to find conditions allowing such control of the reaction.

5.9A. Halogenation

Treatment of benzene with chlorine or bromine in the absence of sunlight and the presence of iron or ferric halide produces the substitution shown. Light (especially high frequency) is usually excluded (pp. 132–133). The reaction is best carried out below 200°C and in the presence of a trace of moisture. These conditions are often abbreviated **ddc**—that is, dark, damp, cool.

$$\text{Benzene} + \text{Cl}_2 \; (\text{or Br}_2) \xrightarrow[\text{ddc}]{\text{Fe}} \text{C}_6\text{H}_5\text{Cl(Br)} + \text{HCl (or HBr)}$$

5.9B. Nitration

One of the most general of the aromatic substitution reactions, and also one of the most useful, is the introduction of the nitro group. It can be accomplished using a wide range of reagents, but one of the oldest and most common is a mixture of concentrated nitric and sulfuric acids (**ma**). The sulfuric acid is used in a catalytic amount so that sulfonation will not be an important side reaction.

$$\text{Benzene} + \text{HNO}_3 \xrightarrow{\text{H}_2\text{SO}_4} \text{C}_6\text{H}_5\text{NO}_2 + \text{H}_2\text{O}$$

5.9C. Sulfonation

The very useful aryl-sulfonic acids are frequently prepared by the direct treatment of the aromatic nucleus with fuming sulfuric acid.

$$\text{Benzene} \xrightarrow[7\%\ \text{SO}_3]{\text{HOSO}_3\text{H}} \text{C}_6\text{H}_5\text{SO}_3\text{H} + \text{H}_2\text{SO}_4$$

5.9D.   Friedel-Crafts Reaction

Organic chemists have a habit of attaching the name(s) of the originator of a reaction to it if the process turns out to be widely used. When you recall that we remember best by association, you will find that this little mark of respect may be of some assistance in your study of organic chemistry.

When an aromatic ring is treated with a halogen derivative (usually chloro) of either an alkane or an acid in the presence of a Lewis acid, a remarkable substitution reaction takes place.

$$\text{C}_6\text{H}_6 + CH_3CH_2Cl \xrightarrow{\text{AlCl}_3} \text{C}_6\text{H}_5CH_2CH_3 + HCl$$

$$\text{C}_6\text{H}_6 + CH_3CH_2\overset{\overset{\textstyle O}{\|}}{C}Cl \xrightarrow{\text{AlCl}_3} \text{C}_6\text{H}_5\overset{\overset{\textstyle O}{\|}}{C}CH_2CH_3 + HCl$$

Although both these reactions are limited in certain ways, they still are the methods of choice for such a large group of useful synthetic procedures that the naming of the reaction is amply justified.

5.10
ELECTROPHILIC AROMATIC SUBSTITUTION

In our treatment of the structure of benzene, we indicated that its apparent unsaturation did not lead, under usual conditions, to typical reactions of unsaturated carbon. Resonance of such a system tends to increase significantly the stability of the molecule, and its reactions are of the substitution type, so as to preserve the aromatic structure. There is, however, one way in which aromatic and unsaturated compounds do show a marked similarity —they are both centers of high electron density and, therefore, subject to electrophilic attack.

Perhaps the most studied of all organic reaction mechanisms is the nitration of aromatic compounds, and it will serve as a good model for our introduction to aromatic substitution in general. A number of physical studies have revealed that when nitric acid ionizes in sulfuric acid with a very low water concentration, the nitronium ion (NO_2^+) is formed.

$$H_2SO_4 + HNO_3 \rightleftharpoons NO_2^+ + HSO_4^- + H_2O$$

It is suggested that this electrophilic species is that which is important in aromatic nitration.

The nature of the reaction itself must involve the interruption of the aromatic system at some point during the process. Actually, there is excellent evidence that an intermediate is formed and, furthermore, that this arrangement of atoms is of such high energy that it is thought to be very similar to the transition state. For the purpose of discussing the mechanism of electrophilic aromatic substitution, it is convenient to use the older Kekulé structure of benzene containing "double bonds."

The intermediate carbonium ion (a phenonium ion) is fairly stable because, although the aromatic system is disrupted, the positive charge can be delocalized through resonance.

The intermediate can rapidly lose a proton to give the nitrated product.

The other common aromatic substitution reactions also involve electrophiles and appear to proceed through a resonance-stabilized carbonium ion. Not all of these low electron density species are ions.

In the Friedel-Crafts alkylation, there is very good evidence of carbonium ions. It is shown in the form of rearranged products resulting from 1,2-hydride shifts of the type we discussed in connection with alcohol dehydration; for example,

$$\text{C}_6\text{H}_6 + \text{CH}_3\text{CH}_2\text{CH}_2\text{Cl} \xrightarrow{\text{AlCl}_3} \text{C}_6\text{H}_5\text{CH}(\text{CH}_3)_2 + \text{HCl}$$

major product

(+ a significant amount of PhCH₂CH₂CH₃)

The suggested mechanism for the major product is the formation of a primary carbonium ion, which rearranges to the more stable secondary carbonium ion prior to attack on the ring.

$$\text{CH}_3\text{CH}_2\text{CH}_2\text{Cl} + \text{AlCl}_3 \rightarrow \text{AlCl}_4^- + \text{CH}_3\text{CH}_2\text{CH}_2^+$$

$$\rightleftharpoons (\text{CH}_3)_2\text{CH}^+$$

5.11
THE SECOND SUBSTITUTION

As has been pointed out earlier in the nomenclature section, all disubstituted benzene derivatives can exist in three isomeric forms. Therefore, it is of some interest to examine the distribution (relative yields) of those that result when a substituted benzene ring is employed as starting material.

Inasmuch as there are two *ortho*, two *meta*, and one *para* hydrogen(s), it would seem reasonable statistically to expect a 40:40:20 ratio of products. Once again, the experimental evidence does not support this hypothesis; in fact, it shows the orientation of the second group to be very dependent on the nature of the group already attached to the ring. The net effect is to make the reaction more specific and, hence, more useful.

The directive influence of the group present on the ring was at one time correlated with the presence or absence of a multiple bond on the atom attached to the ring. There are *many* exceptions, and today we have better methods of prediction.

ortho-para directors　　　　　　　　*meta* directors

(H may be R or Ar)

These generalizations do not solve all of the synthetic problems of aromatic compounds. For example, they do not tell us the amount by which *meta* will exceed *ortho-para* when nitrobenzene is substituted. Nor do they predict an excess of either *ortho* or *para* in any instance. Keep in mind that all isomers are produced but that these directive effects predict the isomer(s) which will predominate.

Let us look at some specific examples of the percentage distribution of the isomers formed by nitration of some compounds having both types of directive groups attached to the aromatic nucleus. When nitrobenzene is further nitrated at 25°C, the following isomers are formed:

*Acetic anhydride, rather than the more usual H_2SO_4, was selected because a greater amount of comparable data is available. Much the same trends would be observed in ma.

We can shorten the method of writing the data to

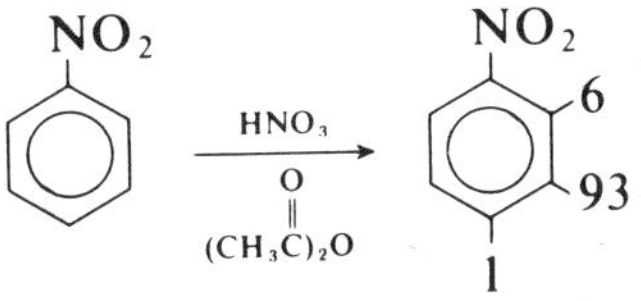

NO_2 → NO_2 6, 93, 1
HNO₃, (CH₃C)₂O

Using this same notation for other types of compounds, we obtain

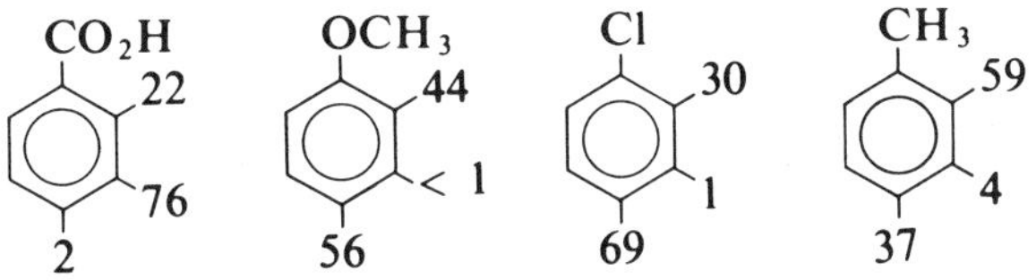

CO_2H 22, 76, 2
OCH_3 44, < 1, 56
Cl 30, 1, 69
CH_3 59, 4, 37

nitration at 25°C

These figures are only for nitration at 25°C. Let us compare the difference in yields when we nitrate or sulfonate toluene at the same temperature.

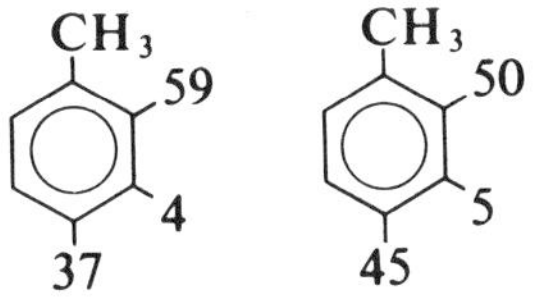

CH_3 59, 4, 37
CH_3 50, 5, 45

nitration at 25°C   sulfonation at 25°C

Let us look at what happens when we sulfonate toluene at different temperatures.

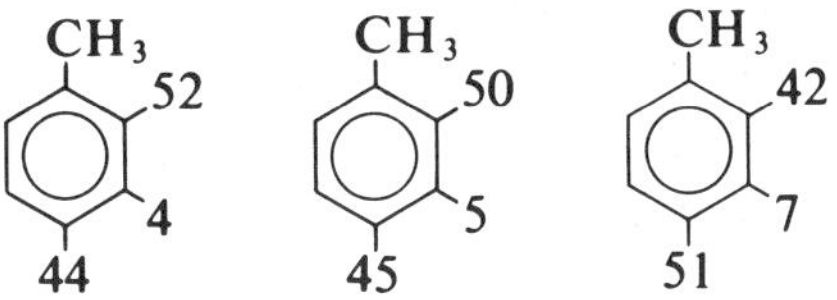

CH_3 52, 4, 44
CH_3 50, 5, 45
CH_3 42, 7, 51

5°C   25°C   65°C

There is evidence that sulfonation under these conditions is reversible; thus, higher temperature favors the more stable, less sterically crowded p position. When you wish to predict the results of treating toluene with fuming sulfuric acid, you say that the methyl group is an *ortho-para* director producing these two isomers. In a practical laboratory situation, if you wish to produce p-toluenesulfonic acid, you would examine the literature to find out the conditions of temperature, pressure, reagents, concentrations, and so on, that would enhance the production of the

para isomer. In this case, it appears that increasing the temperature has this effect. As you will see, it is also possible to make
some very useful predictions based on the mechanism of the
reaction.

Perhaps the greatest aid these considerations give is in the
selection of the proper sequence of reactions to employ in the
proposed synthesis of a new disubstituted benzene. Always keep
in mind that the substitution carried out first will control the
position of the second substitution.

5.12
MECHANISM OF THE DIRECTIVE EFFECT

A question of great mechanistic importance is that of a reasonable explanation for the observed selectivity in the introduction
of the second substituent in aromatic systems. A very convincing
argument can be constructed on the basis of the inductive and
resonance effects that we have used to discuss the stability of
reactive intermediates. When the various types of substituents
are arranged as *ortho-para* or *meta* directors, it is obvious that,
with the exception of halogen, the former are electron donating
and the latter are electron withdrawing.

o, p directors—R, RO, OH, NH$_2$—electron donating (X is
electron withdrawing, but directs *o, p*)

m directors—NO$_2$, CO$_2$H, CHO, SO$_3$H, CN—electron withdrawing

With this information, let us consider the intermediates for
the nitration of toluene and nitrobenzene. Possible intermediates

in nitration of toluene are

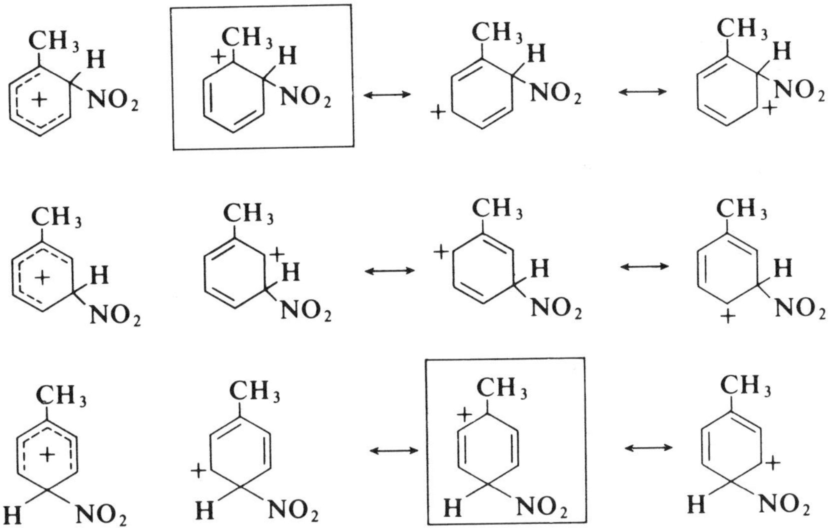

The general formula of the various intermediate states (drawn at the left) can be translated into the several resonance contributors on the right. These may be taken as models of the transition states. The forms in the squares have special significance. First, consider the *ortho-para* directing methyl group. It is known from other experiments that it is an electron donating group, and you should expect it to be especially effective in stabilizing a positive charge on the carbon to which it is attached. Both *ortho* and *para* nitration of toluene involve a transition state, or, rather, a likely model of the transition state, which is a resonance hybrid including such a form as a contributor. Inasmuch as that particular contributor is more stable (i.e., a more important contributor), it is reasonable to predict that the hybrid will also be more stable, and thus that the methyl group should direct *ortho-para*. In other words, we observe that the *meta* substitution transition state model has no unusually important form and, therefore, would be less stable and less important. Possible intermediates in nitration of nitrobenzene are shown on the following page. Our argument in the case of the nitration of toluene can be applied in reverse for nitrobenzene and other *meta* directors. These groups are known to be electron withdrawing in their inductive effect and would, therefore, be expected to destabilize the resonance contributors indicated in the boxes. With this analysis, you should expect the *meta*-nitration transition state, which possesses no such form, to be the most important of the three possibilities.

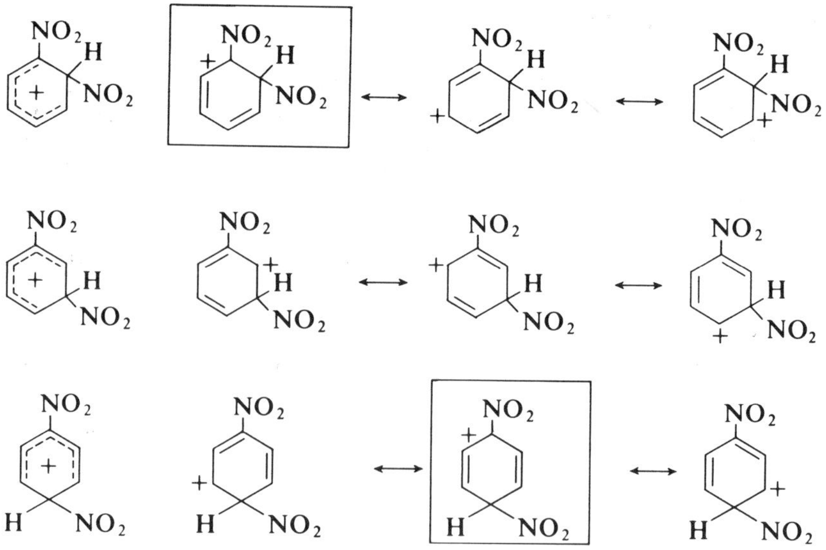

The interesting case of the halogens, which are electron withdrawing but *o, p* directing, results from a balance between inductive and resonance effects. A detailed treatment of this aspect of the reaction can be found in the list of Suggested Additional Readings.

5.13
KÖRNER—AN ORGANIC DETECTIVE

Let us pause for a look at a fine point—the problem of determining which one of the three isomeric disubstituted benzenes prepared in the laboratory has the *ortho, meta,* or *para* structure. In 1874, W. Körner undertook the study of the three dibromobenzenes to answer this question. The method of proof he developed, bearing his name, must be rated as one of the truly classic deductive feats of experimental organic chemistry. Very simply stated, he considered the results that would be observed if each of the three dibromobenzenes were nitrated. As you can see from the following diagram, each of the original compounds gives a different number of trisubstituted isomers.

Thus, all that was required was to nitrate each of the dibromobenzenes, isolate the six isomeric dibromonitrobenzenes, and assign the structures of the original compounds on the basis of the number of derived isomers. If you have done any work in

Wilhelm G. Körner (German, 1839–1925). The problem of the structure of a particular isomer of di- or trisubstituted benzenes was not only a very important one, but demanded great laboratory skill in its solution. The purely deductive answer which Körner provided had the additional advantage of not depending on the assumption of the structure of any other substituted benzene. Körner was a student of Kekulé and first introduced the terms ortho, meta, and para.

Courtesy of the Edgar Fahs Smith Memorial Collection.

the laboratory, you should appreciate the complexity of this task. When it is further recalled that these isomers would be produced in widely varying amounts (traces in some cases), that they would all have somewhat similar physical constants, and that the laboratory apparatus of 100 years ago was much cruder than that of our day, it must be admitted that this study was not only a masterful bit of deduction, but also executed with great skill. You should convince yourself that this method really gives the required information. Today, work of this kind is most often done by the faster, more reliable, instrumental methods (see Appendix II).

5.14
ADDITIONAL REACTIONS OF BENZENE

The substitution reactions we have been discussing are the most frequently mentioned and associated with the aromatic ring, but several others are both useful and characteristic.

5.14A. Side Chain Halogenation

By using light and/or heat, and by omitting the iron or iron salt, it is possible to halogenate the side chain rather than the ring.

$$\text{RCHR}' \xrightarrow[\text{(or Br}_2)]{\substack{h\nu \\ \text{Cl}_2}} \underset{\text{(major product)}}{\text{RCR}'\text{—Cl (or Br)}} + \text{HCl (or HBr)}$$

$h\nu$ = radiant energy

The influence of the benzene ring on the side chain is clearly illustrated by the fact that as long as there are hydrogens on the carbon adjacent to the ring [usually called the *alpha* (α) carbon], the halogenation will take place on it in a step-by-step manner, with only small amounts of products resulting from reaction in other parts of the chain. If there are no *alpha* hydrogens, halogenation will take place on the alkane group in a random and indiscriminate fashion. The conditions of the reaction suggest that it is one involving radicals; refer to our earlier discussion of this mechanism (pp. 71–73).

The reason attack takes place mainly on the α carbon is the great stability of the benzylic radical, which, like the corresponding ions, can show resonance.

Fortunately, the change in conditions required to introduce a second halogen (increased temperature, longer time, 2 moles of halogen, etc.) is sufficient so that either the α halo or the α, α dihalo compound can be prepared by this method.

5.14B.   Addition

Using high temperatures, high pressures, and active catalysts, it is possible to add 3 moles of hydrogen to the benzene ring. In the process, the resonance system is destroyed and a cyclohexane ring is formed. The difficulty of reducing the benzene ring can be seen by comparison with the reduction of 1,3,5-hexatriene under the same conditions.

$$CH_2{=}CH{-}CH{=}CH{-}CH{=}CH_2 + 3\ H_2 \xrightarrow[\substack{1\text{-}2\ hr \\ 25°C \\ \text{moderate pressure}}]{PtO_2}$$

$$CH_3CH_2CH_2CH_2CH_2CH_3$$

A similar process of some industrial importance is the addition of 3 moles of chlorine to produce a mixture of hexachlorocyclo-hexanes.

5.14C.   Oxidation

With the exception of a few industrial applications, the oxidation of aromatic systems of laboratory interest are those involving an alkyl side chain attached to benzene.

$$\underset{\text{heat}}{\overset{KMnO_4}{\longrightarrow}}$$

CH$_2$R → CO$_2$H

The entire side chain is lost (as CO_2 and H_2O), with the exception of the carbon adjacent to the ring, which becomes the carboxyl carbon. This fact illustrates both the great stability of the aromatic ring and the unusual character of the carbon attached to it. One should also be aware of the fact that it is not always possible to be selective in the side chain to be oxidized; if more than one is present, all will be oxidized.

$$\overset{[O]}{\longrightarrow}$$

CH$_3$ ... CH$_2$CH$_3$ → CO$_2$H ... CO$_2$H

5.15
NAPHTHALENE—ANOTHER AROMATIC COMPOUND

A number of aromatic compounds can be thought of as benzene rings sharing a common edge or pair of carbon atoms. Some of them have been known for a long time and others are of quite recent origin. Perhaps the best known is **naphthalene**. As was the case with benzene, this molecule can be represented by more than one Lewis structure (resonance contributors) and, therefore, would be expected to show aromatic character.

For this reason it is now considered preferable to write the naphthalene structure, and that of other aromatic molecules, as we have written benzene.

Naphthalene, like benzene, shows a marked tendency to undergo substitution reactions rather than addition reactions.

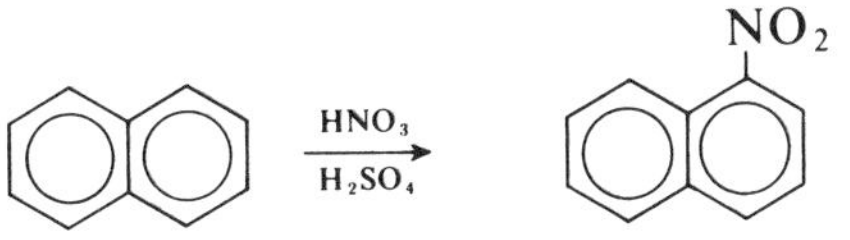

α (or 1)-nitronaphthalene*
100%
(by hydrogenation)

no β-nitronaphthalene
is formed by direct
nitration

It also has the very sizable resonance energy (by hydrogenation) of 61 kcal/mole, although this figure is obviously less than that of two benzene rings. This indication that the naphthalene system is somewhat less aromatic than benzene is also found in the easier reduction of one of the rings, as opposed to the reduction of benzene.

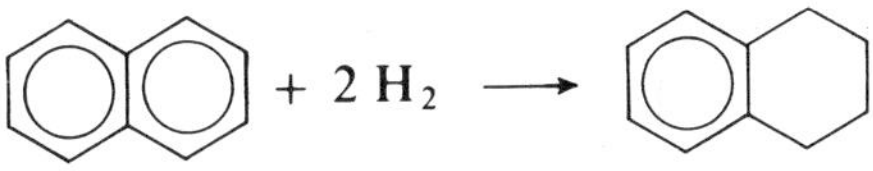

tetralin

This reaction requires conditions much milder than those for total reduction, so that it is possible to avoid complete reduction of the π system. Still another piece of evidence of this weakened aromaticity of naphthalene is the fact that one of the rings can be oxidized and the other left intact.

You have seen how stable the benzene ring is to oxidizing agents. When a compound such as isopropylbenzene is oxidized, the ring is not affected and the carbon attached to the ring remains with it taking the form of a carboxyl group. Such is the case with naphthalene.

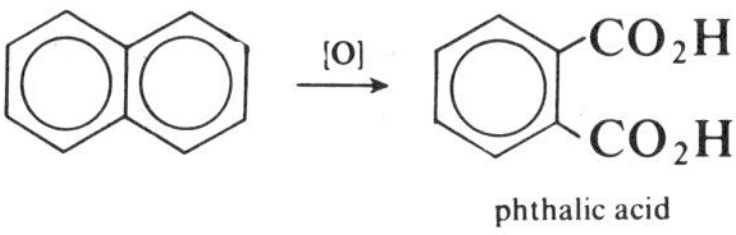

phthalic acid

---

*For more highly substituted naphthalenes, the ring is numbered:

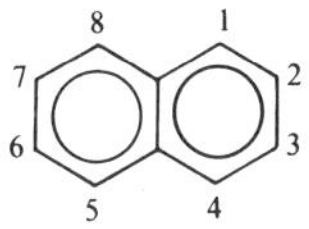

For example,

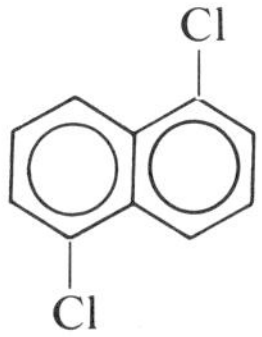

is 1,5-dichloronaphthalene.

No matter which side of the molecule is regarded as the stable benzene ring, the result will be the same.

The results are predictable when groups are attached to the ring. The following example not only illustrates what happens but also gives us a clearer picture of the structure of the naphthalene ring. If we nitrate naphthalene (obtaining α-nitronaphthalene) and oxidize this product, we obtain 3-nitrophthalic acid. However, when nitronaphthalene is reduced to α-naphthylamine, which is in turn oxidized, we simply obtain phthalic acid.

The explanation lies in the fact that oxidation, which is the removal of electrons, occurs faster at an electron-rich site than at an electron-deficient one.

SUGGESTED ADDITIONAL READINGS

Historical

O. Theodor Benfey (ed.), "Kekulé Centennial," *Advances in Chemistry Series No. 61*, American Chemical Society, Washington, D.C.: 1966.

Aromatic Character and Resonance Energy

Allinger and Allinger, pp. 50–56.
Breslow, pp. 6–11.
Cason, Chapter 12.

Gould, pp. 412–17.
Morrison and Boyd, pp. 314–23.
Roberts and Caserio, Chapter 9 and pp. 767–68.
Royals, Chapter 5.
Stock, Chapter 1.

C. R. Noller, "A Physical Picture of Covalent Bonding and Resonance in Organic Chemistry," *J. Chem. Educ.*, **27**, 504 (1950).

A. Gero, "The Concept of Resonance Energy in Elementary Organic Chemistry," *J. Chem. Educ.*, **29**, 82 (1952).

A. Gero, "Kekulé's Theory of Aromaticity," *J. Chem. Educ.*, **31**, 201 (1954).

R. Breslow, "Aromatic Character," *Chem. Eng. News*, June 28, 1965, pp. 90–99.

E. E. van Tamelen, "Benzene—the Story of Its Formulas," *Chemistry*, **38** (1), 6 (1965).

Electrophilic Aromatic Substitution

Breslow, Chapter 5-1.
Cason, Chapter 17.
Cram and Hammond, Chapter 19.
Gould, pp. 419–52.
Morrison and Boyd, Chapter 11.
Roberts and Caserio, pp. 783–815.
Stock, Chapters 2–4 and 7.

L. N. Ferguson, "The Orientation and Mechanism of Electrophilic Aromatic Substitution," *J. Chem. Educ.*, **32**, 42 (1955).

K. L. Marsi and S. H. Wilen, "Friedel-Crafts Alkylation," *J. Chem. Educ.*, **40**, 214 (1963).

H. Duewell, "Aromatic Substitution," *J. Chem. Educ.*, **43**, 138 (1966).

H. Meislich, "Teaching Aromatic Substitution," *J. Chem. Educ.*, **44**, 153 (1967).

SUMMARY

1. Resonance is found in compounds in which the bonding electrons can be considered to be arranged in more than one low energy (stable) manner. This property leads to a greater stability than might be expected for the system.

2. Compounds, such as benzene, that are in resonance by virtue of continuous cyclic conjugation are especially stable. They are called aromatic compounds.

3. Aromatic compounds typically react by substitution.

4. The mechanism of aromatic substitution often involves the electrophilic attack of some reagent on the electron-rich aromatic ring followed by the loss of a proton.

5. The position a second substituent takes is strongly influenced by the first substituent. The rate of the reaction is also affected.

6. The directive effect of substituents can be understood in terms of their stabilization of transition state models by resonance and inductive effects.

7. In addition to substitution reaction, aromatic compounds also undergo a few other reactions of interest.

$$\text{benzene} + 3 H_2 \xrightarrow{PtO_2} \text{cyclohexane}$$

$$\text{Ar–R} \xrightarrow{[O]} \text{Ar–CO}_2H$$

8. Naphthalene is one of many aromatic compounds other than benzene. In many respects its chemistry is similar to benzene.

PROBLEMS

1. Define and illustrate the following terms:
   a. unsaturation   b. aromatic
   c. addition   d. substitution
   e. resonance   f. radical
   g. transition state   h. carbonium ion
   i. nucleophile   j. reactive intermediate

2. Draw the structure of each of the following compounds:
   a. 2,3-dichlorotoluene   b. *m*-nitrobenzoic acid
   c. 3,5-dinitroaniline   d. α-chlorotoluene
   e. *p*-phenylphenol   f. 1,3,5-trinitrobenzene
   g. α′,α″,α‴-tribromo-1,3,5-
        trimethylbenzene
   i. *o*-chloropropylbenzene   j. benzoic acid
   k. benzenesulfonic acid   l. 1,2-diphenylhexane
   m. *p*-iodobenzenesulfonic acid   n 3,5-dichlorobenzaldehyde
   o. 3,5-dinitronaphthalene   p. 3-chlorocyclopentene
   q. 2,5-dibromo-2,5-   r. 2-bromo-2-butene
        dimethylhexane
   s. *p*-isopropyltoluene   t. aniline

3. Write the IUPAC name of the following compounds:

a. (structure: benzene ring with Cl and NO₂)

c. (structure: benzene ring with CH₃ and HO₂C)

e. (structure: benzene ring with CH₃)

b. (structure: two benzene rings linked by CH₂)

d. (structure: benzene ring with CH₂Br)

f. (structure: benzene ring with CH₂CH₂Br)

g.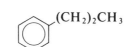

h. CO$_2$H

O$_2$N   Cl

i. NO$_2$

j. HO—

k. CO$_2$H

NO$_2$

l. Cl   Cl

m. SO$_3$H

CH$_3$

n. CHO

o. Br

Br   Br

4. Complete the following reactions (use NR if no reaction takes place under the conditions given). Name all organic compounds.

a.   Br

+ CH$_3$CH$_2$Cl $\xrightarrow{\text{AlCl}_3}$

b.   CN

+ HONO$_2$ $\xrightarrow{\text{H}_2\text{SO}_4}$

c.   OH

+ HOSO$_3$H $\xrightarrow{7\% \text{ SO}_3}$

d.   (CH$_2$)$_2$CH$_3$

$\xrightarrow{\text{KMnO}_4}$

e.   CH$_3$CHCH$_3$

+ Cl$_2$ $\xrightarrow{hv}$

f.   CH$_3$CHCH$_3$

+ Cl$_2$ $\xrightarrow{\text{Fe}}$

g. $\text{C}_6\text{H}_5\text{CO}_2\text{H}$ + Br$_2$ $\xrightarrow{\text{Fe}}$

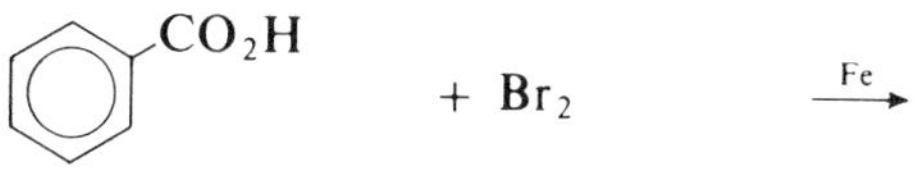

h.   OH (phenol) + Al$_2$O$_3$ $\longrightarrow$

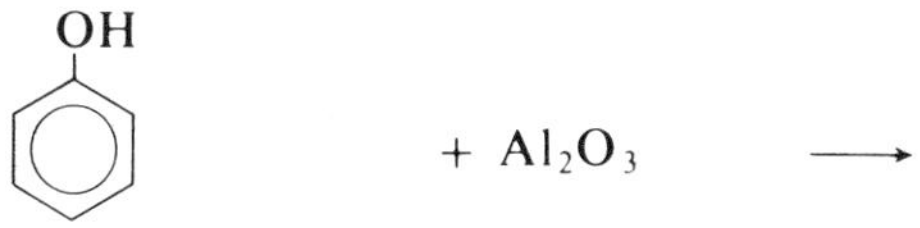

i.   Br (1,4-dibromobenzene) + CH$_3$CCl ($\overset{\text{O}}{\underset{\parallel}{}}$) $\xrightarrow{\text{AlCl}_3}$

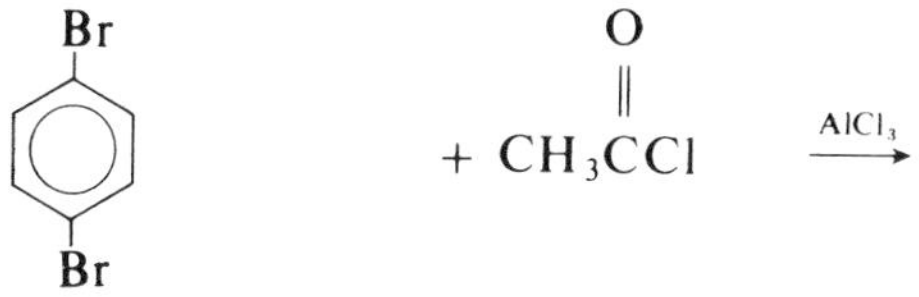

5. Predict the products that will be formed in the highest yield in the following reactions, and name *all* organic compounds (consider only monosubstitution):

   a.   (benzene) + Br$_2$ $\xrightarrow{\text{Fe}}$

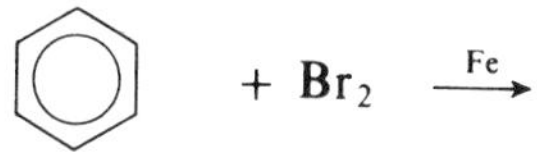

   b.   CH$_3$ (toluene) $\xrightarrow[\text{H}_2\text{SO}_4]{\text{HNO}_3}$

   c.   CO$_2$H (benzoic acid) $\xrightarrow[\text{SO}_3]{\text{H}_2\text{SO}_4}$

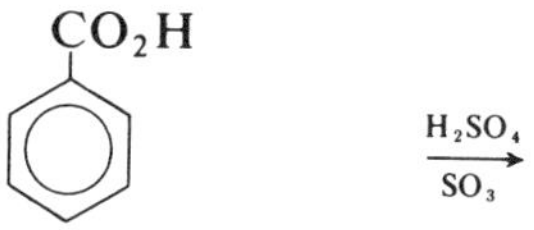

   d.   Br (bromobenzene) + Cl$_2$ $\xrightarrow{\text{FeCl}_3}$

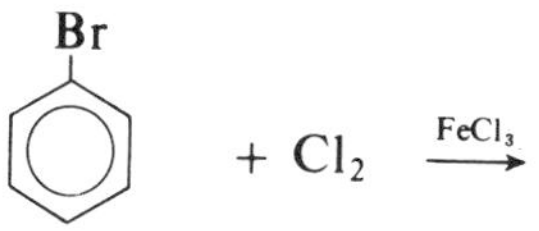

   e.   OCH$_3$ (anisole) + CH$_3$CH$_2$Cl $\xrightarrow{\text{AlCl}_3}$

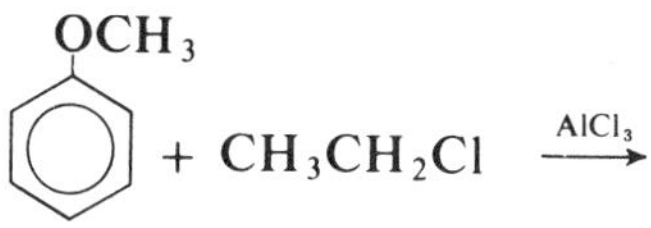

6. From the following observations, what can you deduce about the unknown compound?
   a. An aromatic compound reacts with nitric/sulfuric acid mixture to produce only one mononitro derivative.
   b. A compound with a very low hydrogen-to-carbon ratio is very inert toward strong oxidizing agents.

c. A hydrocarbon reacts with $KMnO_4$ solution to yield one dicarboxylic acid as the only organic product.

d. An aromatic compound reacts readily with bromine by both addition and substitution.

e. An organic compound containing carbon, hydrogen, and chlorine reacts with an oxidizing agent to produce a carboxylic acid containing only carbon, hydrogen, and oxygen.

7. Compound (A), $C_{10}H_8$, yields two mononitronuclear substitution products. Upon oxidation, (A) gives (B), $C_8H_6O_4$, which also yields two mononitronuclear substitution products. Give the structure and reaction products of (A) and (B). Name all organic compounds.

8. The following statements describe the reactions of different compounds. Relate in one or two sentences what that particular piece of information tells you about each of the compounds. For each of the compounds, draw a structure consistent with the information given. Write equations for all reactions and name all organic compounds.

   a. In the presence of iron, compound (A) readily reacts with bromine by substitution to give one mono-bromo product.

   b. In the presence of light and without iron, compound (B) reacts with bromine to produce one mono-bromo product.

   c. Compound (C) reacts with strong oxidizing agents to produce one acidic product without the loss of CO_2.

9. Given benzene, low molecular weight alcohols, and inorganic chemicals, suggest reasonable synthetic routes to the following compounds:

   a. α- and β-bromopropylbenzene
   b. o-, m-, and p-chlorobenzoic acid
   c. o-, m-, and p-nitrotoluene

   One of these compounds should be very difficult to prepare in good yield by the simple methods we have discussed so far. If you carefully consider all that we have said about aromatic substitution and the reasons for its mechanism, you should be able to decide which one is difficult.

10. An unknown compound (A) is treated with C_3H_7Cl in the presence of aluminum chloride to produce (B), C_9H_{12}. When this reaction is repeated with (B) as the starting material, two compounds, (C) and (D), are formed in good yield. Their molecular formula is $C_{12}H_{18}$. When they are oxidized, two isomers, (E) and (F), with formula $C_8H_6O_4$, are produced. Isomer (E) yields one mononitronuclear substitution product, whereas (F) produces two.

Oxidation of (B) yields (G), which can give three mononitronuclear substitution products. Give the reactions, the structures, and the names of all the compounds.

11. An unknown compound (A) $C_{12}H_{12}O$ is treated with H_2SO_4 to give (B), $C_{12}H_{10}$. When (B) is reacted with HBr, (C)—$C_{12}H_{11}Br$— is produced. Deduce possible structural formulas for (A), (B), and (C), and name them.

12. An organic compound (A), $C_{12}H_{14}$, undergoes an interesting series of reactions with bromine. When a cold solution of bromine in carbon tetrachloride is added to (A), a very rapid reaction takes place and a new compound (B), $C_{12}H_{14}Br_2$, is produced. Compound (B) reacts with more bromine in the presence of light to give (C), $C_{12}H_{13}Br_3$. In the absence of light and with an iron catalyst, (B) reacts with bromine to give a mixture of three isomeric compounds of molecular formula $C_{12}H_{13}Br_3$. Strong oxidation of (A) produces 2-phenyladipic acid, and still stronger oxidation gives a compound $C_7H_6O_2$, which is also an acid. Complete all reactions by drawing structures that would be expected to show the chemistry described. Name all compounds.

13. An unknown alcohol will not dehydrate, but, when treated with bromine, it reacts smoothly by substitution to produce three isomeric mono-bromo products. Treatment of each of these with excess HI produces three isomeric brominated hydrocarbons. A fourth isomer of these last three compounds can be prepared by treatment of the original alcohol with HBr. Draw structures for all organic compounds and name them.

14. From questions 4 and 5, select a reaction typical of each of the various types of mechanisms we have discussed in this chapter. Indicate by drawings the most important arrangements of atoms between reactants and products. If there are any important side reactions, discuss them and the reason they occur.

15. Predict the relative acidities of the following series of phenols by considering inductive and resonance effects:

$$R = CH_3, Br, H, NO_2$$

6

Alcohols and Alkyl Halides: Nucleophilic Substitution

6.1
INTRODUCTION

The simple organic molecules that contain either a halogen or a carbinol group are of great interest for both synthetic and mechanistic applications. It is useful to classify these compounds on the basis of the nature of the carbon atom to which the halogen or oxygen is attached.

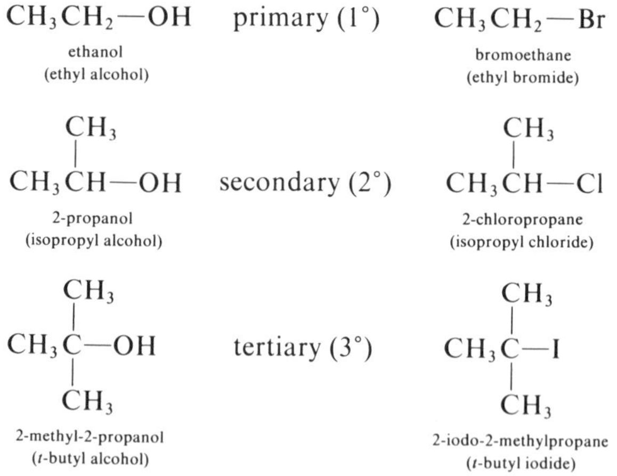

$$CH_3CH_2\!-\!OH \qquad \text{primary (1°)} \qquad CH_3CH_2\!-\!Br$$

ethanol
(ethyl alcohol)

bromoethane
(ethyl bromide)

$$CH_3\overset{\overset{\displaystyle CH_3}{|}}{CH}\!-\!OH \qquad \text{secondary (2°)} \qquad CH_3\overset{\overset{\displaystyle CH_3}{|}}{CH}\!-\!Cl$$

2-propanol
(isopropyl alcohol)

2-chloropropane
(isopropyl chloride)

$$CH_3\overset{\overset{\displaystyle CH_3}{|}}{\underset{\underset{\displaystyle CH_3}{|}}{C}}\!-\!OH \qquad \text{tertiary (3°)} \qquad CH_3\overset{\overset{\displaystyle CH_3}{|}}{\underset{\underset{\displaystyle CH_3}{|}}{C}}\!-\!I$$

2-methyl-2-propanol
(*t*-butyl alcohol)

2-iodo-2-methylpropane
(*t*-butyl iodide)

144

The nomenclature of the alcohols and alkyl halides is illustrated for both IUPAC and common usage.

6.2
PHYSICAL PROPERTIES OF ALCOHOLS AND
ALKYL HALIDES (TABLE 6.1)

Both the alcohols and the alkyl halides have much higher boiling points than hydrocarbons of the same number of carbon atoms. This condition is in part owing to their higher molecular weight but for the alcohols we take into account the effect of **hydrogen bonding** (see Figure 6.1). This effect is found where both hydrogen attached to an electronegative atom and an atom with a free pair of electrons are present—for example, water and ammonia.

TABLE 6.1   PHYSICAL PROPERTIES OF SOME COMMON ALCOHOLS AND ALKYL HALIDES

Name	Formula	Boiling point, °C*	Melting point, °C	Solubility,[†] g/100 ml H_2O	Density,[†] g/ml
Methanol	CH_3OH	64	−97	miscible	0.793
Ethanol	CH_3CH_2OH	78	−115	miscible	0.789
Propanol	$CH_3CH_2CH_2OH$	97	−126	miscible	0.804
Butanol	$CH_3(CH_2)_3OH$	118	−90	7.9	0.810
2-Methyl-1-propanol	$(CH_3)_2CHCH_2OH$	108	−108	10.0	0.802
2-Butanol	CH_3CH_2CHOH $\quad\quad\;\; \vert$ $\quad\quad\;\; CH_3$	100	−114	12.5	0.806
2-Methyl-2-propanol	$(CH_3)_3COH$	83	26	miscible	0.789
Dodecanol	$CH_3(CH_2)_{11}OH$	255	26	insoluble	0.831 (24°)
Tetradecanol	$CH_3(CH_2)_{13}OH$	263	39	0.02 (20°)	0.824 (38°)
Hexadecanol	$CH_3(CH_2)_{15}OH$	344	50	insoluble	0.818 (50°)
Chloromethane	CH_3Cl	−24	−97	soluble	0.92
Bromomethane	CH_3Br	3.6	−95	slightly soluble	1.73 (0°)
Iodomethane	CH_3I	42	−66	slightly soluble	2.28
Bromoethane	CH_3CH_2Br	38	−119	slightly soluble	1.46
Bromopropane	$CH_3CH_2CH_2Br$	71	−110	slightly soluble	1.35
2-Bromopropane	$(CH_3)_2CHBr$	59	−91	slightly soluble	1.31
2-Bromo-2-methyl-propane	$(CH_3)_3CBr$	73	−20	insoluble	1.22

*Boiling points are at 760 mm, unless indicated otherwise.

[†] Solubility and density data are given at 20°C except if indicated otherwise.

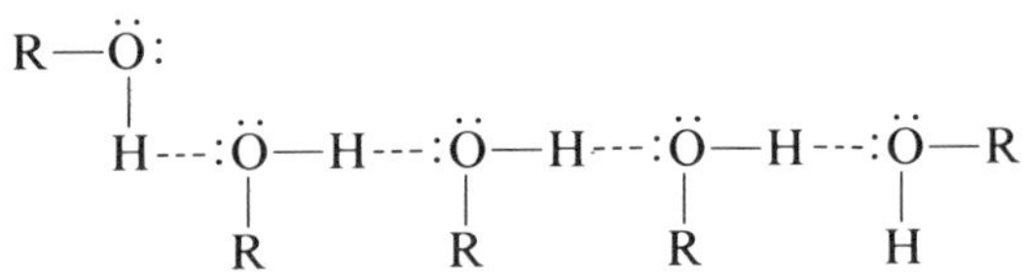

$$R—\overset{..}{\underset{|}{O}}:$$

$$H\text{---}:\overset{..}{\underset{|}{O}}—H\text{---}:\overset{..}{\underset{|}{O}}—H\text{---}:\overset{..}{\underset{|}{O}}—H\text{---}:\overset{..}{\underset{|}{O}}—R$$

$$\qquad R \qquad\quad R \qquad\quad R \qquad\quad H$$

FIGURE 6.1. Hydrogen Bonding.

The importance of hydrogen bonding is evident from the fact that the alcohols have higher boiling points than hydrocarbons of the same molecular weight. In other compounds with oxygen and nitrogen functional groups, this type of bonding is also observed; see especially the proteins (pp. 281, 284). Hydrogen bonding also explains the fact that the lower homologous alcohols are highly soluble (completely miscible) in water, whereas the alkyl halides are nearly insoluble. Both classes of compounds are quite soluble in most organic solvents. With increasing chain length, the polar portion of the alcohols becomes a smaller percentage of the total molecule, and the water solubility decreases. The borderline between what is arbitrarily defined as soluble and insoluble alcohols (3.0 g/100 ml H_2O) is reached at four to five carbon atoms. Branching of the carbon chain greatly increases water solubility. Table 6.1 gives the physical data for a limited number of representative compounds.

6.3
THE CHEMISTRY OF THE ALCOHOLS AND ALKYL HALIDES

The bulk of the chemistry of these compounds, in terms of both their preparation and their reactions, is so closely related to other functional group types that it will be more logical to discuss it along with them. However, there is one class of reactions that you should understand at this point. It involves the direct displacement of an alkyl halide with hydroxide ion and the reverse reaction between an alcohol and a halide ion. In both reactions, the attacking reagent is an anion and the site of the reaction is a carbon atom with a low electron density (because of the electron-withdrawing or electronegative halogen or oxygen). Therefore, these reactions are known as **nucleophilic substitutions** (S_N).

We shall begin by considering the conversion of alkyl halides to alcohols. The reagent and substrate are apparently the same ones used earlier for the elimination of HX and the introduction of a double bond. From this point of view, it is surprising that the desired reaction takes place at all, but this organic reaction is one of many that are strongly dependent on both solvent and structure. Primary alkyl halides show little tendency to eliminate under normal conditions (OH^- in water) and the yield of alcohol is frequently quite good.

$$RCH_2-X + OH^- \rightarrow RCH_2-OH + X^-$$

In alcohol as the solvent, elimination takes place with very little substitution by OH^-. On the other hand, tertiary alkyl halides in most cases give only the corresponding alkene(s), regardless of the solvent used.

$$CH_3\underset{\underset{CH_3}{|}}{\overset{\overset{CH_3}{|}}{C}}-X + OH^- \rightarrow \overset{CH_3}{\underset{CH_3}{>}}C=CH_2$$

100%

Secondary alkyl halides are intermediate between these two cases, and conditions can sometimes be found that will give a satisfactory yield of the desired product.

6.4
NUCLEOPHILIC SUBSTITUTION AT SATURATED CARBON

A reaction of very great importance to the synthetic organic chemist is the treatment of alkyl halides with a wide variety of negative ions in a substitution process.

$$R-X \begin{cases} + \ ^-OH \rightarrow R-OH \\ + \ ^-CN \rightarrow R-CN \\ + \ ^-OR \rightarrow R-OR \end{cases}$$

Nucleophiles other than anions can also be used; for example,

$$R-X + \overset{..}{N}H_3 \rightarrow R-NH_3^+ \ X^-$$

Because of the importance of these reactions, they have been studied extensively with regard to their mechanism. The result is that we understand a good deal about the details of this process.

If a substitution reaction of this type is studied kinetically, the rate law is sometimes of the **second order** or **bimolecular**.

$$\text{rate} = k_2 \, [S] \, [N]$$

In other words, the rate depends on the concentration of both substrate (S) and nucleophile (N). As a specific example, we might consider ethyl chloride and hydroxide ion:

$$CH_3CH_2\overset{\frown}{-}Cl + {}^-OH \rightarrow CH_3CH_2{-}OH + Cl^-$$

$$\text{rate} = k_2 \, [C_2H_5Cl] \, [OH^-]$$

This information has the very important result of ruling out possible mechanisms with a transition state of highest energy that does not involve both species. For example, it would be possible that ionization occurs first and is followed by a very fast reaction

$$CH_3CH_2\overset{\frown}{-}Cl \xrightarrow{\text{slow}} CH_3CH_2^+ + Cl^-$$

$$CH_3CH_2^+ + {}^-OH \xrightarrow{\text{fast}} CH_3CH_2{-}OH$$

between the carbonium ion and hydroxide ion. Such a reaction would have an energy diagram as shown in Figure 6.2,

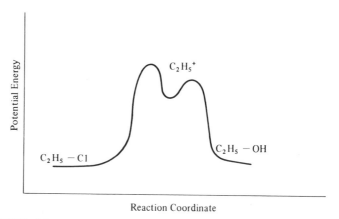

FIGURE 6.2.   Potential Energy Diagram for a Carbonium Ion Intermediate.

in which the transition state leading to the carbonium ion requires a greater activation energy and, therefore, is slower than the subsequent one leading to the product.

This mechanism just excluded does, in fact, occur in a large number of substitution reactions. The factors promoting it are (1) the absence of strong nucleophiles, (2) solvents of great ionizing power, and (3) alkyl halides leading to stable carbonium ions.

Consider the reactions

$$CH_3-\underset{\underset{CH_3}{|}}{\overset{\overset{CH_3}{|}}{C}}-X + H_2O \rightarrow CH_3-\underset{\underset{CH_3}{|}}{\overset{\overset{CH_3}{|}}{C}}-OH + HX$$

$$CH_3-\underset{\underset{CH_3}{|}}{\overset{\overset{CH_3}{|}}{C}}-X + CH_3\overset{\overset{O}{||}}{C}-OH \rightarrow CH_3-\underset{\underset{CH_3}{|}}{\overset{\overset{CH_3}{|}}{C}}-O-\overset{\overset{O}{||}}{C}-CH_3 + HX$$

It is clearly another substitution reaction, and the evidence indicates that it involves the slow (rate-determining) formation of the *t*-butyl cation

$$CH_3-\underset{\underset{CH_3}{|}}{\overset{\overset{CH_3}{|}}{C}}-X \rightarrow CH_3-\underset{\underset{CH_3}{|}}{\overset{\overset{CH_3}{|}}{C}}^{+} + X^-$$

The kinetics are **first order** or **unimolecular**, even in ionizing solvents other than acetic acid or water.

$$\text{rate} = k_1\,[(CH_3)_3CX]$$

Of even greater importance are the stereochemical observations.

When these two reactions (first and second order) are carried out with optically active substrates—for example, 2-bromobutane (single enantiomer)—very different configurations are found in the product. In the first case (S_N2 or **bimolecular nucleophilic substitution**), inversion is observed, whereas in the second (S_N1 or **unimolecular nucleophilic substitution**), racemization is the usual outcome. A close inspection of the probable paths of these two reactions will show the reasonableness of these results.

S_N2

transition state

The general method of approach for the nucleophile in an S_N2 reaction is from the opposite side of the molecule relative to the group being displaced (the **leaving group**). The result of such an attack will be to "flip" the other three groups from one side of the carbon atom to the other. This process is referred to as **Walden inversion** and produces a product of the opposite configuration.

Courtesy of the Edgar Fahs Smith Memorial Collection.

Paul Walden *(Russian-German, 1863–1958). Here is another example of the true physical-organic chemist. Much of Walden's early work was in the electrical conductivity of salts. With Ostwald and independently he studied the properties of electrolytes, especially the effect of dilution and viscosity. These are all areas of physical chemical research which are becoming increasingly important in organic chemistry. Walden is best remembered for his stereochemical studies and especially for the Walden inversion. Later he studied the problem of ionization in nonaqueous solvents, both inorganic and organic.*

The intermediate carbonium ion of an S_N1 reaction is known to be planar and, therefore, should be open to attack from either side with equal ease. It would result in the production of an equal number of the two enantiomers, or a racemic mixture. In actual fact, S_N1 reactions usually occur with a mixture of racemization and inversion. Apparently the leaving group (Br^- in our example) is still close enough to shield partially the front side of the carbonium ion from nucleophilic attack.

6.5

NUCLEOPHILIC REACTIONS OF CARBINOL CARBON

The reverse of the nucleophilic reactions just discussed—that is, the reaction of alcohols with halide ions—is also of great synthetic and mechanistic significance. If water soluble alcohols are treated with concentrated hydrochloric acid saturated with zinc chloride, the observations can be used to determine the class of the alcohol. In this **Lucas test**, the approximate rate of reaction is dependent on the structure of the alcohol. Thus, a tertiary alcohol will give a second layer (alkyl chloride) in a few seconds. Secondary alcohols will react in under 3 minutes and primary alcohols generally require heat to react at all. There are exceptions; for example, benzyl alcohol reacts very rapidly. In the absence of the Lewis acid $ZnCl_2$, only tertiary alcohols react rapidly enough to be useful.

These observations are consistent with a carbonium ion mechanism. The first step is the protonation of the hydroxyl group followed by loss of water to give the more-or-less free carbonium ion.

$$R_3C-\ddot{O}H + \overset{+}{H^+} \rightarrow [R_3C-\overset{+}{\ddot{O}}H_2{}^+]$$

$$\rightarrow [R_3C^+] + H_2O \xrightarrow{\; Cl^- \;} R_3C-Cl$$

In synthetic applications, it is more usual to employ an inorganic acid halide; the most common is thionyl chloride. This reagent is preferred because the by-products are gases and therefore easy to remove. The mechanism appears to involve an intermediate ester that decomposes to give the observed products.

$$ROH + SOCl_2 \rightarrow \left[R\overset{O}{\underset{Cl}{\diagdown\diagup}}S=O \right] + HCl \rightarrow RCl + SO_2$$

The stereochemical outcome of the Lucas reaction is nearly complete racemization. In the case of thionyl chloride, the result can be nearly complete inversion or retention of configuration depending on the solvent. With low concentrations of chloride ion (nonpolar solvent), the intramolecular decomposition shown in the preceding equation takes place. In more polar solvents, in which the HCl formed in the first step can ionize, chloride ion makes an S_N2 attack on the ester, and Walden inversion results.

These reactions are of special importance inasmuch as the simple alkyl halides are not found in nature but are required in many organic preparative schemes.

6.6
QUALITATIVE IDENTIFICATION OF ALCOHOLS

From a practical point of view the alcohols may be considered neutral compounds. Thus, the nonwater soluble homologs will not be soluble in dilute aqueous acid or base as the amines and carboxylic acids. These higher molecular weight compounds will dissolve and/or react with cold concentrated sulfuric acid; this is evidence that the unknown is a neutral compound, but does not distinguish it from aldehydes or ketones. The use of infrared spectroscopy is very helpful (see pp. 342–345).

A number of chemical methods that aid in classifying an unknown alcohol are available. The Lucas test described earlier in this chapter is useful, but limited to alcohols of about six carbon atoms. Primary and secondary alcohols can be distinguished from tertiary alcohols by the use of chromic anhydride in sulfuric acid.

$$\left.\begin{array}{c} RCH_2OH \\ R_2CHOH \end{array}\right\} \xrightarrow[H_2SO_4]{CrO_3} \left\{\begin{array}{c} RCO_2H \\ R_2C{=}O \end{array}\right.$$

The oxidation is very rapid and a green to blue color is observed. Tertiary alcohols fail to show any change within about two seconds and any longer reaction time should be ignored. Aldehydes give a positive test, but as you will see in Chapter 9 there are methods for avoiding this difficulty. An aldehyde and ketone test that is useful with a particular type of alcohol structure is the iodoform reaction (p. 233).

$$\begin{array}{c} OH \\ | \\ RCHCH_3 \end{array} \xrightarrow[I_2]{Na^+OH^-} RCO_2^-\ Na^+ + CHI_3$$

The final step in the chemical identification of an unknown compound is its conversion to another compound of known structure. This **derivative** should have certain characteristics.

1. The derivative should be a crystalline solid melting between 50 and 250°C.

2. The derivative should differ from the original compound in its physical properties, especially in its melting point.

3. The derivative prepared should differ in melting point from the same derivative of the other compounds being considered as the structure of the unknown.

In addition to these necessary characteristics, it is very desirable if the derivative is formed rapidly in high yield and is easily purified. The most generally useful derivatives are those which can be formed from many members of a given homologous series. Representative examples will be provided for a number of functional group classes in the following chapters.

The most useful derivatives of the alcohols are urethanes and benzoate esters.

$$ROH + ArN{=}C{=}O \rightarrow ArNH\overset{\overset{\displaystyle O}{\|}}{C}OR$$

an isocyanate   a urethane

Ar = 1-naphthyl or phenyl

Because the isocyanates react rapidly with water the alcohol must be carefully dried before reaction. This derivative is not very useful with tertiary alcohols.

$$ROH + ArCOCl \rightarrow ArCO_2R + HCl$$

a benzoyl   a benzoate
chloride

Ar = 4-nitrophenyl or 3,5-dinitrophenyl

6.7
DISPLACEMENT REACTIONS LEADING TO ETHERS

The ethers, which are of great importance as solvents in organic reactions, are frequently prepared by variations of methods we have discussed earlier, that is, dehydration and substitution. They may be considered to be derived from water by replacement of both hydrogen atoms by alkyl and/or aryl groups. They are also related to the alcohols.

$$H{-}O{-}H \qquad R{-}O{-}H \qquad R{-}O{-}R'$$

water   alcohol   ether

6.8
NOMENCLATURE OF THE ETHERS

The **ethers** are most frequently known by their common name, which consists in naming the alkyl (or aryl) groups in order of increasing complexity followed by the word ether. In the symmetrical (or simple) ethers, it is usual to omit the prefix "di-."

$$CH_3-O-CH \begin{array}{c} \diagup CH_3 \\ \diagdown CH_3 \end{array} \qquad CH_3CH_2-O-CH_2CH_3$$

methyl isopropyl
ether

(di) ethyl ether

⟨benzene ring⟩—O—CH$_3$

methyl phenyl ether
(anisole)

The IUPAC names of these compounds are 2-methoxypropane, ethoxyethane, and methoxybenzene. With the exception of complicated molecules, especially those with several functional groups, this method is rarely used.

You should note that substituents in symmetrical parent compounds may require primes to show their location clearly; for example,

⟨benzene ring⟩—O—⟨benzene ring⟩—NO$_2$ = 3'-methyl-4-nitrodiphenyl ether

CH$_3$

This system is also used with common names of aliphatic compounds and aromatic side chains.

6.9
PHYSICAL PROPERTIES OF ETHERS (TABLE 6.2)

Ethers are rather inert and frequently good solvents, especially in extraction procedures for substances of low polarity. Ethyl ether, the most frequently used member of the series, dissolves most organic substances and very few inorganic (ionic) compounds. It has a fairly low water solubility and can be easily removed because of its low boiling point. This last point is of some importance, because a high temperature distillation would affect a great many heat-sensitive organic compounds.

TABLE 6.2   PHYSICAL PROPERTIES OF SOME COMMON ETHERS

Name	Formula	Boiling point, °C	Melting point, °C	Solubility,* g/100 ml H_2O	Density,* g/ml
Methyl ether	CH_3OCH_3	−24	−140	3700 (18°)	2.09 (g/l)
Ethyl ether	$CH_3CH_2OCH_2CH_3$	35	−116	7.5	0.714
n-Butyl ether	$[CH_3(CH_2)_3]_2O$	142	−95	slightly soluble	0.769
Anisole	$C_6H_5OCH_3$	154	−37	insoluble	0.994
Phenyl ether	$(C_6H_5)_2O$	259	27	slightly soluble	1.072
Ethylene oxide	$CH_2{-}CH_2$ $\diagdown O \diagup$	11	−111	miscible	0.887 (7°)

*Solubility and density data are given at 20 °C, except if indicated otherwise.

Although ethyl ether is a very useful laboratory solvent, it does have some drawbacks. For example, it dissolves in water to the extent of about 7.5%, and water dissolves in it up to about 1.5% at room temperature. Therefore, there is loss involved in an extraction procedure. Ether is highly flammable and thus is a source of some danger in the laboratory if open flames are ever used. Another dangerous aspect of this chemical is its tendency to form explosive peroxides by reaction with air:

$$CH_3CH_2{-}O{-}CH_2CH_3 + O_2 \rightarrow CH_3\underset{\underset{O{-}OH}{|}}{CH}{-}O{-}CH_2CH_3$$

Suitable methods of inhibiting peroxide formation have been found (store in the dark with fresh Grignard Mg metal and absence of O_2), so that, when used and stored properly, ether is not subject to the violent explosions characteristic of peroxides. A very common method to remove peroxides from ether is to wash with aqueous ferrous ion.

6.10
PREPARATION OF ETHERS

For symmetrical ethers, it is possible to carry out an intermolecular dehydration. To do so successfully and to avoid the formation of an alkene, we must control the reaction conditions carefully. Usually, this situation requires a lower temperature and a large excess of alcohol.

$$CH_3CH_2OH \xrightarrow[140°C]{H_2SO_4} CH_3CH_2OCH_2CH_3 + H_2O$$
(excess)

The most general method is the **Williamson synthesis**:

$$RCH_2\!-\!X + R'O^-Na^+ \rightarrow RCH_2\!-\!O\!-\!R' + Na^+X^-$$

This reaction has as its chief limitation the fact that the sodium alkoxides are strong bases, and, therefore, elimination (especially of 3° alkyl halides) is a serious competing reaction. Thus,

$$CH_3CH_2CH_2OH + Na \rightarrow CH_3CH_2CH_2O^-Na^+ + \tfrac{1}{2}H_2$$

$$CH_3CH_2CH_2O^-Na^+ + CH_3(CH_2)_3Br \rightarrow$$

$$CH_3CH_2CH_2O(CH_2)_3CH_3 + Na^+Br^-$$

But*

$$CH_3\!-\!\underset{\underset{CH_3}{|}}{\overset{\overset{CH_3}{|}}{C}}\!-\!X + CH_3O^-Na^+ \rightarrow CH_2\!=\!C\!\!\begin{smallmatrix}CH_3 \\ \\ CH_3\end{smallmatrix} + CH_3OH + Na^+X^-$$

major product

Courtesy of the Edgar Fahs Smith Memorial Collection.

Alexander W. Williamson *(English, 1824–1904). Still another of the students of Liebig, Williamson was professor of chemistry at University College, London, for his entire career. He is remembered for his synthesis of ethers, but it was much more than simply a new synthetic method. At the time there was much confusion over the relationship of alcohols and ethers. It was Williamson who recognized the salt-forming character of the former and the lack of this property in the latter. With this understanding he was not only able to make ethers but to contribute greatly to our knowledge of organic structure.*

*In this case, a simple reversal of reactant structures will allow the desired compound to be prepared:

$$(CH_3)_3CO^-Na^+ + CH_3X \rightarrow (CH_3)_3C\!-\!O\!-\!CH_3 + Na^+X^-$$

In the preparation of aryl methyl ethers, which have great synthetic value, dimethyl sulfate is frequently used:

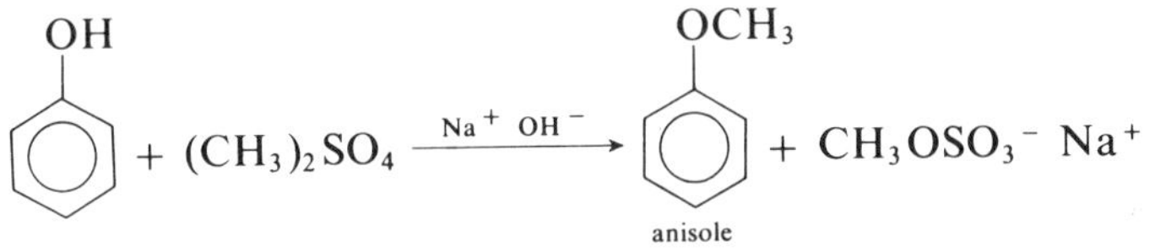

The aryl methoxy group can be useful in organic synthesis, as illustrated by the following example.

The aromatic ring of a phenol is subject to the usual types of substitution reactions we have associated with benzene. One outstanding fact is that the hydroxyl group makes the ring very much more reactive (p. 133).

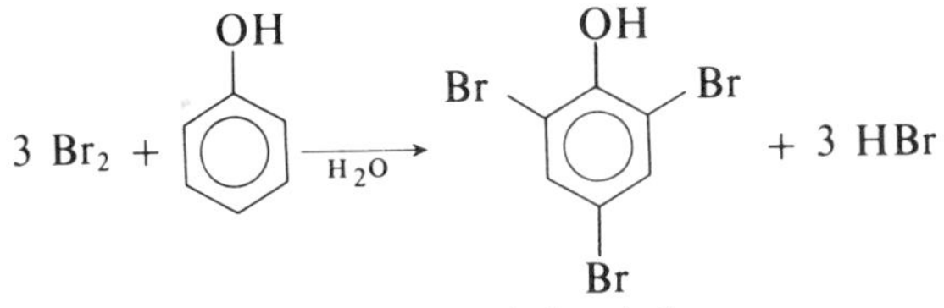

This difficulty can be overcome by preparing the methyl ether and then removing it after the required substitution reaction has been carried out:

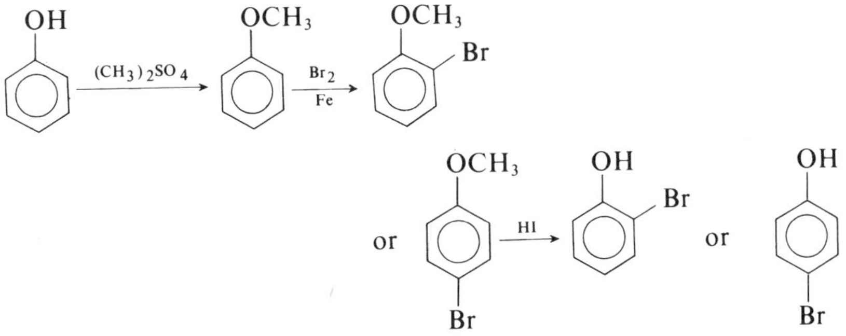

One type of ether with wide synthetic applications is the three-membered, cyclic **epoxide**. Ethylene oxide and the epoxides in general are so useful as synthetic intermediates that we should learn something about their preparation. In general, there are two methods: (1) oxidation of alkenes with peracids,

$$\underset{\substack{\text{peroxybenzoic acid}\\ \text{(often just perbenzoic acid)}}}{\underset{\displaystyle \underset{}{}}{\text{C}_6\text{H}_5\overset{\displaystyle O}{\overset{\|}{\text{C}}}-\text{O}-\text{OH}}} + \overset{}{\text{C}}=\overset{}{\text{C}} \rightarrow \overset{}{\text{C}}\underset{\text{O}}{-}\overset{}{\text{C}} + \text{C}_6\text{H}_5\text{CO}_2\text{H}$$

and (2) the base-catalyzed ring closure of a 1,2-halohydrin.

$$-\overset{|}{\underset{|}{\text{C}}}-\overset{|}{\underset{|}{\text{C}}}- + \ ^-\text{OH} \rightarrow \overset{}{\text{C}}\underset{\text{O}}{-}\overset{}{\text{C}} + \text{H}_2\text{O} + \text{X}^-$$

$$\underset{\text{HO X}}{}$$

The second reaction also depends on alkenes as starting materials and raises an interesting question concerning the direction of addition of the hypohalous acids.

$$\overset{}{\text{C}}=\overset{}{\text{C}} + \text{HOX} \rightarrow -\overset{|}{\underset{\text{HO}}{\text{C}}}-\overset{|}{\underset{\text{X}}{\text{C}}}-$$

There is evidence that the reaction actually involves the halogen and water, in equilibrium with the hypohalous acid, rather than the acid itself. Thus, a reasonable mechanism would be the formation of an intermediate carbonium ion, by reaction with halogen, followed by the addition of water and the loss of a proton.

$$\overset{}{\text{C}}=\overset{}{\text{C}} + \text{X}^{\delta+}\cdots\text{X}^{\delta-} \rightarrow -\overset{|}{\underset{\text{X}}{\text{C}}}-\overset{|}{\underset{+}{\text{C}}}- \xrightarrow{\text{H}_2\ddot{\text{O}}}$$

$$-\overset{|}{\underset{\text{X}}{\text{C}}}-\overset{|}{\underset{\text{OH}_2{}^+}{\text{C}}}- \xrightarrow{-\text{H}^+} -\overset{|}{\underset{\text{X}}{\text{C}}}-\overset{|}{\underset{\text{OH}}{\text{C}}}-$$

Such a mechanism would require that the more stable carbonium ion be formed; therefore, it predicts the orientation that should be observed.

$$\text{CH}_3\text{CH}=\text{CH}_2 + \underset{\underset{\text{H}_2\text{O} + \text{X}_2}{\|}}{\text{HOX}} \rightarrow \underset{\underset{\text{X}}{|}}{\text{CH}_3\overset{+}{\text{CH}}\text{CH}_2} +$$

$$\text{H}_2\text{O} \xrightarrow{-\text{H}^+} \underset{\text{HO X}}{\text{CH}_3\text{CHCH}_2}$$

A very useful reagent for the preparation of epoxides by this method is *N*-bromosuccinimide (NBS). The intermediate 1,2-halohydrin need not be isolated, if the epoxide is desired.

cyclohexene   succinimide
oxide

These useful compounds can be produced industrially by direct oxidation using a silver catalyst and carefully controlled conditions.

$$CH_2\!=\!CH_2 + \tfrac{1}{2} O_2 \xrightarrow{\text{Ag}} CH_2\!-\!CH_2$$
$$\underset{O}{}$$

6.11
AN ETHER REACTION

Ethers are identified by cleavage to simpler products and characterization of these fragments. The most common reagent for this process is hydriodic acid (HI). The first step, which can be observed if a limited amount of acid is used, results in a mixture of alcohols and alkyl iodides:

$$\begin{array}{c} CH_3 \\ {>}CHOCH_3 + HI \rightarrow \\ CH_3 \end{array} \begin{array}{c} CH_3 \\ {>}CHOH + \\ CH_3 \end{array} \begin{array}{c} CH_3 \\ {>}CHI + CH_3OH + CH_3I \\ CH_3 \end{array}$$

$$\xrightarrow[\text{(excess)}]{\text{HI}} CH_3CH_2CH_3 + CH_4$$

A small excess is usually employed and only the alkyl iodides are found as products. At still higher concentrations, reduction to the hydrocarbons results.

    The cleavage of aryl-alkyl ethers can proceed in only one direction because of the fact that phenols are unreactive toward the HI:

SUGGESTED ADDITIONAL READINGS

Nucleophilic Substitution at Saturated Carbon

Breslow, Chapter 3.
Cason, Chapter 6.
Cram and Hammond, Chapters 13–14.
Gould, Chapter 8.
Morrison and Boyd, pp. 466–83.
Roberts and Caserio, pp. 287–306.
Saunders, Chapters 3 and 5.

K. M. Ibne-Rasa, "Equations for Correlation of Nucleophilic Reactivity," *J. Chem. Educ.*, **44**, 89 (1967).

J. O. Edwards, "Bimolecular Nucleophilic Displacement Reactions," *J. Chem. Educ.*, **45**, 386 (1968).

Industrial Methods

Stille, Sections 3.6, 4.4, and 6.1–6.2.

Qualitative Organic Analysis

Pasto and Johnson, Part III, especially Section 12.3.
Shriner, Fuson, and Curtin, Chapters 1–2 and various sections dealing with alcohols.

SUMMARY

1. Hydrogen bonding in the alcohols and similar compounds has a marked effect on their physical and chemical properties.

2. Both the alcohols and the alkyl halides usually react by a nucleophilic substitution mechanism.

$$\left.\begin{array}{l} R{-}OH \\ R{-}X \end{array}\right\} + :N^- \rightarrow R{-}N + \left\{\begin{array}{l} OH^- \\ X^- \end{array}\right.$$

Like the elimination reactions, substitution reactions can precede in either one or two steps. Elimination and substitution are frequently competing reactions.

3. After an unknown compound has been tentatively identified it is converted to a new compound of known structure called a derivative.

4. Structurally the ethers can be considered as derived from water or alcohols.

5. The ethers are useful as solvents because of their low reactivity and the great solubility of many organic compounds in them. The flammability and tendency to form peroxides, which is characteristic of ethers, makes them hazardous if not used with care.

6. Several methods are available for the preparation of ethers:

$$ROH \xrightarrow[\text{heat}]{H^+} ROR + H_2O$$
$$\text{(excess)}$$

$$RX + RO^- Na^+ \longrightarrow ROR + Na^+ X^-$$

$$ROH + (CH_3)_2SO_4 \xrightarrow{OH^-} ROCH_3 + CH_3OSO_3^-$$

The displacement of an alkyl halide by an alkoxide ion (Williamson synthesis) can have elimination as a serious competing reaction. The use of methyl sulfate for the formation of aryl methyl ethers is applied as a protective group in phenol chemistry.

7. The three-membered cyclic ethers (epoxides) can be prepared readily and show useful reactivity. For example:

$$\underset{\diagup}{\overset{\diagdown}{C}}=\underset{\diagdown}{\overset{\diagup}{C}} \xrightarrow[\text{OH}^-]{\text{NBS}} -\underset{\diagdown_{\textstyle O}\diagup}{C-C}-$$

$$H_2C-CH_2 + RMgX \rightarrow RCH_2CH_2OH$$
$$\diagdown_{\textstyle O}\diagup$$

8. The cleavage of ethers with HI is a useful synthetic method; especially with aryl alkyl ethers.

$$ArOR \xrightarrow{HI} ArOH + RI$$

PROBLEMS

1. Give the IUPAC and a common name for each of the following compounds:

a. $CH_3CH_2CHCH_2OH$
   $|$
   CH_3

c. —CH_2CH_2OH

d. $CH_3CH_2CHCH_2Cl$
   $|$
   CH_2
   $|$
   CH_3

b. —Br

e. 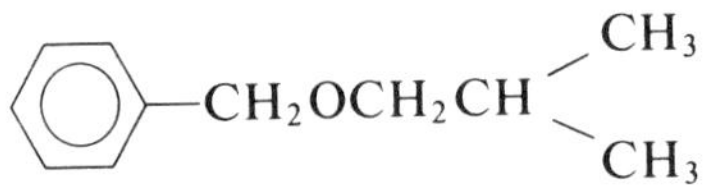 ![benzene ring]—CH_2OCH_2CH〈$^{CH_3}_{CH_3}$

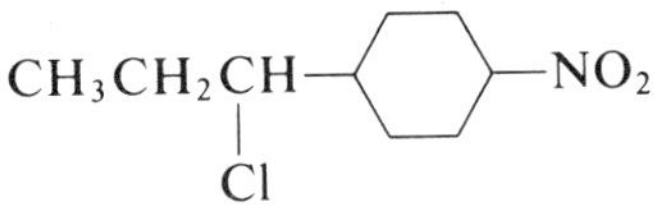

i. CH_3CH_2CH—〈cyclohexane ring〉—NO_2 with Cl on the CH

f. 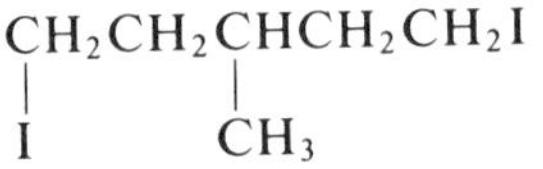 $CH_2CH_2CHCH_2CH_2I$ with I and CH_3 substituents

j. CH_3
CH_3CCH_2OH
CH_3

g. 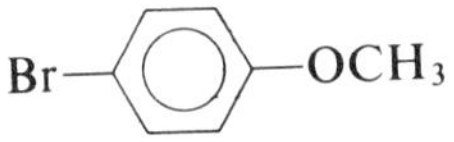 Br—〈benzene ring〉—OCH_3

h. $BrCCl_3$

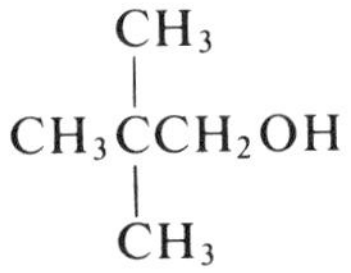

k. 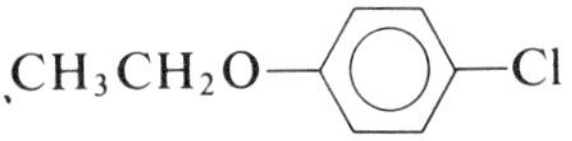 CH_3CH_2O—〈benzene ring〉—Cl

2. Draw the structure corresponding to each of the following names:
   a. isopropyl ether
   b. 2,2-dichloro-3-methylbutane
   c. 3-methoxycyclohexanol
   d. 2,3,4-tribromohexane
   e. β-phenylethyl alcohol
   f. 2-iodoethanol
   g. cyclobutyl bromide
   h. α-chlorotoluene
   i. 1,4-cyclohexandiol
   j. 2-methoxy-2-butene

3. Complete the following reactions and name all organic compounds:
   a. 3-methyl-1-pentanol $\xrightarrow{H_2SO_4}$

   b. 2-butene + NBS $\xrightarrow[H_2O]{OH^-}$

   c. 2-methyl-1-bromocyclohexane + sodium methoxide →

   d. sodium 2-methylcyclopentoxide + bromomethane →

   e. anisole $\xrightarrow{HNO_3}$ $\xrightarrow[\text{excess}]{HI}$

   f. propyne + H_2O $\xrightarrow[H^+]{HgSO_4}$

   g. 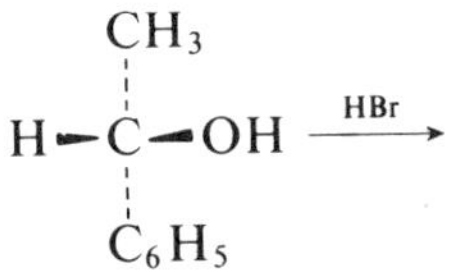 CH_3
   $H{-}C{-}OH$ $\xrightarrow{HBr}$
   C_6H_5

4. Given methanol, ethanol, phenol, and any inorganic chemicals, suggest reasonable reaction series to prepare each of the following compounds:

   a. 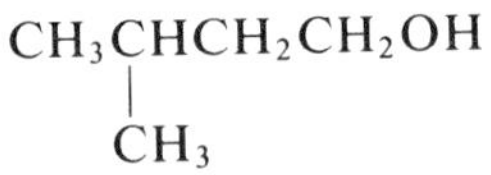 $CH_3CHCH_2CH_2OH$
   CH_3

   b.  OH
   〈benzene ring〉
   $CHBr$
   CH_3

c.   (structure: cyclohexane with OH and Cl substituents)   OH
     Cl

f. $CH_3CH_2CHCH_2CH_2Br$
        |
        CH_3

d. $CH_3CHCH_2CH_2CH_3$
        |
        Br

g. $CH_3CH{-}CHCH_3$ (with epoxide O bridge)

e. $CH_3CH_2O{-}$ (cyclohexyl ring)

h.   (cyclohexane with two OH substituents)   OH

     OH

5. Compound (A) has a molecular formula $C_{10}H_{20}O$. Reaction with HI can produce two alkyl iodides, (B) and (C). Alkyl iodide (B) reacts with alcoholic KOH to produce (D), with a general formula C_nH_{2n-2}. Compound (D) gives a positive Baeyer test, and the product, on further oxidation, gives a single carboxylic acid. Alkyl iodide (C) reacts with alcoholic KOH to give a mixture of two alkenes, (E) and (F). The former, the major product, can be oxidized to a single carboxylic acid. This fact is also true of the minor product (F), but it also gives an equimolar amount of CO_2. Draw structures for all the unknown compounds, complete all reactions, and name all the organic compounds.

6. A saturated, five-carbon alcohol (A) reacts with sulfuric acid to give a mixture of alkenes (B) and (C). It also reacts with HBr to give a mixture of alkyl bromides (D) and (E). Alkenes (B) and (C) can be converted to (E) by the addition of HBr in the absence of peroxides. We convert (B) to (D) by adding HBr in the presence of peroxides. Treatment of (D) with alcoholic KOH gives only (B), but the same reaction of (E) gives (C) with a small amount of (B). Suggest suitable structures and names for all compounds, and complete all reactions.

7. A compound (A) $C_{10}H_{10}O$ reacted with sodium to give a derivative. Treatment of (A) with 80% H_2SO_4 in the presence of $HgSO_4$, and then with H_2O, gave (B), $C_{10}H_{12}O_2$. Boiling with hydriodic acid converted (B) to (C), C_9H_9OI, a compound that upon oxidation yielded (D), $C_9H_8O_3$. Upon further oxidation, (D) yielded (E), $C_8H_6O_4$, which is capable of forming only one mononuclear substitution product. Provide structures and names for all compounds.

8. Nucleophilic substitution reactions have been shown to take place by several different mechanisms. Select two of the most important of these and indicate what kinds of experimental evidence would be useful in distinguishing between them. Include in your discussion

the results you would expect to obtain from each experiment. Illustrate each point with specific examples.

9. Briefly explain the following differences in reactivity. Use diagrams where helpful.

A. The following reactions were observed under S_N1 conditions:
   a. $CH_2\!=\!CHCH_2CH_2Cl$ is less reactive than

$$CH_2CH\!=\!CHCH_2Cl$$

toward alcoholic $AgNO_3$.

b. 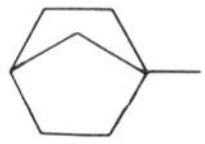 —Cl is very unreactive toward alcoholic $AgNO_3$.

c. 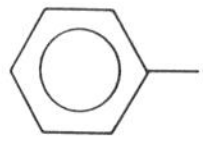 —CH_2Br is more reactive than 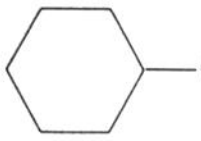 —CH_2Br toward aqueous NaOH.

d. $CH_3CH\!=\!CHCH_2Cl$ yields the same products as

$$\underset{\underset{Cl}{|}}{CH_3CHCH}\!=\!CH_2$$

with aqueous NaOH.

B. The following reactions were observed under S_N2 conditions:
   a. $(CH_3)_3CCH_2Cl$ is very unreactive toward nucleophiles.
   b. $CH_3CH\!=\!CHCH_2Cl$ may yield a mixture of isomeric products with alcoholic KCN.
   c. CH_3CH_2I is more reactive than CH_3CH_2Cl toward KCN.
   d. Some alkyl halides are more reactive toward

$$CH_3CH_2O^-Na^+$$

than toward $CH_3CH_2S^-Na^+$ in elimination, but less reactive in substitution.

7

Acids and Esters

Acids represent the highest oxidation state of carbon commonly found in organic compounds. This fact makes them very stable toward further oxidation. For this reason, they are widely found in natural products, along with the esters, which are produced by reaction between acids and alcohols. This same stability that makes them abundant also aids in their separation and purification. With these factors considered, you can understand why compounds belonging to these functional group classes were among the earliest examples of organic compounds studied.

Greek and Latin, as you probably now realize, have played a large part in the nomenclature of organic compounds. The natural source of several acids are exhibited in their common names: for example, *formica*, ants, formic; *acetum*, vinegar, acetic; *butyrum*, butter, butyric; and *stear*, beef suet, stearic. This last example is the common name for octadecanoic acid $[CH_3(CH_2)_{16}CO_2H]$, which is commonly found in the form of a triacid ester of glycerol as a constituent of fats (p. 263).

7.2
CARBOXYLIC ACID NOMENCLATURE

The **carboxylic acids** may be named from the hydrocarbons. The -e is dropped from the hydrocarbon name and **-oic acid** is added; for example,

$CH_3CH_2CH_2CH_3$ $CH_3CH_2CH_2CO_2H$
butane   butanoic acid

$CH_2{=}CHCH_2CH_3$ $CH_2{=}CHCH_2CO_2H$
1-butene   3-butenoic acid

However, the common names are usually used. For the first six, they are

HCO_2H	formic acid
CH_3CO_2H	acetic acid
$CH_3CH_2CO_2H$	propionic acid
$CH_3(CH_2)_2CO_2H$	*n*-butyric acid
$CH_3(CH_2)_3CO_2H$	*n*-valeric acid
$CH_3(CH_2)_4CO_2H$	*n*-caproic acid

A useful mnemonic device for remembering the first six acids is as follows: "For all purchases, buy very cautiously."

The simple dicarboxylic acids, to which we shall confine our attention, are even less frequently referred to by their IUPAC names.

Formula	Common name	IUPAC name
HO_2CCO_2H	oxalic acid	ethanedioic acid
$HO_2CCH_2CO_2H$	malonic acid	propanedioic acid
$HO_2C(CH_2)_2CO_2H$	succinic acid	1,4-butanedioic acid
$HO_2C(CH_2)_3CO_2H$	glutaric acid	1,5-pentanedioic acid
$HO_2C(CH_2)_4CO_2H$	adipic acid	1,6-hexanedioic acid
$HO_2C(CH_2)_5CO_2H$	pimelic acid	1,7-heptanedioic acid

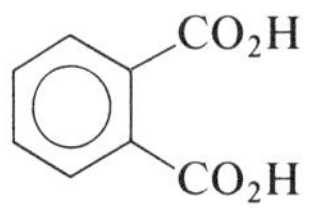

phthalic acid

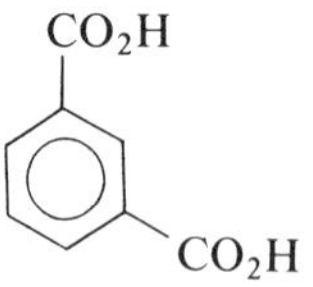

isophthalic acid

CO$_2$H

terephthalic acid

CO$_2$H

A mnemonic device for the aliphatic dicarboxylic acids is as follows: "Oh my such good apple pie."

7.3

THE CARBOXYL GROUP AND WHY IT IS ACIDIC

The functional group characteristic of the most common type of organic acid is usually called the **carboxyl group** (but remember the sulfonic acids, pp. 121–122). This name is obtained from the names of its parts, because it is a complex group and has more than one functional component.

$$\underset{\text{CARBonyl}}{-\overset{\overset{\textstyle O}{\|}}{C}-} \; + \; \underset{\text{hydrOXYL}}{OH} \; = \; \underset{\text{carboxyl}}{-\overset{\overset{\textstyle O}{\|}}{C}-OH} \qquad \begin{array}{c} (-COOH) \\ \text{or} \\ (-CO_2H) \end{array}$$

As might be expected, the carboxyl group will in some ways resemble each of these groups, but because they are linked in the particular arrangement shown, the group will have a nature (physical and chemical) of its own.

The most striking example of this fact is the acidity shown by the carboxyl group. The hydrogen bound to the oxygen is capable of being partially ionized as a solvated proton, thereby showing acidic properties.

$$R-\overset{\overset{\textstyle O}{\|}}{C}-OH + nH_2O \rightleftharpoons R-\overset{\overset{\textstyle O}{\|}}{C}-O^- + H^+(H_2O)_n \text{ or} \\ [H^+ \text{ (aq)}]$$

This relation is also true of alcohols having the same hydrogen-to-oxygen linkage, but these compounds are many millions of times weaker acids than the carboxylic acids and nearly always weaker than H$_2$O. It is not difficult to understand the great difference in Brønsted (i.e., proton) acidity between acids and alcohols when the concept of resonance is employed.

The degree of acidity of any acid is determined by the extent of its ionization in a particular solvent, usually water. For ex-

ample, an inorganic acid, such as nitric acid, ionizes almost
completely and is therefore a strong acid.

$$HNO_3 \xrightleftharpoons{H_2O} H^+(aq) + NO_3^-$$

A phenol ionizes slightly, producing a few solvated protons;
for example,

$$ArOH \xrightleftharpoons{H_2O} H^+(aq) + ArO^-$$

which is therefore a very weak acid.

Between these two examples fall the carboxylic acids:

$$\overset{O}{\underset{\|}{R C} O H} \xrightleftharpoons{H_2O} \overset{O}{\underset{\|}{R C} O^-} + H^+(aq)$$

The extent of the ionization depends upon the nature of the
specific organic acid.

7.4
ACIDITY—ENERGY AND EQUILIBRIUM

One of the most important considerations concerning ionic
charge in organic reactions is the manner in which it is transferred from one part of a molecule to another. A useful way of
illustrating and understanding these processes is to consider the
ionization of various substituted carboxylic acids.

The most common class of organic acids, those characterized
by the carboxyl group ($-CO_2H$), are typical weak acids, and
their ionization in water may be described in terms of an
equilibrium constant.

$$RCO_2H + H_2O \rightleftharpoons RCO_2^- + H_3O^+$$

$$K_{eq} = \frac{[RCO_2^-][H_3O^+]}{[RCO_2H][H_2O]}$$

The tabulated values of equilibrium constants given later in this
chapter indicate that structural changes in acids can cause
significant differences in their acidity. It will be interesting to
attempt to explain these observations.

Before there is any hope of accomplishing this aim, it is
necessary that you understand clearly the factors which are most
important in determining the position of equilibrium. You
should recall that the equilibrium constant is dependent on both

temperature and solvent; but to compare structural effects, you can hold both these variables constant—for example, 25°C in water. One factor still remains: the stability of both the reactants and the products—that is, the acid and the **conjugate base**. The error of failing to consider both species may be avoided if you remember that what must be evaluated is the energy difference between them. Therefore, the greater the energy difference in favor of products (lower energy), the further the equilibrium will be shifted in their direction.

An easy-to-understand example is the difference in acidity as shown by alcohols and carboxylic acids. The equilibria are

$$ROH + H_2O \rightleftharpoons RO^- + H_3O^+$$
$$RCO_2H + H_2O \rightleftharpoons RCO_2^- + H_3O^+$$

The two reactants are both stable organic molecules, and those energy differences that exist would be expected to be very small. When the products are considered, we find that the carboxylate anion is capable of resonance stabilization by virtue of the

***John D. Roberts** (American, 1918–   ). Roberts has made great contributions to our understanding of the nature of organic reactions and especially to the development of new methods of studying them. His interest and ability in teaching research is evident from the large number of his papers which include undergraduate co-authors. He has taught at several of the foremost universities and is currently chairman at Cal. Tech. His study of the relative importance of inductive and resonance effects, using a nonaromatic molecule of rigid geometry, is just one of a long list of important accomplishments.*

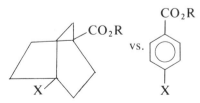

He is the co-author of an outstanding recent organic textbook.

following contributors:

$$\left[R-C\begin{array}{c} \diagup O \\ \diagdown O^- \end{array} \leftrightarrow R-C\begin{array}{c} \diagup O^- \\ \diagdown O \end{array} \right]$$

Such resonance is not possible for the alkoxide anion, which results from the ionization of alcohols. This fact leads to an increase in the energy difference between reactants and products (decrease in relative stability of products). Therefore, you should predict, correctly, that carboxylic acids will ionize to a greater extent than alcohols.

7.5
THE INDUCTIVE EFFECT

Table 7.1 lists the equilibrium constants for a series of saturated carboxylic acids containing different substituents located in various positions. A study of these data allows us to examine the effect of these groups on acidity.

TABLE 7.1   SUBSTITUENT EFFECTS ON ACIDITY

Acid	Structure	$K, H_2O, 25°C$
Acetic	CH_3CO_2H	1.75×10^{-5}
Propionic	$CH_3CH_2CO_2H$	1.4×10^{-5}
Chloroacetic	$ClCH_2CO_2H$	1.55×10^{-3}
Trichloroacetic	Cl_3CCO_2H	3.0×10^{-1}
α-Chlorobutyric	$CH_3CH_2CHClCO_2H$	1.4×10^{-4}
β-Chlorobutyric	$CH_3CHClCH_2CO_2H$	8.9×10^{-5}
γ-Chlorobutyric	$CH_2ClCH_2CH_2CO_2H$	3.0×10^{-5}

The first point that should be noticed in Table 7.1 is that acetic and propionic acids have nearly the same ionization constants, exactly what would be expected on the basis of the small electron-donating tendency of the methyl group. The reactants should be of about equal stability, and there is a similar situation in the product anions, except that the negative charge on the carboxylate group will be slightly stabilized for acetate over propionate. This small effect reflects the somewhat greater electron release of ethyl groups relative to methyl groups.

If the difference in energy of the

$$CH_3 \rightarrow O\!\!\stackrel{\displaystyle \nearrow O}{\searrow}_{O^-} \quad \text{more stable than} \quad CH_3 \rightarrow CH_2 \rightarrow C\!\!\stackrel{\displaystyle \nearrow O}{\searrow}_{O^-}$$

products (anions) is greater than the reactants (acids), there will be a difference in the equilibrium (acidity), with the acid having the more stable anion, also having the greater acidity.

A very different observation is made when chlorine is substituted for hydrogen. Although the reactants might be of similar energy, the products should be of considerably different stability. We can see the reason by examining the dipole created by the much more electronegative chlorine.

$$\overset{\delta-}{Cl} \leftarrow \overset{\delta+}{CH_2}{-}C\!\!\stackrel{\displaystyle \nearrow O}{\searrow}_{O^-}$$

Such a dipole has the effect of counteracting the increased negative charge of the carboxylate anion—that is, of spreading it over the molecule. This process leads to a lowering of the energy of the system or to increasing its stability. Effects resulting from the polarity of the molecule are known as **inductive effects** and play a very important part in numerous organic reactions. Also, in the reactant molecule this same property leads to a destabilization of chloroacetic acid, as opposed to acetic acid, inasmuch as the dipole of the neutral carboxyl group is in the direction opposite to that of the carbon-chlorine bond.

$$\overset{\delta-}{Cl} \leftarrow \overset{\delta+}{CH_2} \rightarrow \overset{\delta+}{C}\overset{\delta-}{O_2H}$$

Thus, the net result of the two situations—chloroacetic acid less stable than acetic acid, and chloroacetate anion more stable than acetate anion—is to increase the acidity of the acid that is substituted with chlorine, or any other strong electron-withdrawing group.

This inductive effect is also borne out by the great increase in acidity of trichloroacetic acid, in which three carbon-chlorine dipoles delocalize the anion charge and destabilize the reactant.

$$\begin{matrix} \overset{\delta-}{Cl} \\ \overset{\delta-}{Cl}{\leftarrow}\overset{\delta+}{C}{-}\overset{\delta+}{C}\overset{\delta-}{O_2H} \\ \overset{\delta-}{Cl} \end{matrix} \rightleftharpoons \begin{matrix} \overset{\delta-}{Cl} \\ \overset{\delta-}{Cl}{\leftarrow}\overset{\delta+}{C}{-}CO_2{}^- \\ \overset{\delta-}{Cl} \end{matrix}$$

One final point worth noting is the rapid rate at which the inductive effect is reduced as the dipole is removed from the site at which the charge is located. As the carbon-chlorine bond is moved farther from the carboxylate anion resulting from the ionization of chlorobutyric acids, the acidity decreases, until in γ-chlorobutyric acid the value of K is little different from acetic acid.

7.6
THE RESONANCE EFFECT

When the aromatic acids are considered, we must take into account resonance of the π electrons of the ring. Benzoic acid ($K_a = 6.5 \times 10^{-5}$) is stronger than the simple aliphatic acids, which is understood as resulting from increasing stabilization of the anion over the acid:

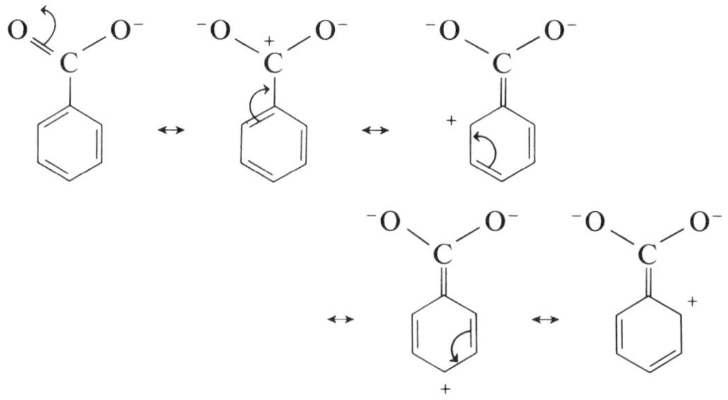

The effect of aromatic substituents involves both inductive and resonance effects and holds only in dilute solution. After you have answered question 16 at the end of this chapter, check your reasoning in the Suggested Additional Readings. We shall have more to say about this effect in later chapters.

7.7
PHYSICAL PROPERTIES OF THE ACIDS (TABLE 7.2)

Like the homologous series of alkanes, the boiling points of the carboxylic acids increase with increasing molecular weight. Unlike the alkanes, there are no gases among the acids, and the first solid acid has only 10 carbon atoms. The presence of the very polar carboxyl group and hydrogen bonding (p. 146) help to account for this much higher range of vaporization temperatures. They also are partially responsible for the fact that the first four acids are water soluble.

The lower aliphatic acids are colorless and have a sharp disagreeable odor. As the molecular weight increases, the vapor pressure decreases and the odor becomes less distinct. The densities of the acids are unusually high; for example, formic and acetic acids are more dense than water.

TABLE 7.2 PHYSICAL PROPERTIES OF SOME COMMON CARBOXYLIC ACIDS

Name	Formula	Boiling point, °C*	Melting point, °C	Solubility,† g/100 ml H_2O	Density,† g/ml
Formic	HCO_2H	101	8	miscible	1.22
Acetic	CH_3CO_2H	118	17	miscible	1.049
Propionic	$CH_3CH_2CO_2H$	141	−21	miscible	0.992
Butyric	$CH_3(CH_2)_2CO_2H$	164	−6	miscible	0.964
Valeric	$CH_3(CH_2)_3CO_2H$	187	−34	3.7 (16°)	0.939
Caproic	$CH_3(CH_2)_4CO_2H$	205		1.0	0.927
Myristic	$CH_3(CH_2)_{12}CO_2H$	149 (1 mm)	54	insoluble	0.858 (60°)
Palmitic	$CH_3(CH_2)_{14}CO_2H$	167 (1 mm)	63	insoluble	0.853 (62°)
Stearic	$CH_3(CH_2)_{16}CO_2H$	184 (1 mm)	70	insoluble	0.941
Benzoic	$C_6H_5CO_2H$	249	122	0.34	1.266 (15°)
o-Nitro-benzoic	$o\text{-}NO_2C_6H_4CO_2H$		147	0.75	1.575
m-Nitro-benzoic	$m\text{-}NO_2C_6H_4CO_2H$		141	0.34	1.494
p-Nitro-benzoic	$p\text{-}NO_2C_6H_4CO_2H$	sublimes	242	0.03	1.550 (32°)
Oxalic	$(CO_2H)_2$	sublimes	189d**	9.0	1.653
Malonic	$CH_2(CO_2H)_2$	d	136	74.0	1.631 (15°)
Succinic	$(CH_2)_2(CO_2H)_2$	235d	182	6.0	1.572 (25°)
Phthalic	$1,2\text{-}C_6H_4(CO_2H)_2$	d	207	0.7	1.593

*The boiling point is at 760 mm unless indicated otherwise.
†Solubility and density data are given at 20°C, except as indicated.
**d = decomposition.

7.8
METHODS OF PREPARATION OF ACIDS

The stability of the carboxylic acids makes possible the most common method of laboratory preparation—oxidation. Several of these reactions have already been discussed as part of the reactions of unsaturated and aromatic hydrocarbons, but they will be reviewed now.

$$RCH{=}C{\overset{R'}{\underset{R''}{\diagup}}} \xrightarrow{[O]} RCO_2H + R'\overset{O}{\overset{\|}{C}}R''$$

$$RC{\equiv}CR' \xrightarrow{[O]} RCO_2H + R'CO_2H$$

$$Ar{-}R \xrightarrow{[O]} ArCO_2H$$

A wide variety of oxidizing agents have been used, including $KMnO_4$, CrO_3, O_3, and so forth.

Several oxidation procedures involving organic compounds of lower oxidation state (alcohols and aldehydes) will be discussed in connection with those compounds (pp. 221 and 226).

7.8A   The Grignard Reaction

One of the most important organic reactions ever developed is utilized in the preparation of carboxylic acids. In 1912, Victor Grignard was awarded the Nobel prize for his work on this synthetic process, which involves the reaction of an alkyl halide (or aryl bromide) with magnesium metal in anhydrous ether.

$$\underset{(ArBr)}{RX} + Mg \xrightarrow[(C_2H_5)_2O]{dry^*} \underset{(ArMgBr)}{RMgX}$$

or

a Grignard reagent

THF

This Grignard reagent is not usually isolated but rather used in solution, and care must be taken to exclude water and oxygen.*

One of the several useful reactions characteristic of Grignard reagents is that with carbon dioxide (often as Dry Ice):

$$RMgX + CO_2 \xrightarrow[THF]{absolute} RCO_2^- MgX^+ \xrightarrow{HX} RCO_2H + MgX_2$$

As an example of the Grignard reaction in the preparation of a carboxylic acid, consider *p*-methylbenzoic acid (*p*-toluic acid):

---

*The Grignard reagent reacts with a great many substances, and care must be used in its preparation and reactions. Other ethers can be used; one of the most popular is THF or tetrahydrofuran, which has a higher boiling point and therefore allows a higher reaction temperature.

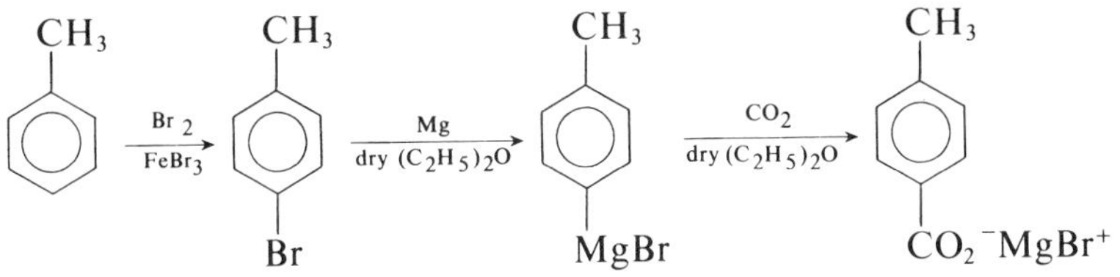

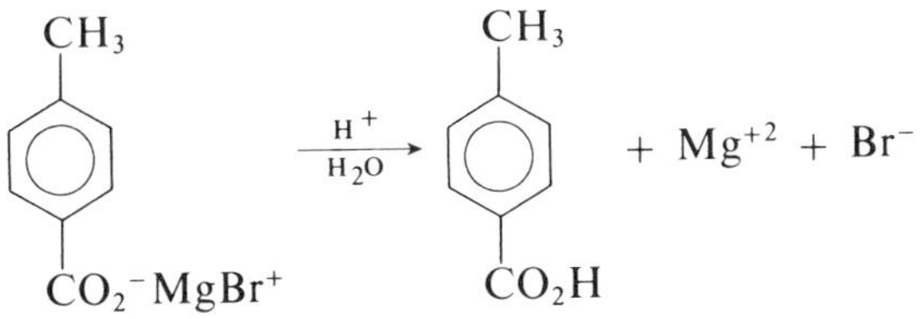

The preparation of p-methylbenzoic acid by oxidation of alkyl side chains would clearly be useless, as the following equation shows:

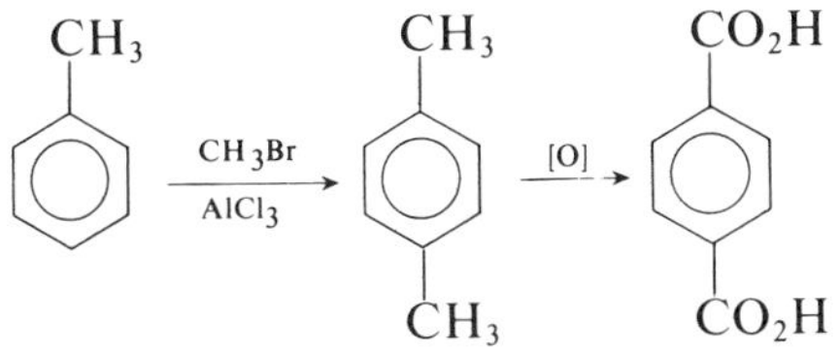

7.8B   Sulfonic Acids

The sulfonic acids of greatest interest are those containing the aryl ring. These are nearly always prepared by sulfonation, as presented in Chapter 5.

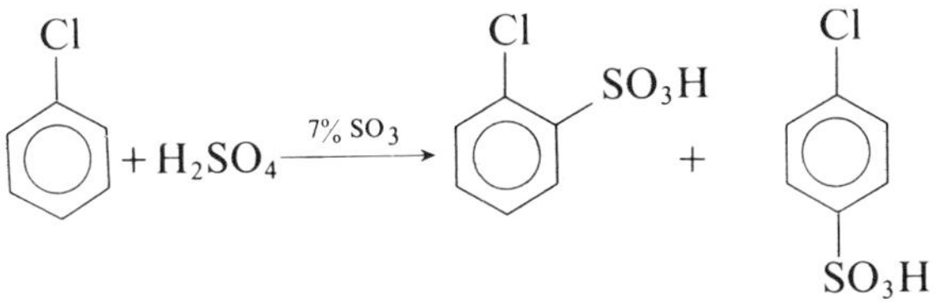

The alkyl sulfonic acids are also produced industrially and are becoming more important, but they are difficult to prepare and purify in the laboratory.

7.9
REACTIONS OF ACIDS INVOLVING THE HYDROGEN ATOM

Two reactions of acids are ionization (acidity) and salt formation. The latter is the expected outcome of neutralization with
base.

$$CH_3\overset{O}{\overset{\|}{C}}OH + Na^+OH^- \rightleftharpoons CH_3\overset{O}{\overset{\|}{C}}O^-Na^+ + H_2O$$

sodium acetate

$$SO_3H + K^+OH^- \rightleftharpoons SO_3^-K^+ + H_2O$$

potassium
benzenesulfonate

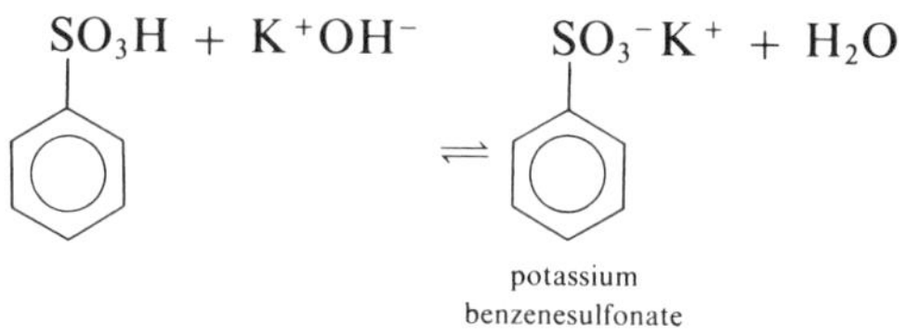

7.10
REACTIONS OF ACIDS INVOLVING THE CARBOXYL GROUP

The salts of acids have reactions of some synthetic interest. The
pyrolysis (strong heating) of aromatic carboxylic acid salts with
soda-lime (NaOH-CaO) results in the loss of CO_2 (decarboxylation).

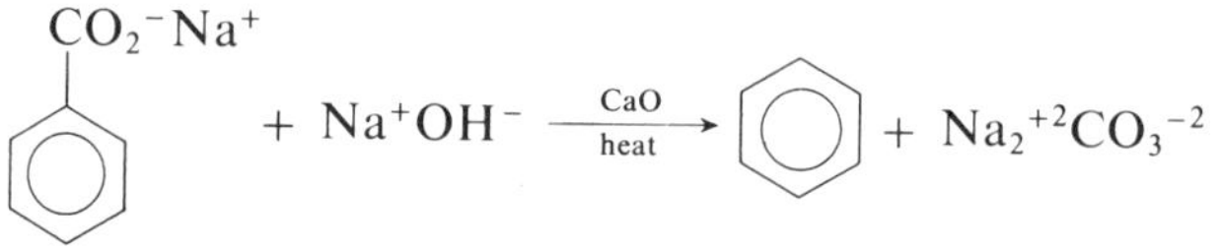

$$+ Na^+OH^- \xrightarrow[heat]{CaO} + Na_2^{+2}CO_3^{-2}$$

This reaction can also be used with some of the very simple
aliphatic acids.

When a similar reaction is carried out with the salt of an aryl-
sulfonic acid in the presence of solid sodium hydroxide, the
product is the sodium salt of the corresponding phenol.

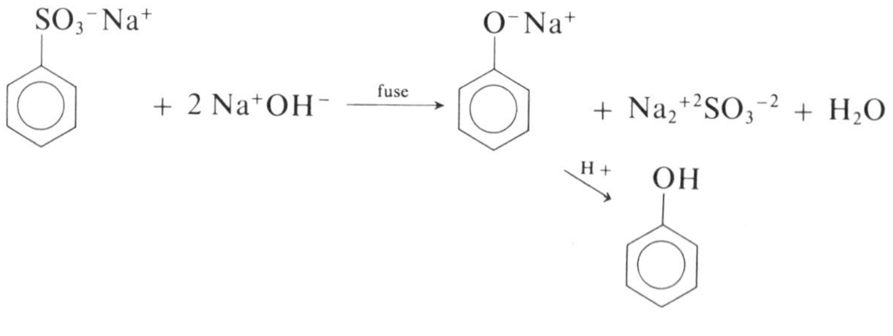

$$+ 2 Na^+OH^- \xrightarrow{fuse} + Na_2^{+2}SO_3^{-2} + H_2O$$

$\searrow H^+$ OH

An additional reaction of salts of carboxylic acids provides a useful method of ring closure in the case of five- and six-membered rings. It requires the use of a dicarboxylic acid as the salt of a divalent metal ion, which, on pyrolysis of the solid, yields the cyclic ketone with the loss of CO_2.

$$(CH_2)_n \overset{CO_2^-}{\underset{CO_2^-}{\diagdown}} M^{+2} \xrightarrow{\text{heat}} (CH_2)_n \underset{}{\boxed{C}}=O + M^{+2}CO_3^{-2}$$

$n = 4$ or 5 $M = Ca, Ba, Th, etc.$

Before leaving the reactions of carboxyl groups, we should point out one of the newer methods that has proved to be of great synthetic value. Until the development of the very reactive metal hydrides, it was not possible to reduce the carboxyl group to a primary alcohol except by an indirect route through the ester or acyl halide.

$$RCO_2H + LiAlH_4 \xrightarrow[\text{(2) } H_2O]{\text{(1) absolute ether}} RCH_2OH + LiOH + Al(OH)_3$$

The yields in reactions of this type are usually very high, and, when combined with the Grignard reaction, the reduction is very useful in preparing longer chain alcohols:

$$RBr + Mg \xrightarrow[\text{THF}]{\text{absolute}} RMgBr \xrightarrow[\text{(2) } H^+]{\text{(1) } CO_2} RCO_2H \xrightarrow[\substack{\text{in absolute ether} \\ \text{(2) } H_2O}]{\text{(1) } LiAlH_4} RCH_2OH$$

7.11
REACTIONS INVOLVING THE REPLACEMENT OF THE HYDROXYL GROUP

Among the most useful and general reactions of the acid groups (both CO_2H and SO_3H) are those in which the —OH portion is converted to some new functional group. Two of these derivatives of acids will be discussed in the present chapter and a third in Chapter 8.

In many synthetic and analytical cases, the very reactive **acyl halides** (especially chlorides) are of interest (p. 182). They are prepared by using the acid halides of inorganic acids.

$$RCO_2H + SOCl_2 \rightarrow RCOCl + SO_2 + HCl$$
$$\text{thionyl}$$
$$\text{chloride}$$

The hydrohalogen acids (HX) are not used. The reason is that the energy barrier for the forward reaction is much greater than that for the reverse, and thus the equilibrium favors the reaction reading from right to left:

$$RCO_2H + HCl \rightleftharpoons RCOCl + H_2O$$

7.12
QUALITATIVE IDENTIFICATION

With care, carboxylic and sulfonic acids present little difficulty in identification. The lower molecular weight carboxylic acids and many of the sulfonic acids are water soluble. In this case, it is only necessary to test the aqueous solution with litmus or phenolphthalein and observe the red color of the former or the amount of base required to produce a red color in the latter.

This second test amounts to the usual acid-base titration and is an extremely useful aspect of the analytical scheme for acids. Using a dried, weighed sample of the acid and a standard solution of base—for example, 0.10 N NaOH—it is quite possible to obtain a satisfactory endpoint in aqueous alcohol solution. As a result of this procedure, the **neutralization equivalent** or equivalent weight* of the acid can be calculated.

$$\text{neutralization eq} = \frac{(1000)(\text{g of acid})}{(\text{ml base})(N \text{ base})} \quad \text{or} \quad \frac{\text{mg of acid}}{\text{meq of base}}$$

Inasmuch as there are relatively few polybasic acids, chances are very good that this experimental value will be either the molecular weight or one-half of it (dicarboxylic acids will have two equivalents per mole; i.e., eq wt = $\frac{1}{2}$ mole wt). This technique not only positively identifies the unknown compound as an acid but also comes very close to telling you which homolog it is. The method is as precise as permitted by the analytical balance, the normality of the NaOH, and the buret you use, but, in general, two significant figures will allow the required decisions to be made.

With compounds that are not water soluble, solubility in a 5% solution of sodium bicarbonate is clear evidence of strongly acidic nature.

$$RCO_2H + Na^+HCO_3^- \rightarrow RCO_2^-Na^+ + H_2O + CO_2$$

---

*The equivalent weight is that weight of acid which will react with 1 mole of hydroxide ion or yield 1 mole of replaceable hydrogen ion.

The water insoluble carboxylic acids are sufficiently soluble in aqueous alcohol to permit titration. Another technique is to dissolve the acid in excess standard aqueous base and back-titrate (see the saponification equivalent, p. 188).

7.13
PREPARATION OF A DERIVATIVE

To complete the identification of an unknown acid, we must prepare a suitable derivative. Probably the one most often employed is the *p*-bromophenacyl ester, according to the equation found later in this chapter. Review the characteristics of a suitable derivative described on p. 153.

7.14
NOMENCLATURE OF ACID HALIDES AND ESTERS

If you start with a given acid—say, propionic or benzoic acid—and replace the —OH group with —Cl, you have an example of an **acid chloride.**

$$\underset{\substack{\text{propionic acid}\\ \text{(propanoic acid)}}}{CH_3CH_2\overset{\displaystyle O}{\overset{\|}{C}}OH} \qquad \underset{\substack{\text{propionyl chloride}\\ \text{(propanoyl chloride)}}}{CH_3CH_2\overset{\displaystyle O}{\overset{\|}{C}}Cl}$$

benzoic acid

benzoyl chloride

The examples given are typical because the names for these compounds are formed by changing the **-ic acid** ending of the appropriate acid to **-yl chloride**.

Esters are frequently stumbling blocks as far as names are concerned. Yet they are very easily and simply named if one follows the rules. Using propionic acid and benzoic acid as the parent compounds, let us look at two examples:

$$\underset{\substack{\text{methyl propionate}\\ \text{(methyl propanoate)}}}{CH_3CH_2\overset{\displaystyle O}{\overset{\|}{C}}OCH_3} \qquad \underset{\text{ethyl benzoate}}{\overset{\displaystyle O}{\overset{\|}{C}}OCH_2CH_3}$$

The R (or Ar) linked to the carboxyl carbon atom is part of the parent acid and determines the fundamental name of the resulting ester. The **-ic acid** is dropped and the suffix **-ate** is added. The —OH of the —CO_2H is also replaced by an —OR' or —OAr'. The name of the $R'(Ar')$ precedes the modified acid name.

Perhaps it will be helpful to summarize the method of naming esters as follows:

$$R-\underset{\underset{2}{\underbrace{}}}{\overset{\overset{O}{\|}}{C}}-O-\underset{\underset{1}{\underbrace{}}}{R'}$$

1. Name the R' group.
2. Name the acid changing **-ic acid** to **-ate**.

Let us now try additional examples:

$$CH_3CH_2CH_2\overset{\overset{O}{\|}}{C}OCH\overset{CH_3}{\underset{CH_3}{\diagdown}}$$

isopropyl butyrate
(isopropyl butanoate)

cyclohexyl p-chlorobenzoate

You should note that the names of the esters are *two words*. This fact is also true of the IUPAC names, which differ from the common names only in using the IUPAC acid names and in usually adding the suffix **-oate** (examples of IUPAC names are given in parentheses). The names of salts are very similar to those of the esters, but the presence of an anion instead of an alkyl or aryl group removes any difficulty.

$$\text{—}CH_2CO_2{}^-\ Na^+$$

sodium phenylacetate

$$CH_3CO_2\text{—}$$

phenyl acetate

In the case of the ester, the two words phenyl acetate should be noted.

7.15
PREPARATION OF ESTERS

An acid derivative that is of great interest is the one resulting from the replacement of the hydroxyl group of the acid by an **alkoxy** (RO—) group of an alcohol. The structure of the ester is most clearly seen by the indirect method of preparation through the acyl chloride or the acid anhydride to be discussed in Chapter 8.*

$$RCOCl + R'OH \rightarrow RCO_2R' + HCl$$
$$(RCO)_2O + R'OH \rightarrow RCO_2R' + RCO_2H$$

Although these reactions are very useful methods of preparation of esters, an older reaction is the **Fischer esterification**, which is an acid-catalyzed equilibrium between the acid and the alcohol.

$$CH_3CO_2H + CH_3CH_2OH \overset{H^+}{\rightleftharpoons} CH_3CO_2CH_2CH_3 + H_2O$$

The chief disadvantage of this reaction is that the equilibrium in some cases is slow in being reached and may have an unfavorable equilibrium constant resulting in a low yield of product. Special considerations of cost and techniques available frequently make this method useful industrially.

Still another method of preparation is available—the reaction of the salt of an acid with an alkyl halide. In fact, this process is used for the preparation of solid derivatives for the identification of the carboxylic acids.

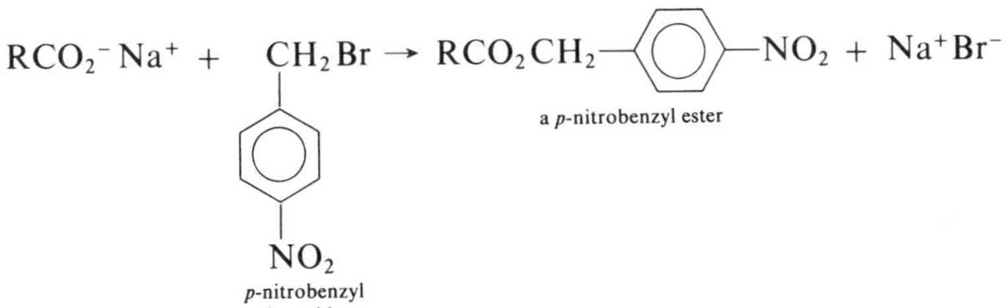

a *p*-nitrobenzyl ester

p-nitrobenzyl
bromide

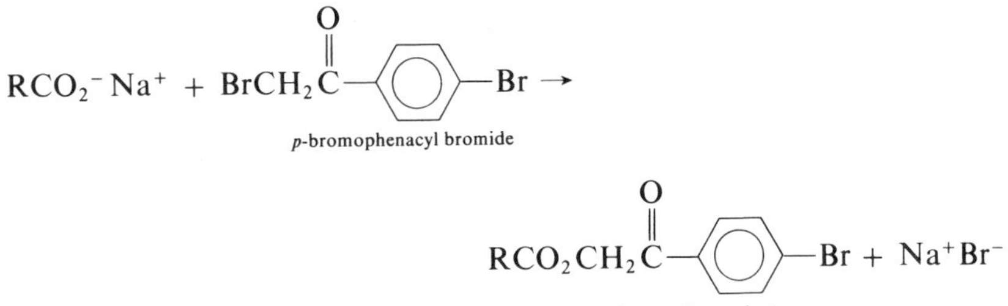

p-bromophenacyl bromide

a *p*-bromophenacyl ester

---

*The reaction between acetyl chloride and low molecular weight alcohols is exothermic to the extent that it is sometimes used as a qualitative test. Keep in mind the fact that water and lower amine homologs would also heat the test tube; therefore, this test alone, like most others, is not conclusive.

Esters of another type prepared by a still different route are of value as derivatives for the identification of alcohols and phenols.

$$ROH \text{ (or } ArOH) + Ar'COCl \rightarrow RO_2CAr' \text{ (or } ArO_2CAr') + HCl$$

Ar' often = Ph or

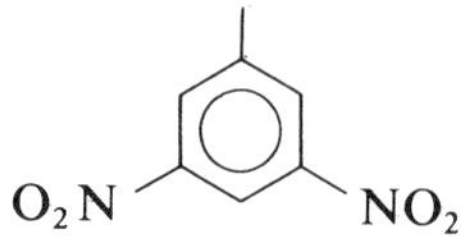

$O_2N \qquad NO_2$

Before leaving the subject of ester preparation, we should point out that a method similar to one used previously may be applied to the preparation of sulfonic acid esters.

$$C_6H_5SO_2Cl + ROH \rightarrow C_6H_5SO_2OR + HCl$$

benzenesulfonyl chloride   a benzenesulfonate

The benzenesulfonyl chloride required is obtained in a manner analogous to that used for the carboxylic acid chlorides:

$$C_6H_5SO_2OH + SOCl_2 \rightarrow C_6H_5SO_2Cl + SO_2 + HCl$$

A still better method involves the direct chlorosulfonation of the aromatic hydrocarbon:

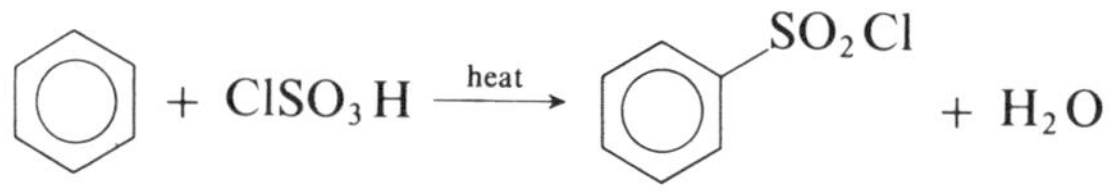

7.16
ESTERIFICATION AND HYDROLYSIS

The reactions by which esters are prepared and split apart are of great practical and theoretical importance; consequently, they have been studied extensively. A wealth of detailed knowledge has been obtained concerning such processes, and a brief look at a few of the most significant facts and methods by which they were obtained will be of value for your understanding of organic reaction mechanisms.

It has been learned that the simple overall reaction

$$\overset{O}{\overset{\|}{RCOH}} + R'OH \rightleftharpoons \overset{O}{\overset{\|}{RCOR'}} + H_2O$$

actually involves a series of steps, and that it can proceed by several different mechanistic pathways. It will be adequate for

the present purpose to consider only the most frequently observed of these—the acid-catalyzed or Fischer esterification.

The presence of a trace of Lewis or mineral acid serves as a
catalyst for both ester formation and hydrolysis or cleavage by
water. Therefore, the reactions presented form an equilibrium
system; the reversible reactions written really describe the
mechanism of both processes. It has been suggested that the
first (fast) step is a reaction between the carboxylic acid and the
mineral acid to produce the organic conjugate acid, which is the
reactive species.

$$
\underset{R-C-OH}{\overset{:\ddot{O}}{\|}} + \overset{+}{H} \rightleftharpoons \underset{R-C-OH}{\overset{:\ddot{O}-H}{|}}{}_{+}
$$

The carbonyl carbon of the carboxyl group, which now bears a
unit positive charge, is very susceptible to nucleophilic attack;
the unshared electron pairs of the alcohol oxygen are readily
available for this purpose.

$$
\underset{\underset{+}{R-C}{-\ddot{O}H}}{\overset{:\ddot{O}H}{|}} + R'-\ddot{O}H \rightleftharpoons \underset{\underset{H\overset{+}{-}\ddot{O}-R'}{R-C-\ddot{O}H}}{\overset{:\ddot{O}H}{|}}
$$

This unstable addition intermediate loses a molecule of water,
and the catalytic proton and the new ester are produced. This
process actually takes place in two steps not shown in the following equation:

$$
\underset{\underset{H\overset{+}{-}\ddot{O}-R'}{R-C-\ddot{O}H}}{\overset{:\ddot{O}H}{|}} \rightleftharpoons \underset{R-C-\ddot{O}R'}{\overset{:\ddot{O}}{\|}} + H_2O + H^+
$$

A vital piece of evidence in establishing this mechanism is the
source of the oxygen atom, which, in the final product, is on the
—OR' fragment. The general reaction, which is, of course, not
intended to give any mechanistic detail, suggests that the acid
has its hydroxyl hydrogen replaced by an alkyl group. This fact
is in direct conflict with the mechanism suggested previously,
which requires that the oxygen in question be supplied by the
alcohol. The question was solved by the clever application of
the generally useful technique of **isotope labeling**.

During the first half of the twentieth century, isotopes and the instruments for making use of them have become increasingly available to the chemist. In the present case, it was necessary to prepare an alcohol with a hydroxyl group containing a concentration of O^{18} greater than the natural abundance. This "tagged" molecule was allowed to react with an organic acid, and the heavy isotope concentration in the products was determined.

$$RCO_2H + R'O^{18}H \left\{ \begin{array}{l} \longrightarrow \overset{\displaystyle O}{\overset{\|}{R C}} O^{18}R' + H_2O \\[2mm] \overset{\not\longrightarrow}{} \overset{\displaystyle O}{\overset{\|}{R C}} OR' + H_2O^{18} \end{array} \right.$$

As is indicated, the O^{18} was found in the ester and not in the water.

Although the acid-catalyzed hydrolysis of esters does occur, a much more useful reaction is the base-catalyzed hydrolysis or **saponification**.

$$\overset{\displaystyle O}{\overset{\|}{R C}} OR + Na^+OH^- \longrightarrow \overset{\displaystyle O}{\overset{\|}{R C}} O^- Na^+ + ROH$$

As with all compounds containing a carbonyl group, the esters tend to have a polarization that promotes nucleophilic attack. In this case, the very strong nucleophile, hydroxide ion, is the attacking species.

$$R \overset{+\delta}{\underset{OR}{C}} \overset{-\delta O}{\overset{\|}{}} \!\! :\ddot{O}H^- \longrightarrow \left[R - \overset{O^-}{\underset{OR}{C}} - OH \right] \longrightarrow RCOH + RO^-$$

$$RCO_2H + RO^- \longrightarrow RCO_2^- + ROH$$

The stronger carboxylic acid is found as the salt, whereas the much weaker acid (alcohol) is obtained as the neutral molecule. This fact accounts for the irreversibility of this reaction sequence and greatly increases its usefulness.

7.17
PHYSICAL PROPERTIES OF ESTERS (TABLE 7.3)

Volatile esters have characteristic fruity odors. Methyl butyrate has a pineapplelike fragrance, and isoamyl valerate (IUPAC

TABLE 7.3　PHYSICAL PROPERTIES OF SOME COMMON ESTERS

Name	Formula	Boiling point, °C*	Melting point, °C	Solubility,† g/100 ml H$_2$O	Density,† g/ml
Methyl acetate	CH$_3$CO$_2$CH$_3$	57	−98	31.9	0.972
Ethyl butyrate	CH$_3$(CH$_2$)$_2$CO$_2$CH$_2$CH$_3$	120	−98	0.68 (25°)	0.879
Isoamyl acetate	CH$_3$CO$_2$(CH$_2$)$_2$CH(CH$_3$)$_2$	142		0.16 (25°)	0.867
Isoamyl valerate	CH$_3$(CH$_2$)$_3$CO$_2$(CH$_2$)$_2$CH(CH$_3$)$_2$	204		slightly soluble	0.881
Ethyl phenylacetate	C$_6$H$_5$CH$_2$CO$_2$CH$_2$CH$_3$	227		insoluble	1.033
Ethyl palmitate	CH$_3$(CH$_2$)$_{14}$CO$_2$CH$_2$CH$_3$	191 (10 mm)	25	insoluble	0.858 (25°)
Ethyl β-naphthoate	β-C$_{10}$H$_7$CO$_2$CH$_2$CH$_3$	308	32	insoluble	1.117
Dimethyl sebacate	(CH$_2$)$_8$(CO$_2$CH$_3$)$_2$	144 (5 mm)	27	insoluble	0.988 (28°)
Dicyclohexyl phthalate	1,2-C$_6$H$_4$(CO$_2$C$_6$H$_{11}$)$_2$		66	insoluble	1.383

*Boiling point is at 760 mm, unless otherwise indicated.
†Solubility and density data are given at 20°C, except as indicated.

name—isopentyl pentanoate) has the odor of apples. Mixtures of esters are responsible for the flavor and aroma of many fruits and flowers. Artificial flavorings are often mixtures of synthetic esters. An artificial raspberry flavor uses nine esters. An ingredient of lacquers is amyl acetate (banana oil), which is employed as a solvent. The other physical properties of the esters show trends similar to classes of compounds already discussed. You should note the reduced boiling points as compared with acids, which is related to much poorer hydrogen bonding.

7.18
REACTIONS OF ESTERS

In the presence of aqueous acid, esters undergo hydrolysis (splitting by water) to produce the original acid and alcohol.

$$RCO_2R' + H_2O \underset{}{\overset{H^+}{\rightleftharpoons}} RCO_2H + R'OH$$

This reaction is just the reverse of the acid-catalyzed process of esterification we discussed earlier in this chapter. It therefore

Courtesy of the Edgar Fahs Smith Memorial Collection.

Ludwig Claisen (German, 1851–1930). Another student of Kekulé, Claisen taught and carried on active research programs at a number of leading German universities. His activities are well remembered since there are a number of reactions and pieces of apparatus named after him. Among these reactions is an ester condensation:

$$2CH_3CO_2C_2H_5$$

$$+ C_2H_5O^{-+}Na \rightleftharpoons$$

$$\overset{O}{\overset{\|}{CH_3CCH_2CO_2C_2H_5}}$$

ethyl acetoacetate

might seem that neither of these processes would be of much value as preparative methods. Now is a good time to recall, from introductory chemistry, that systems in equilibrium can be forced to react in either desired direction by adding reactant or by removing product. For example, a large excess of water shifts the preceding reaction to the right (hydrolysis), whereas a large excess of alcohol shifts it to the left (esterification). Through the use of this application of the principles embodied in the **law of mass action**, it is often possible either to prepare or to hydrolyze esters; for example, esterification is favored if the water is removed as it is formed.

An extension of the Grignard reaction involves the use of esters and should be considered here.

$$RCO_2R' + R''MgX \xrightarrow[\text{THF}]{\text{absolute}} [RCOR''] + R'OMgX$$

$$[RCOR''] + R''MgX \xrightarrow[\text{THF}]{\text{absolute}} R-\overset{\overset{\displaystyle R''}{|}}{\underset{\underset{\displaystyle R''}{|}}{C}}-OMgX \xrightarrow{H^+} R-\overset{\overset{\displaystyle R''}{|}}{\underset{\underset{\displaystyle R''}{|}}{C}}-OH$$

The reaction with the carbonyl group of the ester is just like our earlier example of a Grignard reagent and carbon dioxide, except that alkoxide (OR') is displaced by R'' from the Grignard reagent. With an ester, the initial product is a ketone, which also shows a marked tendency to react with the alkyl magnesium halide and hence is not isolated, as indicated by the brackets. Thus, the final product is always a tertiary alcohol having two identical groups attached to the carbinol group; for example,

$$CH_3CH_2CO_2CH(CH_3)_2 + 2\ CH_3MgBr \xrightarrow[\text{(2) 2 H}_2\text{O}]{\text{(1) absolute ether}}$$

$$CH_3CH_2\overset{\overset{\displaystyle OH}{|}}{\underset{\underset{\displaystyle CH_3}{|}}{C}}CH_3 + \begin{cases} Mg(OH)_2 \\ MgBr_2 \\ (CH_3)_2CHOH \end{cases}$$

With less active metals than Mg (e.g., Zn or Cd), the ketone may be isolated.

Unlike acids, esters can be reduced to the corresponding alcohol under fairly mild conditions.

$$RCO_2R' + H_2 \xrightarrow[\text{PtO}_2,\ \text{etc.}]{\text{Pt, Pd,}} RCH_2OH + R'OH$$

The catalysts employed cover a very wide range, but are generally finely divided metallic materials (especially copper chromite) somewhat similar to those required for the reduction of alkenes. Lithium aluminum hydride also works very well with esters.

7.19
ANALYSIS OF ESTERS

The identification of esters involves the hydrolysis, isolation, characterization, and preparation of derivatives of both the acid and the alcohol portions of the unknown compound. This process is frequently accomplished by the use of a base and is known as saponification.

$$RCO_2R' + Na^+OH^- \xrightarrow{\text{H}_2\text{O}} RCO_2^-Na^+ + R'OH$$

It can also be carried out quantitatively in a manner analogous to that employed with the acids, and the resulting **saponification equivalent** is equal to the equivalent weight of the ester. In practice, the ester is hydrolyzed in an excess of standard base. The excess is titrated with standard acid.

$$\text{saponification eq} = \frac{\text{mg of ester}}{[(\text{ml base})\,(N\text{ base})] - [(\text{ml acid})\,(N\text{ acid})]}$$

The use of the saponification equivalent is essentially the same as the use of the neutralization equivalent. For an ester of a monobasic acid, the value is equal to the molecular weight; for a dibasic acid ester, it will be one-half the molecular weight.

SUGGESTED ADDITIONAL READINGS

Inductive and Resonance Effects

Cram and Hammond, pp. 206–15.
Morrison and Boyd, pp. 599–601 and 745–48.
Roberts and Caserio, pp. 514–17 and 650–52.

N. L. Allinger, "Energy Relations in Teaching Organic Chemistry," *J. Chem. Educ.*, **40**, 201 (1963).

Esterification and Hydrolysis

Breslow, pp. 179–84.
Gould, pp. 314–27.
Morrison and Boyd, pp. 661–65 and 675–79.
Roberts and Caserio, pp. 518–21.
D. A. Semenow and J. D. Roberts, "Uses of Isotopes in Organic Chemistry," *J. Chem. Educ.*, **33**, 2 (1956).

Industrial Methods

Stille, Sections 4.5–4.6 and Chapter 8.

Qualitative Organic Analysis

Pasto and Johnson, Section 12.10–12.13.
Shriner, Fuson, and Curtin, various sections dealing with acids and esters.

SUMMARY

1. The carboxyl group is characteristic of an important class of organic acids. These acids are generally quite stable, and their derivatives are widely distributed in natural products.

2. The acidity of the acids is defined as the position of equilibrium for the ionization of the acid in some solvent. The solvent, usually water, acts as the base in accepting the ionized proton.

$$RCO_2H + n\,H_2O \rightleftharpoons RCO_2^- + H^+ \text{(aq)}$$

3. The order of increasing acidity for some organic compounds is

$$ROH < ArOH < RCO_2H$$

Resonance effects are important in understanding this sequence.

4. Both inductive and resonance effects are important in understanding the effect of various structural arrangements on the acidity of the carboxylic acids.

5. The stability of the carboxylic acids toward oxidation makes their preparation from less highly oxidized compounds attractive.

$$\left.\begin{array}{l} R \\[-2pt] C{=}C \\[-2pt] RC{\equiv}C- \\ RCH_2OH \\ RCHO \end{array}\right\} \xrightarrow{\text{[O]}} RCO_2H$$

6. The Grignard reagent is useful in the preparation of carboxylic acids.

$$RX \xrightarrow[\text{ether}]{\text{Mg}} RMgX \xrightarrow{CO_2} RCO_2^- \; Mg^{+2}X^- \xrightarrow{H^+} RCO_2H$$

7. The alkyl sulfonic acids can be prepared, but in the laboratory the aryl sulfonic acids are more important.

8. Some typical reactions of the acids are

$$RCO_2H + LiAlH_4 \xrightarrow[\text{(2) } H_2O]{\text{(1) ether}} RCH_2OH$$

$$RCO_2H + SOCl_2 \rightarrow RCOCl + HCl + SO_2$$

$$RCO_2H + R'OH \overset{H^+}{\rightleftharpoons} RCO_2R' + H_2O$$

9. The qualitative identification of an unknown organic acid is made easier by the fact that it can be titrated with standard base. From this technique the neutralization equivalent or equivalent weight is obtained.

10. In addition to the acid-catalyzed esterification, several other methods are available.

$$RCOCl + R'OH \rightarrow RCO_2R' + HCl$$

$$(RCO)_2O + R'OH \rightarrow RCO_2R' + RCO_2H$$

Two methods are especially useful for the preparation of derivatives for identification.

11. Acid chlorides and esters of sulfonic acids can be prepared by similar routes.

$$ArSO_3H + SOCl_2 \rightarrow ArSO_2Cl + HCl + SO_2$$
$$ArSO_2Cl + ROH \rightarrow ArSO_3R + HCl$$

Direct chlorosulfonation is also very useful in the laboratory.

$$ArH + ClSO_3H \rightarrow ArSO_2Cl + H_2O$$

12. Basic hydrolysis of esters is called saponification and can be made quantitative for a measurement of the equivalent weight of an ester.

13. Esterification and hydrolysis are the reverse of one another. The mechanism of esterification in acid solution involves the nucleophilic attack of alcohol on the conjugate acid of the carboxylic acid. Saponification proceeds through the attack of hydroxide ion on the polarized carboxyl group of the ester.

14. It has been found that the acyl oxygen bond is important in many cases of esterification and hydrolysis. The technique of isotope labeling has been used in these studies.

15. The principle of mass action can be used to force either esterification or hydrolysis to take place.

16. The following are some typical reactions of esters:

$$RCO_2R' + R''MgX \xrightarrow[\text{(2) H}^+]{\text{(1) ether}} RC\overset{\displaystyle R''}{\underset{\displaystyle R''}{\overset{|}{\underset{|}{OH}}}}$$

$$RCO_2R' \xrightarrow[\text{Pd}]{H_2} RCH_2OH + R'OH$$

17. The qualitative identification of esters requires cleavage to the acid and alcohol portions and their identification.

PROBLEMS

1. Give the structure(s) and name(s) of the vigorous oxidation products of the following:

a. $CH_3\underset{\displaystyle CH_3}{\overset{\displaystyle |}{C}}=CH_2$

b.
$$\begin{array}{ccc} & CH_2 & \\ CH_2 & & CCH_3 \\ | & & \| \\ CH_2 & \!\!\!\!-\!\!\!\!- & CH \end{array}$$

c. 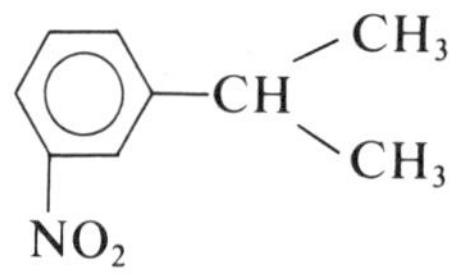   d. $HC\equiv CCH_2CH=CH_2$

e. $CH_3CH_2CH=CHCH_3$

2. Complete the following reactions (name all organic compounds):

a. $CH_3CO_2H + NaOH \xrightarrow{H_2O}$

b. $C_6H_5CO_2H + CH_3OH \xrightarrow{H^+}$

c. $Ca^{+2} \xrightarrow{heat}$

d. $CH_3CH=CHCH_2CH_3 \xrightarrow{KMnO_4}$

e. $CH_3CH=CHCO_2H \xrightarrow{Br_2}$

f. $\xrightarrow{H_2SO_4}$

g. 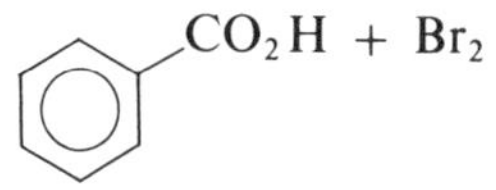 $CO_2H + Br_2 \xrightarrow{Fe}$

h. $CH_3CH_2CO_2CH_2CH_3 + NaOH \xrightarrow{H_2O}$

i. $CH_3CO_2^- Na^+ + $ $\rightarrow$

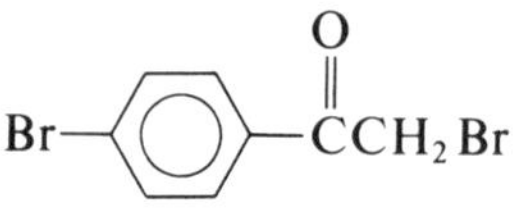

j. 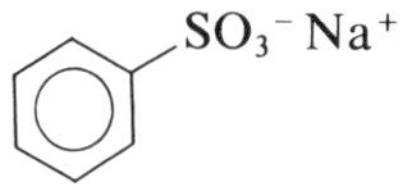 $+ NaOH \xrightarrow{heat}$

3. Complete the following reactions (name all organic compounds):

a. $CH_3CH_2CO_2H + SOCl_2 \rightarrow$

b. $CH_3CH_2COCl + H_2O \rightarrow$

c. $C_6H_5CO_2CH_2CH_3 + NaOH \xrightarrow{H_2O}$

d. $CH_3CH_2CH_2CO_2H + CH_3CH_2OH \xrightarrow{H^+}$

e. $CH_3CH_2COCl + CH_3CH_2O^- Na^+ \rightarrow$

f. 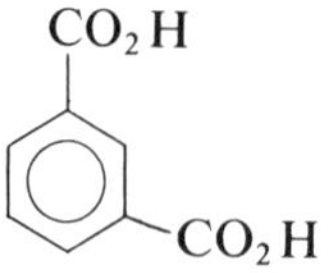 $\xrightarrow{[O]}$

g. CH_3

$\xrightarrow{[O]}$

CH_2CH_3

h. $CH_3CH_2CHCH_2OH \xrightarrow{[O]}$

            |

          CH_3

i. $CH_3CH_2CH_2MgBr + CO_2 \xrightarrow{\begin{array}{c}\text{dry}\\\text{ether}\end{array}}$

For problems 4 through 14, give the structural formulas and names of all lettered compounds, writing equations for each reaction.

4. On vigorous oxidation, two different hydrocarbons give

$$HO_2CCH_2CHCH_2CO_2H$$
$$|$$
$$CH_3$$

as the sole organic compound.

5. $\underset{C_8H_6Br_4}{(C)} \xleftarrow{Br_2} \underset{C_8H_6}{(A)} \xrightarrow[\text{vigorous}]{[O]} \underset{}{(B)} C_7H_6O_2 + CO_2$

            $\downarrow$ HBr

          (D)

        $C_8H_8Br_2$

6. Analysis shows that an unknown compound (A) is an acid containing bromine. A 0.5-g sample required 25.7 ml of 0.1 N NaOH for titration. Treatment with alcoholic KOH gave a new acid, (B). Titration of a 0.5-g sample of (B) required 43.9 ml of 0.1 N NaOH. Oxidation of (B) gave two compounds, a ketone (C) and an acid (D). A 0.2-g sample of (D) required 38.5 ml of 0.1 N NaOH.

7. Compound (A), an aromatic acid, has a neutralization equivalent of 136 ± 1. Upon strong oxidation, a new acid (B) is produced. Titration of 0.208 g of (B) requires 25.00 ml of 0.1 N NaOH. Compound (B) very easily forms a five-membered cyclic anhydride (C).

8. $(A) \xrightarrow{\underset{Fe}{Br_2}} \underset{\text{mixture}}{(C) + (D)} \xrightarrow[\substack{(3)\ H^+}]{\substack{(1)\ Mg\ \}\ \text{absolute}\\(2)\ CO_2\ \}\ THF}} \underset{\text{mixture}}{(E) + (F)}$

  $\downarrow [O]$ $\downarrow [O]$

  (B) (G) + (H)

                                           mixture

      0.24 g (B)

     neutralized by   0.35 g (G)   0.27 g (H)

     19.7 ml NaOH   neutralized by   neutralized by

       (0.1 N)   42.2 ml NaOH   32.5 ml NaOH

                            (0.1 N)   (0.1 N)

9. Compound (A) C_7H_8 was brominated to give (B), C_7H_7Br. Compound (B) was treated with Mg in dry ether, and *n*-propyl bromide was slowly added to the solution. Compound (C), $C_{10}H_{14}$, was isolated, and when (C) was oxidized, (D)—$C_8H_6O_4$—was produced. Compound (D) yielded only one mononitronuclear substitution product.

10. An organic acid (A) has a neutralization equivalent of 180 ± 1. If (A) is treated with concentrated H_2SO_4, a new acid (B) is formed. Acid (B) has a neutralization equivalent of 162 ± 1. Treatment of either (A) or (B) with a nitric-sulfuric acid mixture results in four mononitro derivatives. What additional data are needed to make a final choice among the 6 possibilities for (B) and the 11 possibilities for (A)?

11. Hydrocarbon (A), on strong oxidation, yields an acid (B), with neutralization equivalent 83 ± 2, and a neutral three-carbon compound (C). Acid (B) gives only a single monobromo substitution product.

12. Compound (A), C_8H_6, reacts to give a red precipitate with ammonical cuprous chloride. When treated with sodium, hydrogen gas is released and (B), C_8H_5Na, is produced. Compound (B) is reacted with methyl chloride to form (C), C_9H_8. Compound (C) reacts with HCl to form (D), $C_9H_{10}Cl_2$, and with ethyl chloride in the presence of $AlCl_3$ to form (E), $C_{11}H_{12}$. Then (E) reacts with water in the presence of $H_2SO_4 + Hg^{+2}$ to yield (F), $C_{11}H_{14}O$, which, in turn, reacts with chlorine at an elevated temperature to give (G), $C_{11}H_{13}OCl$. Compound (G) is treated with alcoholic KOH to give (H), $C_{11}H_{12}O$. Finally, (A) through (D) are oxidized to (J), $C_7H_6O_2$; (E) through (H) are oxidized to (K), $C_8H_6O_4$.

13. A compound (A), $C_9H_{10}O_2$, when brominated at an elevated temperature, produced (B), $C_9H_9O_2Br$, and when brominated at a lower temperature with an iron catalyst, produced (E), which has the same molecular formula as (B). When treated with alcoholic KOH, (B) gave (C), $C_9H_8O_2$. Then (A), (B), and (C), on oxidation, gave (D). On bromination, (D) gave one organic product, (F), which is also the oxidation product of (E).

14. Compound (A), $C_7H_{14}O$, reacts with sodium to produce a salt, and releases hydrogen gas. Then (A) reacts with thionyl chloride to yield (C), $C_7H_{13}Cl$, and it releases sulfur dioxide and hydrogen chloride. Compound (A) reacts with hydrobromic acid to give (D), $C_7H_{14}Br_2$. When (A) is passed over hot aluminum oxide (dehydrated), (E)—C_7H_{12}—is produced. When (E) is oxidized, two compounds—(F) and (G)—are formed: the former, $C_2H_4O_2$, is

found to be an acid; the latter, $C_3H_4O_3$, gives a test for both an acid and a ketone. When (A) is oxidized, (F) and (H), $C_5H_8O_2$, are produced.

15. Draw the principal contributors to the resonance hybrid for each of the following compounds:

a. [benzene ring]—CO_2H

b. [benzene ring with O_2N and CO_2H]

c. HO—[benzene ring]—CO_2H

d. [benzene ring with NO_2]—CO_2H

e. [benzene ring with CH_3]—CO_2H

16. On the basis of your answers to question 15, and on any other reasonable arguments, what would you expect the order of increasing acid strength to be?

17. Write a reasonable mechanism for the reaction of toluene with bromine in the presence of ultraviolet radiation and with no Lewis acid catalyst. Is the mechanism of the observed substitution reaction the same in the dark with iron powder? What would you expect the products to be with a second molar equivalent of bromine in each of the above? Explain why you would expect such products.

18. How might you prepare 2-phenylpropanoic acid from ethanol, benzene, and inorganic reagents? Will your synthesis produce more than one isomer of the desired product? Explain how it happens that they are formed.

19. Arrange the following sets of compounds in order of increasing acidity:

   a. CH_3CO_2H, $C_6H_5CO_2H$, CH_3—[benzene ring]—CO_2H

   b. CH_3CHCO_2H, Cl—[benzene ring]—CH_2CO_2H, $CH_2CH_2CO_2H$
        | |
        Cl Cl

   c. [benzene ring]—CO_2H, Cl—[benzene ring]—CO_2H, O_2N—[benzene ring]—CO_2H

   d. $HO_2CCH_2CO_2H$, $HO_2C(CH_2)_2CO_2H$, $HO_2C(CH_2)_3CO_2H$
      (first ionization only)

e. F—CH$_2$CO$_2$H,   I—CH$_2$CO$_2$H,   Br—CH$_2$CO$_2$H,
Cl—CH$_2$CO$_2$H

20. Design a practical synthetic route to each of the following compounds, starting with benzene, alkyl halides of three carbons or
less, and inorganic reagents:

a.

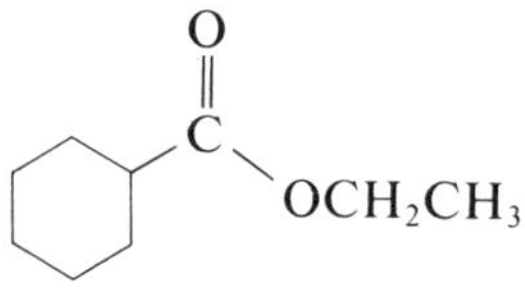

b.

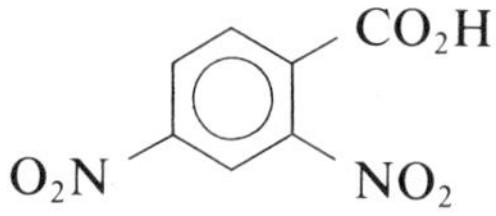

c. (CH$_3$)$_2$CHCO$_2$H

d. HO$_2$C(CH$_2$)$_4$CO$_2$H

e.

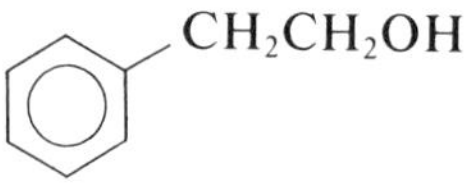

f.

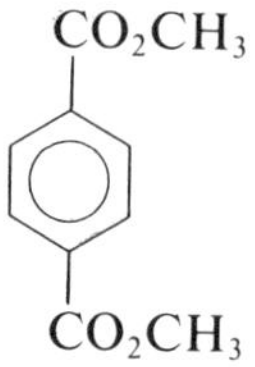

8

Amines and Amides

8.1
THE ORGANIC BASES

Although quite a few organic materials show basic properties—for example, the carboxylate anion and the metal salts of alcohols and phenols—the type to be considered in the present chapter are those containing nitrogen—the amines. The extranuclear electronic configuration of nitrogen places five electrons in the valence shell, and three of these are used in forming the three covalent bonds that are typical of ammonia and its derivatives. The two remaining electrons are available to accept a proton; thus, such nitrogen compounds are classified as bases. Inasmuch as nitrogen is less electronegative than oxygen, it is better able to support a positive charge. The amines are more basic than their oxygen analogues.

$$H_3N\!: + H^+Cl^- \rightarrow H_3N^+\!: H\ Cl^-$$

The neutralization reaction shown in this equation for the inorganic compound ammonia has a direct analogy in organic chemistry. It is based on the fact that the amines, which are derived from ammonia, react in a very similar manner.

$$CH_3NH_2 + H^+ Cl^- \rightarrow CH_3NH_3^+Cl^-$$

methylamine   methylammonium chloride

The product is a typical salt, with a high melting point and great water solubility. It is possible to reverse the reaction and liberate the free amine by treatment with a strong base.

$$CH_3NH_3^+Cl^- + Na^+OH^- \rightarrow CH_3NH_2 + H_2O + Na^+Cl^-$$

8.2
CLASSIFICATION OF AMINES

It is possible to replace more than one of the N—H bonds with a N—C bond; therefore, amines having one, two, or three alkyl (or aryl) groups are known. Our discussion of amines is made more understandable by classifying these different types as primary (1°), secondary (2°), and tertiary (3°), depending on the number of hydrogens replaced. This system causes some confusion at times, because the definitions of primary, secondary, and tertiary are apparently different from those used earlier with alkyl groups. In one case, the question is the number of groups attached to *carbon*, and in the other, the number attached to *nitrogen*.

one group attached   = primary
two groups attached   = secondary
three groups attached = tertiary

Alkyl groups		*Amines*
R—CH$_2$—	primary	R—NH$_2$
$\overset{R}{\underset{R'}{\diagdown}}$CH—	secondary	$\overset{R}{\underset{R'}{\diagdown}}$NH
R—C— with R' above and R'' below	tertiary	R—N— with R' above and R'' below

The confusion arises because of the fact that the one group attached to nitrogen in a primary amine may be a primary, secondary, or tertiary alkyl group. For example, the following are all primary amines:

$$CH_3CH_2CH_2CH_2—NH_2 \qquad \textit{n}\text{-butylamine}$$

$$CH_3CH_2\underset{\underset{CH_3}{|}}{CH}—NH_2 \qquad \textit{sec}\text{-butylamine}$$

$$CH_3—\overset{\overset{CH_3}{|}}{\underset{\underset{CH_3}{|}}{C}}—NH_2 \qquad \textit{tert}\text{-butylamine}$$

Inasmuch as the **amines** are typical organic bases they may conveniently be thought of as ammonia derivatives. Clearly, any number of hydrogens (from one to three) may be replaced by the same or different alkyl or aryl groups, and each of these will be a different amine. The following will illustrate.

$$H—\overset{\overset{H}{|}}{N}—H \qquad \text{ammonia}$$

$$H—\overset{\overset{H}{|}}{N}—CH_3 \qquad \text{methylamine}$$

$$CH_3—\overset{\overset{H}{|}}{N}—CH_2CH_3 \qquad \textit{N}\text{-ethylmethylamine}$$

$$CH_3CH_2—\overset{\overset{CH_3}{|}}{N}—CH_2CH_2CH_3 \qquad \textit{N}\text{-ethyl-}\textit{N}\text{-methylpropylamine}$$

This common method of naming **amines**, really quite systematic, is so useful that the IUPAC names are rarely used. With amines of such simple structure that no ambiguity would result, it is the practice to omit the *N*-, for example, ethylmethylamine. The usefulness of the *N*- may be seen in the case of dimethylpentylamine:

$$CH_3CH_2CH_2\overset{\overset{CH_3}{|}}{\underset{\underset{CH_3}{|}}{C}}CH_2NH_2 \qquad CH_3CH_2CH_2CH_2CH_2N\overset{\diagup CH_3}{\diagdown CH_3}$$

β, β-dimethyl-*n*-pentylamine   *N, N*-dimethyl-*n*-pentylamine
(2,2-dimethyl-1-aminopentane)   (*N, N*-dimethyl-1-aminopentane)

The IUPAC names of the simple aromatic amines are based on the parent compound, aniline:

N-methylaniline   *N,N*-dimethylaniline   *p*-methylaniline

Some of the aromatic amines also have trivial names that are in general use; for example, *p*-methylaniline is known as *p*-toluidine.

8.4
PHYSICAL PROPERTIES OF THE AMINES (TABLE 8.1)

The simplest amines (methyl and ethyl) are gases, very water soluble, and have strong ammonialike odors. Higher members

TABLE 8.1   PHYSICAL PROPERTIES OF SOME COMMON AMINES

Name	Formula	Boiling point, °C*	Melting point, °C	Solubility,† g/100 ml H_2O	Density,† g/ml
Methylamine	CH_3NH_2	−6	−94	very soluble	0.769 (−70°)
Dimethylamine	$(CH_3)_2NH$	7	−96	very soluble	0.680 (0°)
Trimethylamine	$(CH_3)_3N$	3	−117	very soluble	0.662 (−5°)
Ethylamine	$CH_3CH_2NH_2$	17	−84	miscible	0.706 (0°)
Butylamine	$CH_3(CH_2)_3NH_2$	78	−50	miscible	0.740
Isobutylamine	$(CH_3)_2CHCH_2NH_2$	68		miscible	0.736
sec-Butylamine	$CH_3CH_2CHNH_2$ $\quad\quad\quad\;$ | $\quad\quad\quad CH_3$	63		miscible	0.724
tert-Butylamine	$(CH_3)_3CNH_2$	45	−68	miscible	0.696
Aniline	$C_6H_5NH_2$	184	−6	3.7	1.022
Diphenylamine	$(C_6H_5)_2NH$		53	insoluble	1.159
Triphenylamine	$(C_6H_5)_3N$		127	insoluble	0.774 (0°)
o-Nitroaniline	*o*-$O_2NC_6H_4NH_2$	284	72	0.1	1.442 (15°)
m-Nitroaniline	*m*-$O_2NC_6H_4NH_2$	306d**	112	0.1	1.430
p-Nitroaniline	*p*-$O_2NC_6H_4NH_2$	332	148	0.05	1.424

*Boiling point is at 760 mm, unless indicated otherwise.
†Solubility and density data are given at 20°C, except as indicated.
**d = decomposition.

of the homologous series show the usual trends of increasing boiling points and decreasing solubility in water. The odor changes to a disagreeable fishy aroma and rapidly becomes faint with decreased vapor pressure.

The basic nature of the amines makes them soluble as salts in dilute hydrochloric acid. Nearly all of the aliphatic amines are sufficiently basic to show this characteristic. The aromatic amines (anilines) are usually considerably less basic because of resonance, and those with more than one aromatic ring (such as triphenylamine) are too weakly basic to show solubility in dilute HCl (p. 208).

8.5
THE RESONANCE EFFECT

The effectiveness of resonance stabilization in explaining the greater acidity of the carboxyl group as compared with the hydroxyl group suggests that this, too, might be a useful method of transferring ionic charge from one part of a molecule to another. A consideration of the basicity of certain amines demonstrates the extent to which the resonance distribution of electronic charge is, in fact, useful. Table 8.2 shows the appropriate equilibrium constants for these amines.

TABLE 8.2   RESONANCE EFFECT ON BASICITY

Amine	Structure	K_b
Methylamine	CH_3NH_2	4.38×10^{-4}
Aniline	$C_6H_5NH_2$	3.83×10^{-10}
m-Nitroaniline	$m\text{-}O_2NC_6H_4NH_2$	4.00×10^{-12}
p-Nitroaniline	$p\text{-}O_2NC_6H_4NH_2$	1.00×10^{-13}

The most striking fact about the amines listed is the very great difference in basicity between the aliphatic and the aromatic. This fact can be attributed, for the most part, to a **resonance effect**. You recall that the basic nature of the amines is owing to the presence of the unshared electrons on nitrogen making the compounds typical Lewis bases. Resonance is a method for delocalizing the electronic system of molecules, and, for aromatic amines, the phenyl group provides a very convenient π electron system for redistributing nitrogen's electrons. The contributors to the hybrid—which are, of course, unavailable to methylamine—as follows:

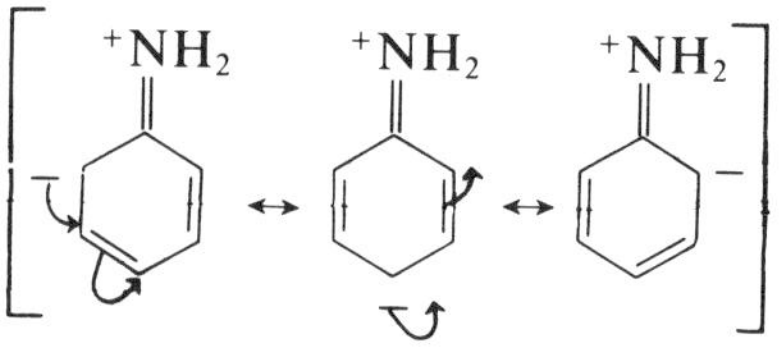

A second factor that must be considered in this discussion is the fact that the **conjugate acid**, or anilinium ion, does not have these resonance possibilities. This fact further lowers the basicity of aromatic amines.

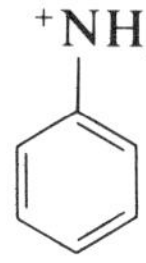

The final example of the basicity of amines to be considered involves both the inductive and the resonance effects. The nitro group, which is known to be a strong electron-withdrawing group (p. 128), would be expected to lower the basicity of aniline still further. This effect is in accord with the facts as presented in Table 8.2, but it is interesting to examine the reasons for the greater effectiveness of the *para* substituent. Let us look at the various contributors possible for each isomer:

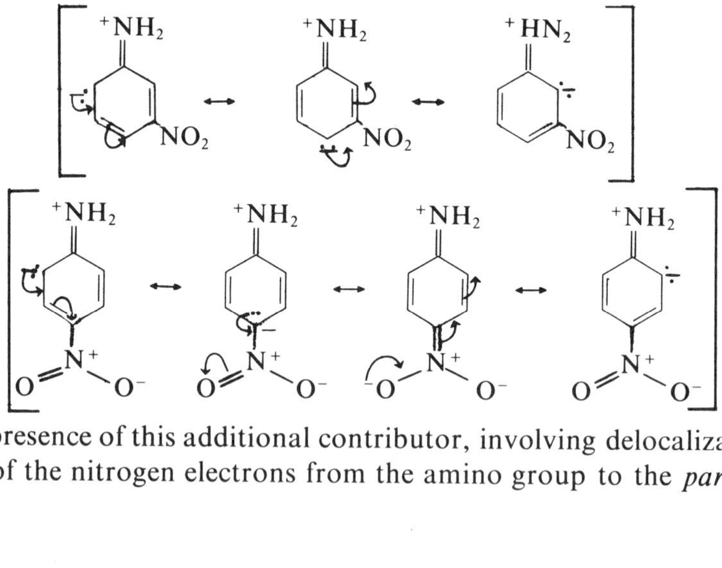

The presence of this additional contributor, involving delocalization of the nitrogen electrons from the amino group to the *para*

nitro group, would be expected to make the *p*-nitroaniline a weaker base than *m*-nitroaniline. This contributor should be important because it places a negative charge on oxygen instead of carbon, which should be favorable owing to the greater electronegativity of oxygen.

8.6
PREPARATION OF AMINES

The great usefulness of amines has caused the discovery and development of numerous synthetic procedures. At this point, we shall consider two of the most useful. The formal resemblance of amines to ammonia indicates one of the early methods —the direct alkylation of ammonia by alkyl halides.

$$2 \overset{\frown}{\overset{..}{N}H_3} + \overset{\frown}{R}—Cl \rightarrow NH_2—R + NH_4^+ Cl^-$$

The resulting amine will also react with more alkyl halide to form the secondary amine. This fact represents one of the principal limitations of the reaction; it is very difficult to obtain high yields of pure amine of any one class. If a reasonable yield of primary amine is to be produced, a very large excess of ammonia must be

August W. von Hofmann (German, 1818–1892). The first director of the Royal College of Chemistry in London and the founder of the German Chemical Society, Hofmann's main field of research was the amines, both aliphatic and aromatic. In this work he is credited with many important discoveries including the first preparation of numerous compounds and several general reactions. He is one of the many first-rank chemists who were students of Liebig.

Courtesy of the Edgar Fahs Smith Memorial Collection.

used; however, it will still be contaminated with secondary and tertiary amine, as well as tetralkylammonium salt.

$$2\ R{-}NH_2 + RCl \rightarrow \begin{array}{c} R \\ \diagdown \\ R \diagup \end{array} N{-}H + RNH_3{}^+Cl^- \ (R_2NH_2{}^+Cl^-)$$

$$2\ \begin{array}{c} R \\ \diagdown \\ R \diagup \end{array} N{-}H + RCl \rightarrow \begin{array}{c} R \\ \diagdown \\ R \diagup \end{array} N{-}R + R_2NH_2{}^+Cl^- \ (R_3NH^+Cl^-)$$

$$\begin{array}{c} R \\ \diagdown \\ R \diagup \end{array} N{-}R + RCl \rightarrow \begin{array}{c} R \\ \diagdown \\ R \diagup \end{array} N \begin{array}{c} R \\ \diagup \\ \diagdown \ R \end{array} {}^+Cl^-$$

a tetralkylammonium salt

A class of reactions resulting in amine formation is the reduction of nitrogen in a higher oxidation state. One of the most useful is the reduction of the nitro group, especially in aromatic compounds.

The reduction of an aliphatic nitro compound also produces an amine, but the ease with which a wide variety of aromatic nitro compounds can be prepared makes the reaction of greater utility in that series. A great many reducing agents are used—for example, H_2/Pt and LAH.

A very useful method of preparing pure primary amines is through the cyano compound or nitrile. It can be obtained by using the displacement of an alkyl halide by cyanide ion (elimination can be a serious competing reaction).

$$Na^+CN^- + R{-}X \rightarrow RCN + Na^+X^-$$

This reaction, and nucleophilic displacement reactions in general, are much more difficult (often not feasible) with aromatic halogen compounds, and thus less useful synthetically.* The resulting nitrile can now be reduced to the corresponding amine:

$$RCN + LiAlH_4 \xrightarrow[\substack{(1)\ \text{absolute} \\ \text{ether} \\ (2)\ H_2O}]{} RCH_2NH_2$$

---

*A possible alternative is

$$ArCONH_2 \xrightarrow[-H_2O]{P_2O_5} ArCN$$

Obviously, this method, which extends the carbon chain, is of value only for the preparation of primary amines. Later in this chapter, we shall use a method for the preparation of secondary and tertiary amines essentially free from the other classes.

8.7
REACTIONS OF AMINES

Amines of all classes will frequently react with alkyl halides to form amines of a higher class, which represents, as indicated earlier, one of the difficulties in the preparation of amines by this procedure, unless equimolar amounts are used.

$$CH_3CH_2NH_2 + CH_3CH_2Cl \rightarrow (CH_3CH_2)_2 NH_2^+ \ Cl^-$$

$$\downarrow Na^+OH^-$$

$$\underset{\text{diethylamine}}{(CH_3CH_2)_2NH} + H_2O + Na^+Cl^-$$

Although aromatic amines will react less readily than will alkyl amines with alkyl halogen compounds to form N-substituted aniline derivatives, aryl halides are generally not reactive enough to permit the reverse sequence at all. In general, the amine must be reasonably nucleophilic for the reaction to have a passable energy barrier.

$$Ar\overset{..}{N}H_2 + RCl \xrightarrow[\text{(2) } Na^+OH^-]{\text{(1) heat}} ArNHR + Na^+Cl^- + H_2O$$

$$RNH_2 + ArCl \rightarrow \text{no reaction}$$

Closely related to these alkylation reactions are the acylations resulting from the corresponding acid halide.

$$\underset{CH_3}{\overset{CH_3}{\diagdown}}CHCH_2\overset{..}{N}H_2 + CH_3\overset{\overset{O}{\|}}{C}Cl \xrightarrow{Na^+OH^-} \underset{\text{N-isobutylacetamide}}{CH_3\overset{\overset{O}{\|}}{C}NHCH_2CH\underset{CH_3}{\overset{CH_3}{\diagup}}}$$

$$+ Na^+Cl^- + H_2O$$

Would you expect this reaction to take place more easily than the S_N2 reaction of amines on alkyl halides? As the name indicates, the product is an amide, which is an acid derivative and may be thought of as resulting from replacement of the carboxyl —OH group by an amino group (which may or may not be substituted). The amides may be prepared directly from the acids, but are more frequently obtained by using either the acid chloride or another derivative—the anhydride.

$$RNH_2 + (R'CO)_2O \xrightarrow{Na^+OH^-} RNHCR' + R'CO_2^-Na^+ + H_2O$$

an anhydride

An acid anhydride is a compound that can be obtained by elimination of a molecule of water from a dicarboxylic acid (or 2 moles of a monocarboxylic acid). The addition of water can regenerate the original acid. Both IUPAC and common names for the anhydrides are made (for simple, symmetrical cases) by replacing **acid** with **anhydride**.

$$
\begin{array}{ccc}
\overset{O}{\overset{\|}{CH_2COH}} & & \overset{O}{\overset{\|}{CH_2C}} \\
| & \xrightarrow{heat} & | \quad \diagdown \\
CH_2COH & & CH_2C \quad O + H_2O \\
\overset{\|}{O} & & \overset{\|}{O} \quad \text{(steam)}
\end{array}
$$

succinic anhydride (limited to
5-, 6-, and 7-membered anhydrides)

Like the acid chloride, the anhydride is very reactive and hydrolyzes easily, but less readily than acid halides. For this reason, special methods of preparation are necessary. Acetic anhydride is not prepared by direct dehydration, but rather by the reaction of acetyl chloride with acetic acid or sodium acetate.

$$
\overset{O}{\overset{\|}{CH_3COH}} + \overset{O}{\overset{\|}{CH_3CCl}} \rightarrow \overset{O}{\overset{\|}{CH_3C}}-O-\overset{O}{\overset{\|}{CCH_3}} + HCl
$$

or

acetic anhydride

$(CH_3CO_2^-Na^+)$

The aromatic amines show the typical substitution reactions of the benzene ring. In fact, they are very reactive, and unless special methods are employed, all three *ortho* and *para* positions are substituted.

These ammonia derivatives are formally similar to acid chlorides in that the —OH of the acid is replaced by the —N⟨ group.

$$CH_3CH_2\overset{\overset{\displaystyle O}{\|}}{C}NH_2$$

propionamide
(propanamide)

$$\underset{\text{α-phenylacetamide}}{\bigcirc\!\!-CH_2\overset{\overset{\displaystyle O}{\|}}{C}NH_2}$$

α-phenylacetamide
(2-phenylethanamide)

As before, the **-ic acid** is dropped, and, in this case, the suffix **amide** is added to obtain the common name.

With the amides it is possible to have substituents other than hydrogen attached to nitrogen. To indicate that the group in question is attached to nitrogen, we use *N-* before the group name.

$$CH_3CH_2\overset{\overset{\displaystyle O}{\|}}{C}N\overset{H}{\underset{CH_3}{\diagup}}$$

N-methylpropionamide
(*N*-methylpropanamide)

$$CH_3CH_2\overset{\overset{\displaystyle O}{\|}}{C}NCH_3$$

N-methyl-*N*-phenylpropionamide
(*N*-methyl-*N*-phenylpropanamide)

$$CH_3\overset{}{\underset{\underset{\displaystyle NH_2}{|}}{C}}H\overset{\overset{\displaystyle O}{\|}}{C}NH_2$$

α-aminopropionamide
(2-aminopropanamide)

The use of α to locate substituents on alkyl chains was introduced previously for aryl side chains (p. 132). In fact, it is quite common with the non-IUPAC names. The second carbon from the functional group is β, as illustrated by 3-phenylpropanamide, which would be β-phenylpropionamide. The IUPAC names simply change **-oic acid** to **-amide**, as shown in parentheses.

Very often in the course of preparing new organic compounds, the reactions available do not lead to the particular molecule desired. A good example of this was seen in Chapter 7, when we discussed the use of the Grignard reaction in making *p*-methyl-

benzoic acid. Another might be the synthesis of a monobro-
minated aniline, for you have just seen that the direct reaction
with bromine leads to the tribromo product.

An interesting method of reducing the reactivity of the aniline
molecule for bromination consists in making the corresponding
acetamide, which is considerably less reactive:

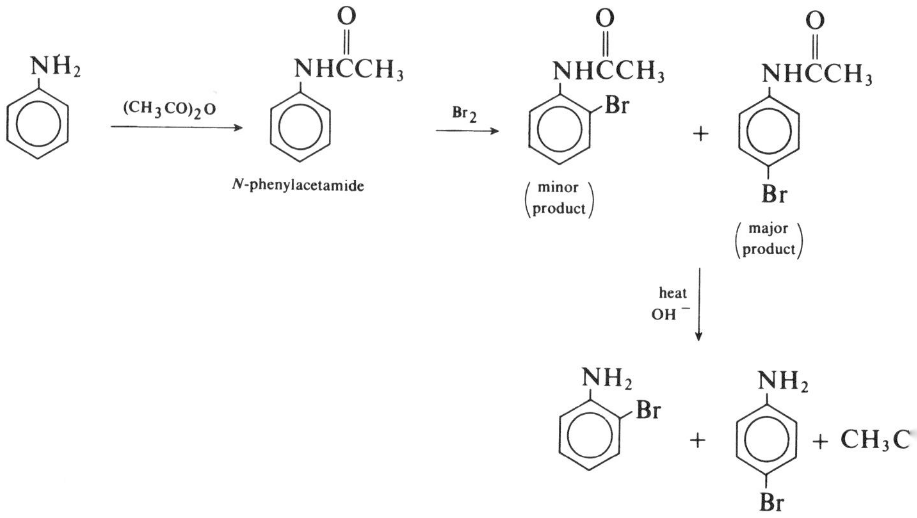

8.10
QUALITATIVE IDENTIFICATION

One of the most important reactions of amines has already been
presented—the formation of salts by neutralization with an acid.
This property is of great importance for the qualitative identification of an unknown amine. First, it explains the characteristic
solubility of water-insoluble amines in 5% hydrochloric acid
solution. Water-soluble amines can usually be identified by
using red litmus paper. Second, it allows their titration and the
calculation of a neutralization equivalent. This method, which
is analogous to that used for the acids (pp. 178–179), provides a
simple laboratory determination of the equivalent weight of the
amine and greatly aids the analyst in determining the structure
of an unknown amine. Titration of amines requires a different
indicator from the phenolphthalein used with acids. Methyl red
or methyl orange is frequently used, the reason being that the

pH of the solution at the endpoint is that of the ammonium salt produced, and, like that of $NH_4^+Cl^-$, lies in the acid pH region.

A useful test for the classification of an unknown amine is the **Hinsberg reaction**. It involves the preparation of a sulfonamide using the acid chloride of benzenesulfonic acid.

benzenesulfonyl chloride   a benzenesulfonamide

Both primary and secondary amines react, whereas tertiary amines do not, thus distinguishing between them. The mono-substituted sulfonamide resulting from a primary amine is soluble in sodium hydroxide solution, but the disubstituted product of a secondary amine is not. The use of these two steps—(1) reaction with benzenesulfonyl chloride in sodium hydroxide solution, and (2) the acidification of the resulting solution—establishes the class of a given amine.

From the preceding equations, it should be clear that the reason for the solubility of the N substituted sulfonamide in NaOH solution is the fact that it can form a salt with its weakly acidic hydrogen attached to nitrogen.

Primary and secondary amines are usually identified by using either the acetamide or the benzamide as a derivative.

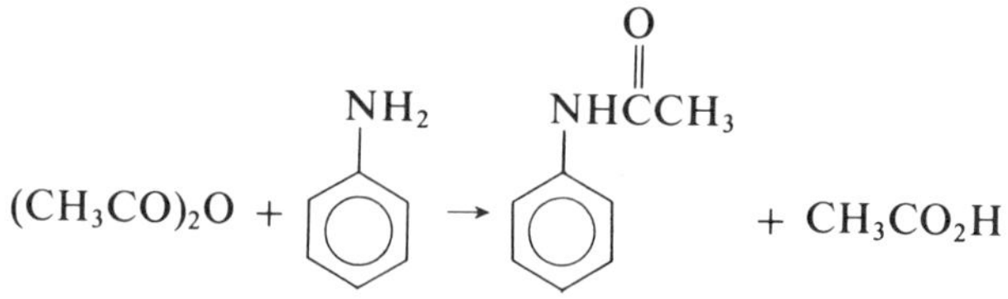

$$(CH_3CO)_2O + \underset{NH_2}{}\text{[phenyl]} \rightarrow \underset{NHCCH_3}{\overset{O}{}}\text{[phenyl]} + CH_3CO_2H$$

N-phenylacetamide
(acetanilide)

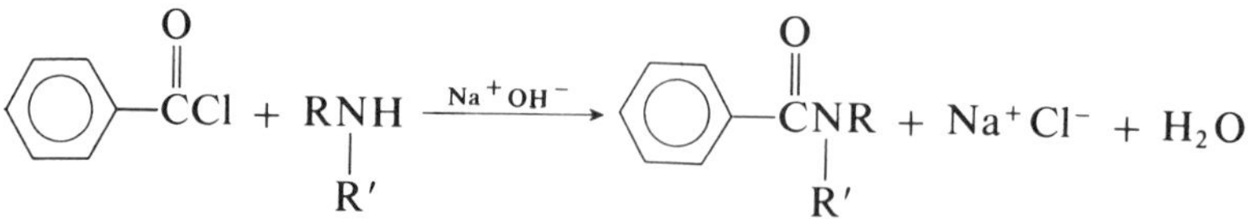

$$\text{[phenyl]}\overset{O}{\underset{}{C}}Cl + \underset{R'}{RNH} \xrightarrow{Na^+OH^-} \text{[phenyl]}\overset{O}{\underset{R'}{C}}NR + Na^+Cl^- + H_2O$$

a benzamide

As indicated in the examples, the formation of amides takes place only with primary and secondary amines, inasmuch as tertiary amines have no hydrogen to be replaced. The most frequently employed derivative of tertiary amines involves a very interesting reaction between the amine and the strongly acidic phenol, picric acid (2,4,6-trinitrophenol).

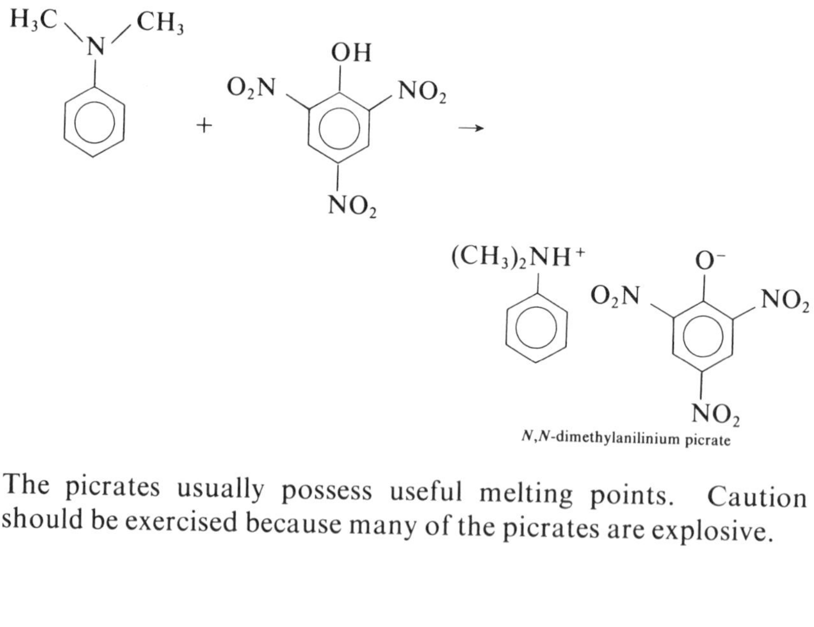

N,N-dimethylanilinium picrate

The picrates usually possess useful melting points. Caution should be exercised because many of the picrates are explosive.

To round out our methods of preparing pure amines, we must introduce one more reaction of amides. With the use of lithium aluminum hydride it is possible to reduce amides to the corresponding amines.

$$
\left.\begin{array}{l}
RCONH_2 \\
RCONH \\
\quad | \\
\quad R' \\
RCON\!-\!R'' \\
\quad | \\
\quad R'
\end{array}\right\} + \xrightarrow[\text{(2) } H_2O]{\text{(1) } LiAlH_4}
\begin{array}{l}
RCH_2NH_2 \\
RCH_2NH \\
\quad | \\
\quad R' \\
RCH_2N\!-\!R'' \\
\quad | \\
\quad R'
\end{array}
$$

Thus, given the proper acid, it is possible to prepare many desired amines, regardless of how many different alkyl or aryl groups are involved.

Ernest Beckmann (German, 1853–1923). Taught at several famous German universities and served as the first director of the Kaiser Wilhelm Institute. He invented a differential thermometer which made possible the precise measurement of small changes in temperature. The rearrangement of oximes to amides and subsequently to amines bears his name and is often a useful method of preparing these compounds.

$$
\begin{array}{c}
R \\
\quad \diagdown \\
\quad\quad C\!=\!N \\
\quad \diagup \qquad \diagdown OH \\
R
\end{array}
\xrightarrow[\text{several steps}]{H^+}
$$

$$
\underset{\displaystyle RCNHR}{\overset{\displaystyle O \atop \displaystyle \|}{}} \xrightarrow[H^+ \text{ or } OH^-]{H_2O}
$$

$$RCO_2H + RNH_2$$

Courtesy of the Edgar Fahs Smith Memorial Collection.

SUGGESTED ADDITIONAL READINGS

Inductive and Resonance Effects

Cason, Chapter 19.
Cram and Hammond, pp. 206–15.
Morrison and Boyd, pp. 599–601 and 745–48.
Roberts and Caserio, pp. 514–17 and 650–52.

N. L. Allinger, "Energy Relations in Teaching Organic Chemistry," *J. Chem. Educ.*, **40,** 201 (1963).

Industrial Methods

Stille, Sections 9.1–9.6.

Qualitative Organic Analysis

Pasto and Johnson, Sections 12.14–12.15.

Shriner, Fuson, and Curtin, various sections dealing with amines and amides.

SUMMARY

1. The most common organic bases are those containing nitrogen in a low oxidation state, that is, the amines (and anilines).

2. The amines may be divided into classes on the basis of the number of groups attached to nitrogen.

3. The basicity of the amines is shown by their salt formation with acids.

$$RNH_2 + HCl \rightarrow RNH_3{}^+Cl^-$$

From this reaction a neutralization equivalent can be obtained.

4. Resonance effects are important in understanding the variations in the basicity of different amines.

5. Some preparations of amines are as follows:

$$RX + NH_3 \rightarrow RNH_2$$

$$RNH_2 + RX \rightarrow R_2NH$$

$$ArNO_2 \xrightarrow{[H]} ArNH_2$$

$$RCN \xrightarrow{LiAlH_4} RCH_2NH_2$$

$$RCONR_2 \xrightarrow{LiAlH_4} RCH_2NR_2$$

6. In addition to the reactions already pointed out, the formation of amides is important.

$$RNH_2 + R'COCl \rightarrow R'CONHR + HCl$$
$$R_2NH + (R'CO)_2O \rightarrow R_2NCOR' + R'CO_2H$$

7. The anhydrides, like the acid chlorides, are reactive acid derivatives useful in further synthesis. They are often prepared using the acid chloride.

$$RCO_2^- Na^+ + RCOCl \rightarrow (RCO)_2O + Na^+ Cl^-$$

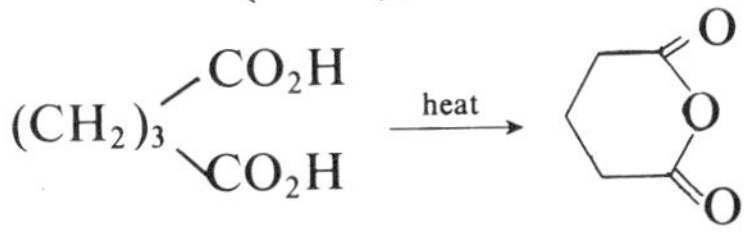

8. Like the aryl methyl ethers, the aryl acetamides are useful in organic synthesis as a protective group.

9. The Hinsberg reaction is useful in deciding the class to which an unknown amine belongs. It involves the reaction (or lack of reaction) of an amine with benzenesulfonyl chloride.

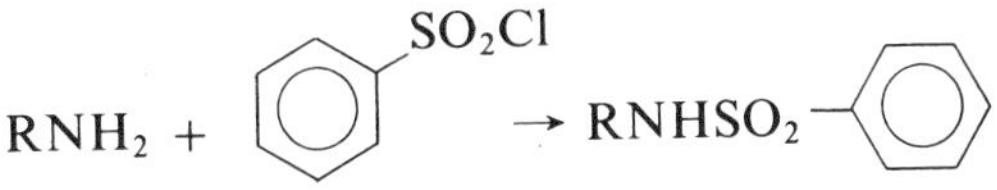

10. The derivatives of primary and secondary amines are usually amides or sulfonamides. Picrates are often used for tertiary amines.

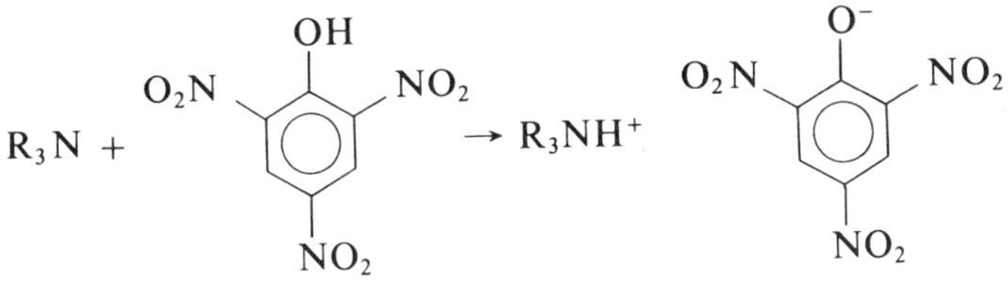

PROBLEMS

1. Give a proper name for each of the following compounds:

   a. CH_3CHNH_2
      $|$
      CH_3

   b.

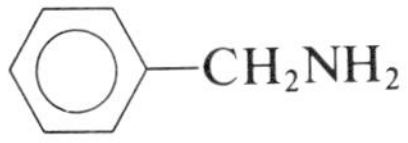

c.

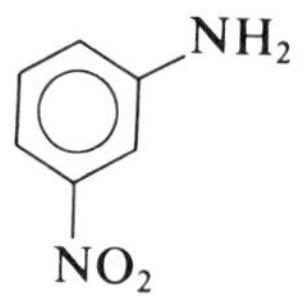

NH_2

NO_2

d. $CH_3CH_2CH_2\overset{\overset{\displaystyle O}{\|}}{C}NHCH_2CH_3$

e. $(CH_3)_3CNHCH_3$

f.

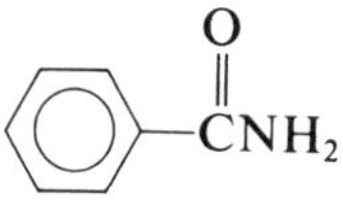

$\overset{\overset{\displaystyle O}{\|}}{C}NH_2$

g. $\underset{NH_2}{\overset{\displaystyle CH_2}{|}}-\underset{NH_2}{\overset{\displaystyle CH_2}{|}}$

h. $CH_3CH_2\underset{\overset{|}{CH_3}}{N}CH(CH_3)_2$

i. $[CH_3CH_2CH_2CH_2\!-\!]_4N^+Cl^-$

j.

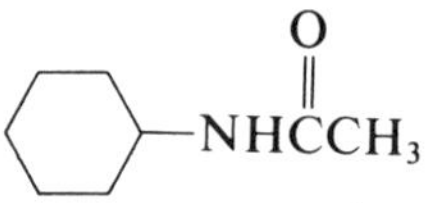

$-NH\overset{\overset{\displaystyle O}{\|}}{C}CH_3$

2. Draw a structure for each of the following compounds:
   a. *N,N*-dibutylacetamide
   b. *N*-methyldiethylamine
   c. diphenylamine
   d. *N*-phenylaniline
   e. *n*-decylamine
   f. 3-chloropropylamine
   g. 2,4-dibromobenzamide
   h. methylpropylhexylamine
   i. trimethylcyclobutylammonium iodide
   j. *N*-chloro-2-naphthylamine

3. Classify each of the amines in questions 1 and 2 as primary, secondary, or tertiary.

4. Complete the following reactions:
   a.

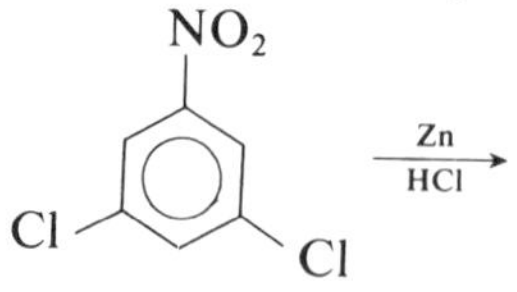

   NO_2

   $\xrightarrow[\text{HCl}]{\text{Zn}}$

   Cl   Cl

b. $CH_3CH_2\overset{\overset{\displaystyle O}{\|}}{\underset{\underset{\displaystyle CH_3}{|}}{CH}}\overset{\displaystyle O}{C}-Cl + CH_3NH_2 \xrightarrow{\text{NaOH}}$

c. $(CH_3)_2CHNH_2 + CH_3I \rightarrow$

d. $CH_3\underset{\underset{\displaystyle \bigcirc}{|}}{CH}NH_2 + CH_3\overset{\overset{\displaystyle O}{\|}}{C}-O-\overset{\overset{\displaystyle O}{\|}}{C}CH_3 \rightarrow$

e. $\underset{\bigcirc}{NH_2} + HCl \rightarrow$

f. $CH_3CH_2\overset{\overset{\displaystyle O}{\|}}{C}-Cl + CH_3NH_2 \xrightarrow{\text{NaOH}}$

g. $CH_3CH_2NH_2 + HCl \xrightarrow{\text{H}_2\text{O}}$

h. (naphthalene with NO_2 substituent) $\xrightarrow{[H]}$

Draw suitable structures for all compounds, name them, and complete all reactions in the following problems 5–10.

5. An organic compound containing nitrogen is reduced and 0.28 g of the product is neutralized with 28.3 ml of 0.1 N HCl.

6. A water-soluble compound has a neutralization equivalent of 73 ± 1. When reacted with benzenesulfonyl chloride in aqueous NaOH, it forms a precipitate.

7. Compound (A) is known to contain chlorine and reacts with ammonia to form compound (B), which reacts with benzene-sulfonyl chloride. When 0.23 g of (B) is neutralized with 0.1 N hydrochloric acid, 21.5 ml are required. Strong oxidation of (B) produces compound (C), which is soluble in 5% sodium bicarbon-ate solution. Titration of 0.28 g of (C) with 0.1 N sodium hydrox-ide requires 22.9 ml.

8. An organic base had a neutralization equivalent of 121 ± 1. Vigorous oxidation of this compound converted it to an acid with a neutralization equivalent of 121 ± 1.

9. Compound (A) is neither acidic nor basic and has a molecular formula $C_5H_{11}ON$. Refluxing with aqueous NaOH produces a new compound (B). Titration of 0.45 g of (B) requires 0.01 mole of hydrochloric acid.

10. An unknown compound (A) was insoluble in water but dissolved in both dilute HCl and NaOH. It contained nitrogen and bromine and would not give a satisfactory neutralization equivalent. Treatment with acetyl chloride converted (A) to a new compound (B), which is in the strong acid class and has a neutralization equivalent of 270 ± 3. When compounds (A) and (B) were oxidized vigorously, compound (C), with a neutralization equivalent of 199 ± 2, was obtained.

11. Given inorganic reagents and alcohols of four carbons or less, how could you convert the following starting material to the required product?
    a. propene to isobutylamine
    b. benzene to N-cyclohexylpropanamide
    c. acetic acid to N,N-diethylacetamide
    d. benzene to N-phenylbenzenesulfonamide
    e. bromobenzene to 1,6-diaminohexane

12. The synthesis of the various isomers of aromatic compounds is an area of organic chemistry requiring skill in selecting the proper sequence of reactions and the appropriate use of protective groups. These facts will be illustrated as you attempt to outline synthetic routes to the following compounds, starting with benzene:
    a. o, m, and p-aminobenzoic acid
    b. o, m, and p-bromoaniline
    c. 2, 3, and α-chloro-4-methylaniline

13. On the basis of resonance and inductive effects, predict the relative order of increasing base strength for the following series of anilines:

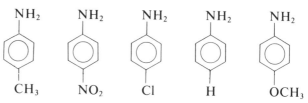

Aldehydes and Ketones

The functional group characteristic of the aldehydes and ketones is an unsaturated linkage involving carbon and oxygen known as the **carbonyl group**. Because of its unsaturation, it will show addition reactions similar to the alkenes, but because of the **heteroatom**,* there will be a difference in the results of such additions.

The extra electrons of the oxygen atom contribute to making the resonance hybrid partly polar. Resonance structures are

$$\underset{/\backslash}{\overset{\overset{\displaystyle O}{\|}}{C}} \longleftrightarrow \underset{/\backslash}{\overset{\overset{\displaystyle O^-}{|}}{C^+}}$$

---

*A heteroatom is defined as a polyvalent atom other than carbon that is not part of a monovalent functional group like OH, OR, NH_2, etc.

The aldehydes take their common names (often used) from the corresponding acid. The **-ic acid** is dropped and **-aldehyde** is added.

$$CH_3CH_2\overset{\overset{\displaystyle O}{\|}}{C}\diagdown H \qquad CH_3CH_2CH_2\overset{\overset{\displaystyle O}{\|}}{C}\diagdown H$$

(CH_3CH_2CHO) $(CH_3CH_2CH_2CHO)$

propionaldehyde   n-butyraldehyde

(propanal)   (butanal)

The ketones are commonly (and usually) designated by simply naming the groups on each side of the carbonyl group and adding the word **ketone**.

$$CH_3\overset{\overset{\displaystyle O}{\|}}{C}CH_2CH_3 \qquad CH_3\overset{\overset{\displaystyle Cl}{|}}{C}H\overset{\overset{\displaystyle O}{\|}}{C}\overset{\overset{\displaystyle Cl}{|}}{C}HCH_3$$

methyl ethyl ketone α,α'-dichlorodiethyl ketone

(2-butanone)   (2,4-dichloro-3-pentanone)

$$\overset{\displaystyle CH_3}{\underset{\displaystyle CH_3}{}}\!\!\diagup\!\!CH\overset{\overset{\displaystyle O}{\|}}{C}\!\!-\!\!\bigcirc \qquad BrCH_2\overset{\overset{\displaystyle O}{\|}}{C}\!\!-\!\!\langle\bigcirc\rangle\!\!-\!\!Br$$

isopropyl cyclohexyl ketone   p-bromophenacyl bromide

(isobutyrylcyclohexane)   (2,4'-dibromoacetophenone)

Inasmuch as the IUPAC names (given in parentheses) are becoming more frequently used, it would be worthwhile to know this system too. The IUPAC names of aldehydes are formed by changing the **-e** of the parent alkane to **-al**. Because the aldehyde group must be at the end of a chain, the number 1 is understood.

$$CH_3\overset{\overset{\displaystyle |}{C}=O}{\underset{\displaystyle H}{|}} \qquad CH_3\overset{\overset{\displaystyle |}{C}HCH_2CH_2\overset{\displaystyle |}{C}=O}{\underset{\displaystyle CH_3 \qquad H}{}} \qquad ClCH_2CH_2\overset{\overset{\displaystyle |}{C}=O}{\underset{\displaystyle H}{|}}$$

acetaldehyde   isovaleraldehyde β-chloropropionaldehyde

(ethanal)   (4-methylpentanal)   (3-chloropropanal)

The IUPAC names of ketones require the change of the **-e** of the parent alkane to **-one**. With these compounds it is necessary to

show the position of the carbonyl group by number. Note the
exceptions in the cyclic example, where 1 is assumed.

$$CH_3CH_2\overset{\overset{\textstyle O}{\|}}{C}CH_2CH_3 \qquad CH_3\overset{\overset{\textstyle O}{\|}}{\underset{\overset{\textstyle |}{CH_3}}{C}H}C\overset{}{\underset{\overset{\textstyle |}{CH_3}}{C}H}CH_3$$

diethyl ketone   diisopropyl ketone   IUPAC only
(3-pentanone)   (2,4-dimethyl-3-pentanone)   (3-methylcyclohexanone)

9.3
PHYSICAL PROPERTIES OF THE ALDEHYDES AND KETONES
(TABLE 9.1)

Because of the polar nature of the carbonyl group, the aldehydes
and ketones have higher boiling points than hydrocarbons of the
same molecular weight; for example, only the simplest compound, formaldehyde, is a gas at room temperature. On the
other hand, they do not form hydrogen bonds as readily as the
acids and alcohols. For this and other physical reasons, the
simple carbonyl compounds change state at lower temperatures
than either of these classes of compounds.

For similar reasons, the solubility of the carbonyl compounds
in polar solvents such as water is intermediate between related
hydroxyl and carboxyl compounds. Table 9.2 shows a comparison of these physical properties for the four types of structural arrangement.

One of the outstanding physical properties of both aldehydes
and ketones is their odor. Whereas some of the very volatile
lower homologs have rather sharp and unpleasant odors—
often because of traces of acids, for example, acetone, acetaldehyde, butyraldehyde—most of the higher molecular weight compounds have very pleasant aromas. In some cases, they are very
fragrant and make up the characteristic scent of many plant
extracts. Vanillin, 3-methoxy-4-hydroxybenzaldehyde, is a good
example; another is "Exaltone," cyclopentadecanone, which is
widely used in fine perfumes.

TABLE 9.1 PHYSICAL PROPERTIES OF SOME COMMON ALDEHYDES AND KETONES

Name	Formula	Boiling point, °C*	Melting point, °C	Solubility,† g/100 ml H_2O	Density,† g/ml
Formaldehyde	HCHO	−21	−92	very soluble	0.815 (−20°)
Acetaldehyde	CH_3CHO	20	−121	miscible	0.783 (18°)
Propionaldehyde	CH_3CH_2CHO	49	−81	16	0.807
Butyraldehyde	$CH_3(CH_2)_2CHO$	76	−99	7	0.817
Benzaldehyde	C_6H_5CHO	178	−26	0.3	1.042 (25°)
Vanillin	$3\text{-}CH_3O\text{-}4\text{-}HOC_6H_3CHO$	285 (in CO_2)	82	1	1.056
p-Hydroxybenz-aldehyde	$p\text{-}HOC_6H_4CHO$	sublimes	116	1.4	1.129 (130°)
Acetone	$(CH_3)_2CO$	56	−95	miscible	0.79
2-Pentanone	$CH_3COCH_2CH_2CH_3$	102	−78	6.3	0.812 (15°)
3-Pentanone	$CH_3CH_2COCH_2CH_3$	103	−42	5	0.816 (19°)
Acetophenone	$C_6H_5COCH_3$	202	21	insoluble	1.028
Benzophenone	$(C_6H_5)_2CO$	306	48(α)**, 26(β)	insoluble	(α)1.146 (20°), (β)1.108
Cyclopentadecanone	$(CH_2)_{14}CO$	120(0.3 mm)	63	slightly soluble	0.890

*Boiling point is at 760 mm, unless indicated otherwise.

†Solubility and density data are given at 20°C, except as indicated otherwise.

**Crystallizes in two different forms, rhombic and monoclinic.

**TABLE 9.2   COMPARISON OF PHYSICAL PROPERTIES
OF VARIOUS FUNCTIONAL GROUPS**

Name	Formula	Molecular weight	Boiling point, °C	Solubility,* g/100 ml H_2O	Density,* g/ml
1-Butanol	$CH_3(CH_2)_3OH$	74	118	7.9	0.810
Butyraldehyde	$CH_3(CH_2)_2CHO$	72	76	3.7	0.817
2-Butanone	$CH_3COCH_2CH_3$	72	80	26	0.805
Butyric acid	$CH_3(CH_2)_2CO_2H$	88	164	5.6 (−1°)	0.959
Propionic acid	$CH_3CH_2CO_2H$	74	141	miscible	0.992

*Solubility and density data are given at 20°C, except as indicated otherwise.

**9.4
PREPARATION**

The preparation of aldehydes and ketones frequently makes use of one of the following methods:

1. oxidation of alcohols;
2. decarboxylation of acids;
3. acylation;
4. dehydrogenation;
5. miscellaneous reactions.

9.4A   Oxidation of Alcohols

The oxidation of primary alcohols under the proper conditions yields aldehydes. The oxidation of secondary alcohols yields ketones.

$$CH_3CH_2CH_2OH \xrightarrow{[O]} CH_3CH_2CHO$$

$$\underset{\underset{OH}{|}}{CH_3CHCH_3} \xrightarrow{[O]} \underset{\underset{O}{\parallel}}{CH_3CCH_3}$$

The oxidizing agents commonly used are potassium dichromate or potassium permanganate.* Aldehydes are very readily oxidized, even more readily than the alcohols from which they are derived, and they will oxidize to the acid.

*When testing for unsaturation with dilute $KMnO_4$ (Baeyer test), you must be aware that any oxidizable substance will decolorize the solution—for example, primary and secondary alcohols and aldehydes.

$$RCHO \xrightarrow{[O]} RCO_2H$$

The aldehydes, however, usually have lower boiling points than the corresponding alcohol; therefore, they may be distilled from the oxidation mixture as they are formed. For example,

$$CH_3CH_2CH_2CH_2OH \xrightarrow[H^+]{K_2Cr_2O_7} CH_3CH_2CH_2CHO$$
$$\text{b.p.} = 118°C \qquad\qquad\qquad\qquad \text{b.p.} = 76°C$$

Thus, if the reaction is carried out at a temperature above 76°C and below 118°C, and if the apparatus is connected to a condenser, the product can be collected before it has an opportunity to be oxidized to butyric acid. The oxidant is added slowly to the alcohol at the same rate as the distillation of the aldehyde; thus, an excess of oxidizing agent is avoided.

9.4B Decarboxylation of Acids

You will recall that when salts of acids are heated in the dry state, ketones are formed:

$$
\begin{array}{c}
CH_3CO_2^- \\
\qquad\qquad Ca^{+2} \xrightarrow{\text{heat}} \\
CH_3CO_2^-
\end{array}
\quad
\begin{array}{c}
CH_3 \\
\qquad C{=}O + CaCO_3 \\
CH_3
\end{array}
$$

Another technique involves passing the vapor of the acid over hot solid thorium or manganese dioxide.

$$2\,CH_3CO_2H \xrightarrow[\text{heat}]{ThO_2} CH_3\overset{\overset{\displaystyle O}{\|}}{C}CH_3 + CO_2 + H_2O$$

This procedure is useful only for preparing symmetrical ketones. The reaction is especially practical for certain cyclic ketones starting with dicarboxylic acids.

$$
\begin{array}{c}
CO_2H \\
| \\
(CH_2)_n \xrightarrow[\text{heat}]{BaO} (CH_2)_n \quad C{=}O \\
| \\
CO_2H
\end{array}
$$
$$n = 4, 5 \text{ for highest yields}$$

9.4C Acylation

The Friedel-Crafts reaction was previously utilized to attach alkyl side chains to an aromatic nucleus (**alkylation**).

Anhydrous aluminum chloride was used as a catalyst. A similar procedure (**acylation**) may be employed to produce ketones (either aryl-alkyl or aryl-aryl) by using an acid halide:

The chief limitation of these reactions is that the ring being substituted upon must be activated; for example,

9.4D Dehydrogenation

By passing alcohol vapors over a hot copper gauze, it is possible to carry out a reaction that appears to be the same as the oxidation presented earlier:

$$RCH_2OH \xrightarrow[\text{heat}]{Cu} RCHO + H_2$$

$$\underset{\displaystyle RCHR'}{\overset{\displaystyle OH}{|}} \xrightarrow[\text{heat}]{Cu} \underset{\displaystyle RCR'}{\overset{\displaystyle O}{\|}} + H_2$$

The reactions actually involve fundamentally different chemistry; it simply happens that the same products result. In the case of the conversion of the primary alcohol to an aldehyde, the resulting advantage of avoiding oxidation to an acid by the use of hot copper mesh is very desirable.

9.4E Miscellaneous Reactions for the Preparation of Carbonyl Compounds

Certain arrangements of atoms are unstable under normal conditions. Two are of special interest in the preparation of aldehydes and ketones.

1. *The 1,1-Chlorohydrin.* The presence of a chlorine and a hydroxyl group on the same carbon atom will, with most organic systems, result in the spontaneous loss of a molecule of hydrogen chloride and the introduction of a carbon-oxygen double bond. Thus, if a reaction might be expected to lead to such a **1,1-chlorohydrin**, it will not form, and the corresponding carbonyl compound is the product obtained:

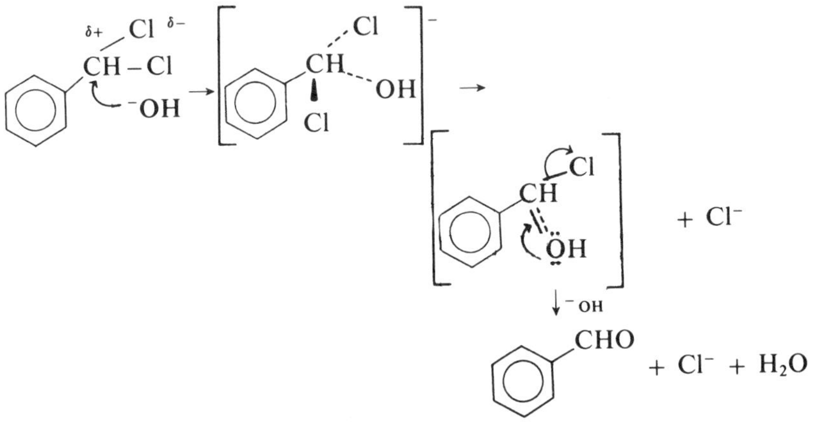

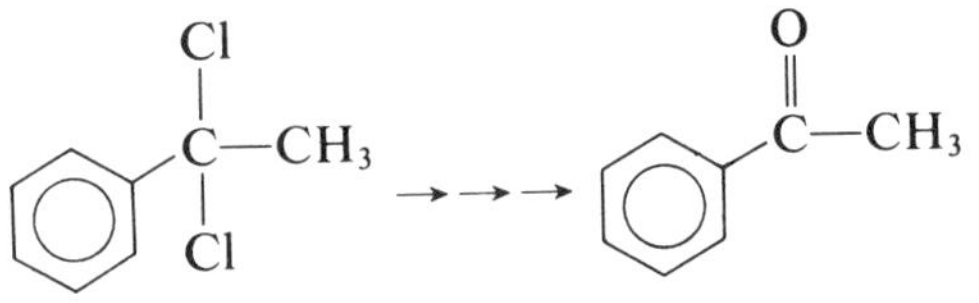

Inasmuch as there are a number of good methods for preparing the aromatic *gem*-dichloro compounds, this method represents a useful approach to several types of aldehydes and phenones (ArCR).
$\overset{\|}{O}$

$$ArC\equiv CH + 2\ HCl \rightarrow ArC\overset{\overset{\displaystyle Cl}{|}}{\underset{\underset{\displaystyle Cl}{|}}{C}}CH_3$$

$$ArCH_2R + Cl_2 \xrightarrow{h\nu} ArC(Cl)_2R$$

2. *The Enol.* The fact that a hydroxyl group attached to a carbon involved in a double bond tends to rearrange to the more stable keto or aldehyde form has been discussed and should be reviewed at this point (p. 91). Such hydration of triple bonds is a useful preparation of acetaldehyde and methyl ketones. Observe that disubstituted alkynes produce a mixture of ketones; thus, they would be used only if no other satisfactory route to the desired ketone were available:

$$CH_3CH_2C{\equiv}CCH_3 + H_2O \xrightarrow[H_2SO_4]{Hg^{+2}} CH_3CH_2COCH_2CH_3$$

$$+ CH_3CH_2CH_2COCH_3$$

An obvious exception is the use of symmetrically substituted alkynes that yield a single product:

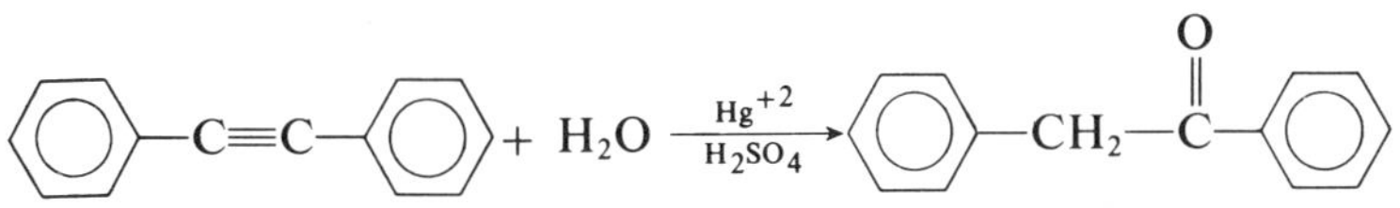

9.5
REACTIONS

The reactions of carbonyl compounds are of three general types:

1. reduction;
2. oxidation;
3. addition.

9.5A   Reduction

Aldehydes or ketones may be reduced in the presence of a catalyst to yield alcohols. Aldehydes are reduced to primary alcohols and ketones are reduced to secondary alcohols, which is the reverse of a preparative method.

$$RCHO \xrightarrow[Ni, Pt, etc.]{[H]} RCH_2OH$$

$$\underset{R'}{\overset{R}{\diagdown}}C{=}O \xrightarrow[Ni, Pt, etc.]{[H]} \underset{R'}{\overset{R}{\diagdown}}CHOH$$

In addition to the catalytic method shown in the preceding general reactions, the metal hydrides are very useful reagents for effecting these reductions. Not only can lithium aluminum hydride be employed, but the milder sodium borohydride is especially important. This latter hydride, because it is not as reactive, allows us to reduce selectively carbonyl groups without touching esters, amides, and so on, in the same molecule:

$$CH_3\overset{\overset{\textstyle O}{\|}}{C}CH_2CH_2CO_2CH_2CH_3 + NaBH_4 \rightarrow$$

$$CH_3\overset{\overset{\textstyle OH}{|}}{C}HCH_2CH_2CO_2CH_2CH_3$$

The advantages of this method are obvious, in that many compounds which would be impossible to prepare by the usual reductive methods are available in high yield.

9.5B Oxidation

By using the usual oxidizing agents, we oxidize aldehydes to the corresponding acids.

$$RCHO \xrightarrow{\text{[O]}} RCO_2H$$

Ketones are not readily oxidized.

$$\overset{R}{\underset{R}{>}}C=O \xrightarrow{\text{[O]}} \text{no reaction}$$

Mild oxidizing agents, such as Ag^+ or Cu^{+2} ions in alkaline solution, will readily oxidize aldehydes, whereas much stronger reagents capable of breaking carbon-carbon bonds are required to oxidize ketones. These latter reagents and ketones do not lead to useful laboratory processes. Some industrial and analytical use is made of the products. The difference in the ease of oxidation of the two subclasses of carbonyl compounds is one of the best methods for their qualitative analysis, and we shall have more to say about them later in this chapter.

9.5C Addition Reactions

Addition reactions of the aldehydes and ketones may be summarized in the following equation:

$$R\overset{\overset{\textstyle O}{\|}}{C}H(R') + HY \rightarrow R\overset{\overset{\textstyle OH}{|}}{\underset{\underset{\textstyle Y}{|}}{C}}H(R')$$

The following are typical examples of HY (as indicated earlier, Y ≠ OH or halogen, except in rare cases):

H—CN   hydrogen cyanide
H—NHOH   hydroxylamine

H—NHNH—⬡   phenylhydrazine

H—CHCHO   aldehydes or ketones
    | containing an α-hydrogen
    R

In each case, the hydrogen becomes attached to the oxygen of the carbonyl group, converting the double bond to a single bond. Grignard reagents (RMgX) and sodium bisulfite ($Na^+HSO_3^-$) also add to carbonyl groups in a superficially different manner (see parts 4 and 5).

1. Hydrogen cyanide adds to aldehydes, methyl, and cyclic ketones (but not other ketones) to form cyanohydrins. The failure with higher ketones is because **steric crowding** results in an unfavorable equilibrium value for product.

$$
\underset{}{\overset{O}{\overset{\|}{CH_3CH}}} + HCN \rightleftharpoons \underset{\underset{CN}{|}}{\overset{OH}{\overset{|}{CH_3CH}}}
$$

acetaldehyde
cyanohydrin

These compounds are useful for preparing α-hydroxy acids because the cyano group is readily hydrolyzed.

$$
RCN \xrightarrow[\text{H}^+]{2H_2O} \overset{O}{\overset{\|}{RCOH}} + NH_4^+
$$

$$
\underset{CH_3CHCN}{\overset{OH}{\overset{|}{CH_3CHCN}}} + H_3O^+ \xrightarrow{H_2O} \underset{CH_3CHCO_2H}{\overset{OH}{\overset{|}{CH_3CHCO_2H}}}
$$

Care must be taken to avoid the elimination of H_2O:

$$
\underset{CH_3CHCO_2H}{\overset{OH}{\overset{|}{CH_3CHCO_2H}}} \xrightarrow{H^+} CH_2\!=\!CHCO_2H
$$

acrylic acid

2. Hydroxylamine and phenylhydrazine add to either aldehydes or ketones in the normal manner. The products are not usually stable and lose the elements of water (in several steps) to yield oximes and phenylhydrazones.

$$
\underset{\text{O}}{\overset{\text{O}}{\underset{\|}{CH_3\overset{\|}{C}H}}} + H{-}\overset{H}{\underset{|}{N}}OH \rightarrow \left[CH_3\overset{HO}{\underset{|}{C}}H\overset{H}{\underset{|}{N}}OH \right] \xrightarrow[\text{(2) }-\text{OH}^-]{\text{(1) }-\text{H}^+} CH_3CH{=}NOH
$$

acetaldehyde oxime

$$
CH_3\overset{\text{O}}{\underset{\underset{CH_3}{|}}{\overset{\|}{C}}} + H{-}NNH{-}\bigcirc \rightarrow
$$

$$
\left[CH_3\overset{HO}{\underset{\underset{CH_3}{|}}{\overset{|}{C}}}{-}\overset{H}{\underset{|}{N}}NH{-}\bigcirc \right] \xrightarrow[\text{(2) }-\text{OH}^-]{\text{(1) }-\text{H}^+} CH_3\overset{}{\underset{\underset{CH_3}{|}}{C}}{=}NNH{-}\bigcirc
$$

acetone phenylhydrazone

These addition compounds, and other similar ones, are useful in the preparation of carbonyl derivatives.

3. Aldehydes or ketones containing an *alpha* hydrogen may add to another carbonyl group in dilute alkali. The reaction is called an **aldol condensation*** (water does not often split out spontaneously). An aldol is a reasonably stable compound.

$$
\underset{\text{O}}{\overset{\text{O}}{\underset{\|}{CH_3\overset{\|}{C}H}}} + H{-}\underset{\text{O}}{\overset{\text{O}}{\underset{\|}{CH_2\overset{\|}{C}H}}} \xrightarrow{\text{dilute OH}^-} CH_3\overset{OH}{\underset{|}{C}}H CH_2\overset{\text{O}}{\overset{\|}{C}}H
$$

aldol (relatively stable)

$$
\downarrow \overset{\text{H}^+ \quad -\text{H}_2\text{O}}{\text{heat}}
$$

$$
CH_3CH{=}CHCHO
$$

crotonaldehyde

Many aldol condensations, which might appear to be good preparative methods, fail to produce useful yields of dimeric† product. The chief reason in cases such as the example given is

---

*Reactions that involve joining of two molecules by the formation of a new bond are called addition reactions. Frequently, the addition is followed by the loss of some simple molecule, such as water; the reaction is then called a **condensation reaction**.

†A dimer is a molecule produced by the addition or condensation of two identical molecules.

that the product (aldol) still has hydrogen on the α-carbon and can undergo further condensation to yield polymers.

Another reaction of some importance that depends on the reactivity of the hydrogens adjacent to a carbonyl group is the halogenation of the α-carbon. This reaction takes place easily in the presence of dilute base:

$$CH_3CH_2CHO + Cl_2 \xrightarrow[\text{base}]{\text{dilute}} CH_3\overset{\overset{\displaystyle Cl}{|}}{C}HCHO \xrightarrow{Cl_2} CH_3\overset{\overset{\displaystyle Cl}{|}}{\underset{\underset{\displaystyle Cl}{|}}{C}}\!\!-CHO$$

Depending on the conditions employed, either one or two halogens may be introduced. Under slightly more vigorous conditions, this reaction has important uses in qualitative identification (p. 233).

4. Grignard reagents add to the carbonyl group, and subsequent hydrolysis yields alcohols. Formaldehyde yields primary alcohols, all other aldehydes yield secondary alcohols, and ketones yield tertiary alcohols.

$$H\overset{\|}{\underset{O}{C}}H + RMgX \xrightarrow[\text{ether}]{\text{absolute}} H\overset{\overset{\displaystyle R}{|}}{\underset{\underset{\displaystyle OMgX}{|}}{C}}H \xrightarrow{H_2O} H\overset{\overset{\displaystyle R}{|}}{\underset{\underset{\displaystyle OH}{|}}{C}}H$$

(primary alcohol – 1°)

$$R'\overset{\|}{\underset{O}{C}}H + RMgX \xrightarrow[\text{(THF)}]{\text{absolute ether}} R'\overset{\overset{\displaystyle R}{|}}{\underset{\underset{\displaystyle OMgX}{|}}{C}}H \xrightarrow{H_2O} R'\overset{\overset{\displaystyle R}{|}}{\underset{\underset{\displaystyle OH}{|}}{C}}H$$

(secondary alcohol – 2°)

$$R'\overset{\|}{\underset{O}{C}}R'' + RMgX \xrightarrow[\text{THF}]{\text{absolute}} R'\overset{\overset{\displaystyle R}{|}}{\underset{\underset{\displaystyle OMgX}{|}}{C}}R'' \xrightarrow{H_2O} R'\overset{\overset{\displaystyle R}{|}}{\underset{\underset{\displaystyle OH}{|}}{C}}R''$$

(tertiary alcohol – 3°)

In theory, the proper Grignard reagent and the proper aldehyde or ketone are all that is required to make any alcohol. In practice, there are certain limitations, but the generalization is true enough to make this synthetic method one of the most important ever developed.

One further application of the Grignard reagent to the preparation of alcohols involves the cyclic ethers or epoxides (pp. 158–159).

$$RMgX + CH_2\!\!-\!\!CH_2 \xrightarrow[\text{(2) } H_2O]{\text{(1) absolute ether}} RCH_2CH_2OH$$

It provides a method of increasing the chain length by two carbon atoms at a time, and it supplements other preparations of primary alcohols—for example, reduction of acids (p. 177) and hydroboration (p. 84).

5. A final addition reaction of value both in the separation and identification of organic compounds involves a carbonyl compound and the inorganic salt sodium bisulfite:

$$\underset{R}{\overset{R'}{\diagdown}}C\!\!=\!\!O + Na^+HSO_3^- \rightleftharpoons R'\underset{R}{\overset{OH}{\underset{|}{\overset{|}{C}}}}SO_3^-Na^+$$

The concentration of product at equilibrium is very dependent on the structure of the carbonyl compound. This fact allows two important applications of the reaction: (1) a qualitative indication of structure (p. 232); and (2) the separation of two carbonyl

Courtesy of the Edgar Fahs Smith Memorial Collection.

F. A. Victor Grignard *(French, 1871–1935). The reagent which bears his name was actually discovered by his professor at the University of Lyons (P. A. Barbier). He introduced Grignard to the subject of magnesium organic halides and asked him to study it further. For a time the reaction was known as the Barbier-Grignard reaction, but Barbier insisted that all of the credit for its development should go to his student.*

compounds of different structure (because of the water solubility of the salt). You should note that the bisulfite addition product is the sodium salt of an α-hydroxysulfonic acid.

9.6
QUALITATIVE IDENTIFICATION OF CARBONYL COMPOUNDS

Inasmuch as they are neutral compounds, the ketones and aldehydes will show solubility in water (less than five carbon atoms) or concentrated sulfuric acid. Therefore, it is necessary at first to distinguish them from the alcohols. One useful method of doing so is to treat the suspected carbonyl compound with a freshly prepared solution of 2,4-dinitrophenylhydrazine:

$$\begin{array}{c} R' \\ R \end{array}\!\!\!C{=}O \ + \ H_2NNH{-}\!\!\langle\bigcirc\rangle\!\!{-}NO_2 \ \rightarrow$$

$$\text{NO}_2$$

$$\begin{array}{c} R' \\ R \end{array}\!\!\!C{=}NNH{-}\!\!\langle\bigcirc\rangle\!\!{-}NO_2 \ + \ H_2O$$

$$\text{NO}_2$$

a 2,4-dinitrophenylhydrazone

Bernhard C. G. Tollens *(German, 1841–1918). Professor of chemistry at the University of Göttingen and interested in the structure of the sugars. It was his work in this area which led to the development of ammoniacal silver nitrate in order to distinguish between carbonyl groups of ketones and aldehydes. Although this reagent does have limitations, it is applicable to many simple carbonyl compounds in addition to the sugars.*

Courtesy of the Edgar Fahs Smith Memorial Collection.

It has been found that this reagent reacts with a very wide variety of carbonyl compounds to give the product shown. This hydrazone is, in nearly all cases, a brightly colored solid, with a sharp melting point, that forms in a very short time.

Once it has been shown that a carbonyl group is present in the unknown, an attempt must be made to distinguish between aldehydes and ketones. As was indicated earlier, the ease of oxidation of aldehydes represents one effective method of determining whether the carbonyl group is present as an aldehyde or ketone. Three common reagents are in use for making this test. **Fehling's** and **Benedict's solutions** contain cupric ions in aqueous sodium hydroxide. **Tollens' reagent** contains silver ions as the diammonia silver complex ions. In oxidizing aldehydes, the cupric (Cu^{+2}) ion is reduced to the cuprous (Cu^{+}) ion. A precipitate of red Cu_2O indicates a positive test.

$$RCHO + 2\,Cu(OH)_2 + Na^+OH^- \rightarrow RCO_2^-\,Na^+ + Cu_2O\!\downarrow + 3\,H_2O$$

In the Tollens' test, the silver ion is reduced to metallic silver and deposits a silver mirror on the glass test tube.

$$RCHO + 2\,Ag(NH_3)_2^+ + 2\,OH^- \rightarrow RCO_2^-NH_4^+ + 2\,Ag\!\downarrow$$
$$+ H_2O + 3\,NH_3$$

The cupric ion test is valid only for certain substituted aliphatic aldehydes (pp. 247–248). The silver ion test works for both aliphatic and aromatic aldehydes.

In the identification of ketones and aldehydes, we are fortunate enough to have available several reactions that will give rather specific information about the structure of the unknown compound. The first of these is the **bisulfite addition reaction**. As indicated earlier, the extent of reaction at equilibrium depends on the structure of the carbonyl compound. It happens that aldehydes and methyl (except for aryl methyl) ketones react to a large extent, whereas more highly branched ketones (even ethyl) react to only a very limited extent. Thus, the rapid formation of the usually crystalline addition compound is good evidence that a compound with one of these structural features is present. An outstanding exception is the class of cyclic ketones. Apparently the approximately planar geometry of the ring is such that the greater bulk does not effectively retard addition of bisulfite.

The further reaction with sodium cyanide is frequently a convenient route to the cyanohydrins.

Another reaction that helps to establish the structure of an unknown organic compound is an application of the halogenation of the α-carbon. When this reaction is carried out in the presence of sodium hydroxide, and the unknown contains a methyl group adjacent to a carbonyl group, a carbon-carbon bond is broken, as shown:

$$CH_3\overset{O}{\overset{\|}{C}}R + 3I_2 \xrightarrow{Na^+OH^-} CI_3\overset{O}{\overset{\|}{C}}R \xrightarrow{Na^+OH^-} CHI_3\downarrow + RCO_2^-Na^+$$

This **haloform test** is most usefully carried out with iodine, because the solid iodoform (which precipitates) is readily observed and can be characterized by its melting point.

The iodoform test will be positive for acetaldehyde and any methyl ketone. The most important addition is a number of secondary alcohols in which the carbon atom with the hydroxyl group (the carbinol group) is adjacent to a methyl group. The sodium hypoiodite formed is a strong enough oxidizing agent to produce the required methyl ketone:

$$2\,Na^+OH^- + I_2 \rightarrow Na^+OI^- + Na^+I^- + H_2O$$

$$\underset{RCHCH_3}{\overset{OH}{\overset{|}{}}} \xrightarrow[Na^+OI^-]{[O]} \left[R\overset{O}{\overset{\|}{C}}CH_3\right] \rightarrow CHI_3 + RCO_2^-Na^+$$

This reaction can, like many others, by very useful if accompanied by other data. Consider the iodoform reaction with ethanol and predict the observation you would make.

9.7
PREPARATION OF CARBONYL DERIVATIVES

The oximes and phenylhydrazones formed by the condensation of hydroxylamine and phenylhydrazine with carbonyl compounds are both useful derivatives. However, there are a number of cases in which the product is an oil, and, therefore, not satisfactory as a derivative. The chemical test suggested for the carbonyl group, the 2,4-dinitrophenylhydrazone formation, is also a fine derivative. By using the same basic reaction, but with this reagent of higher molecular weight, it is possible to avoid oils in nearly all cases. The rapid reaction, the high yields, and the ease of recrystallization make it one of the most generally useful of all derivatives.

One other derivative is in common use—the semicarbazone. This derivative represents still another slight modification of the addition of ammonia-derived substances to carbonyl compounds.

$$\underset{R'}{\overset{R}{>}}C{=}O + H_2NNH\overset{\overset{\displaystyle O}{\|}}{C}NH_2 \rightarrow \underset{R'}{\overset{R}{>}}C{=}NNH\overset{\overset{\displaystyle O}{\|}}{C}NH_2 + H_2O$$

semicarbazide   a semicarbazone

Like the 2,4-dinitrophenylhydrazone, semicarbazones possess most of the desirable attributes for the characterization of organic unknowns.

SUGGESTED ADDITIONAL READINGS

Carbonyl Compounds

Cason, Chapter 15.
Gutsche.
Morrison and Boyd, Chapters 19 and 27.
Roberts and Caserio, Chapters 14–15.

R. V. Cash, "Nucleophilic Reactions at Trigonally Bonded Carbon," *J. Chem. Educ.*, **41**, 108 (1964).

O. H. Wheeler, "The Girard Reagents," *J. Chem. Educ.*, **45**, 435 (1968).

Industrial Methods

Stille, Chapter 7.

Qualitative Organic Analysis

Pasto and Johnson, Section 12.7.

Shriner, Fuson, and Curtin, various sections dealing with carbonyl compounds.

SUMMARY

1. The polarization of the carbonyl group helps to understand many of the reactions of aldehydes and ketones.

$$\overset{\delta+}{\underset{}{>}}C=O^{\delta-}$$

2. Some methods of preparation of carbonyl compounds are

$$\left.\begin{array}{c} RCH_2OH \\ R_2CHOH \end{array}\right\} \xrightarrow{[O]} \left\{\begin{array}{c} RCHO \\ R_2C=O \end{array}\right. \quad \begin{array}{l} \text{Dehydrogenation with Cu is} \\ \text{preferred in many cases} \end{array}$$

$$(RCO_2^-)_2Ca^{+2} \xrightarrow{\text{heat}} R_2C=O + CaCO_3$$

$$ArH \xrightarrow[AlCl_3]{RCOCl} ArCOR$$

$$RC\equiv CH + H_2O \xrightarrow[H^+]{Hg^{+2}} R\overset{\overset{\displaystyle O}{\|}}{C}CH_3$$

$$ArCHCl_2 \xrightarrow{OH^-} ArCHO$$

3. The following represent some typical carbonyl reactions:

$$\left.\begin{array}{c} RCHO \\ R_2C=O \end{array}\right\} \xrightarrow{[H]} \left\{\begin{array}{c} RCH_2OH \\ R_2CHOH \end{array}\right. \quad \begin{array}{l} \text{Especially the use of NaBH}_4- \\ \text{very mild conditions.} \end{array}$$

$$RCHO \xrightarrow{[O]} RCO_2H$$

$$R\overset{\overset{\displaystyle O}{\|}}{C}H(R') + HY \rightarrow R\overset{\overset{\displaystyle OH}{|}}{\underset{\underset{\displaystyle Y}{|}}{C}}H(R')$$

$$HY = HCN, H_2NOH, H_2NNH-\langle\bigcirc\rangle, RCH_2CHO, Na^+HSO_3^-$$

4. Some of the addition reactions of carbonyl compounds are followed by a more or less easy dehydration

$$RCHO + H_2NOH \rightarrow \left[\begin{array}{c} OH \\ | \\ R\overset{}{C}HNHOH \end{array} \right] \rightarrow RCH=NOH$$

$$\overset{O}{\overset{\|}{RCR'}} + H_2NNH-\text{⬡} \rightarrow \left[\begin{array}{c} R \\ \diagdown \\ R' \diagup \end{array} \overset{OH}{\underset{|}{C}}-NHNH-\text{⬡} \right] \rightarrow$$

$$\begin{array}{c} R \\ \diagdown \\ R' \diagup \end{array} C=NNH-\text{⬡}$$

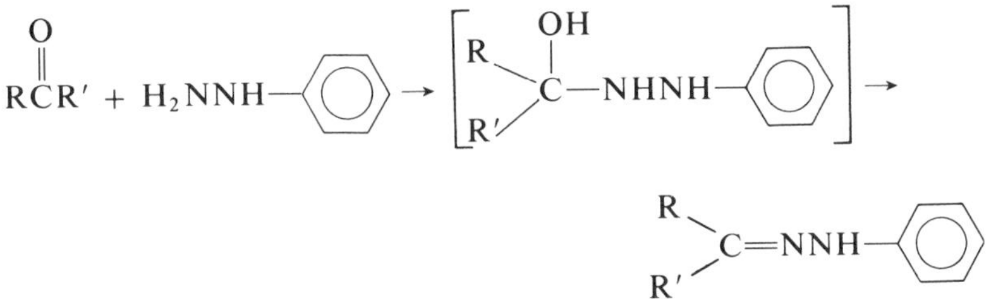

5. One of the most frequent uses of the Grignard reaction is in the preparation of alcohols from carbonyl compounds.

$$\left. \begin{array}{l} H_2C=O + RMgX \rightarrow RCH_2OH \\ RCHO + RMgX \rightarrow R_2CHOH \\ R_2C=O + RMgX \rightarrow R_3COH \end{array} \right\} \quad \text{after hydrolysis}$$

6. The carbonyl compounds are often identified by their characteristic condensation reaction with 2,4-dinitrophenylhydrazine.

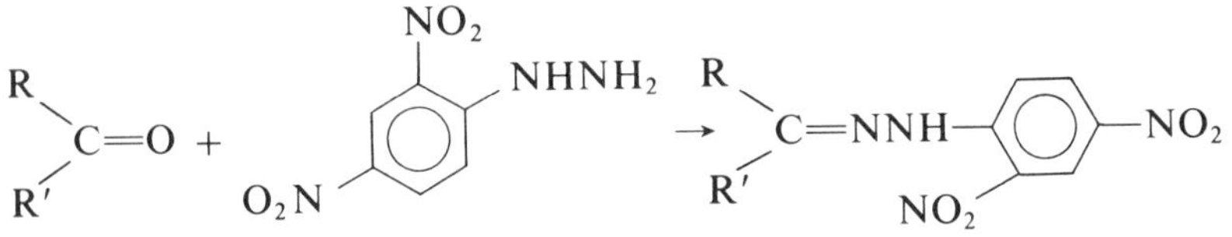

$$\begin{array}{c} R \\ \diagdown \\ R' \diagup \end{array} C=O + \quad \underset{O_2N}{\overset{NO_2}{\text{⬡}}}\text{-NHNH}_2 \rightarrow \begin{array}{c} R \\ \diagdown \\ R' \diagup \end{array} C=NNH-\underset{NO_2}{\text{⬡}}-NO_2$$

The resulting 2,4-dinitrophenylhydrazone is also a good derivative.

7. The aldehydes can be distinguished from the ketones by their much greater ease of oxidation; e.g.,

$$RCHO + 2\,Cu(OH)_2 + OH^- \rightarrow RCO_2^- + Cu_2O + 3\,H_2O$$

The red cuprous oxide precipitate indicates a positive test.

8. Some additional structural information can be gained from the following reactions:

$$RCHO + Na^+HSO_3^- \rightleftharpoons R\overset{OH}{\underset{|}{C}}HSO_3^-\,Na^+$$

The adduct does not form with hindered ketones.

$$\text{R}\overset{\overset{\displaystyle O}{\|}}{\text{C}}\text{CH}_3 \xrightarrow{\text{NaOI}} \text{RCO}_2^- \text{Na}^+ + \text{CHI}_3$$

This reaction is specific for methyl carbonyl compounds or methyl secondary alcohols.

PROBLEMS

1. Give both a common and an IUPAC name for each of the following compounds:

   a. CH_3CHO

   b.
   $$\text{CH}_3\overset{\overset{\displaystyle O}{\|}}{\text{C}}\text{CH}_2\text{CH}_3$$

   c. 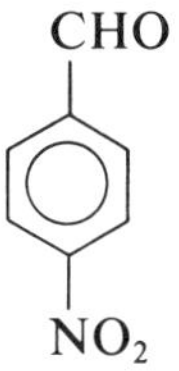   CHO
   NO_2

   d. 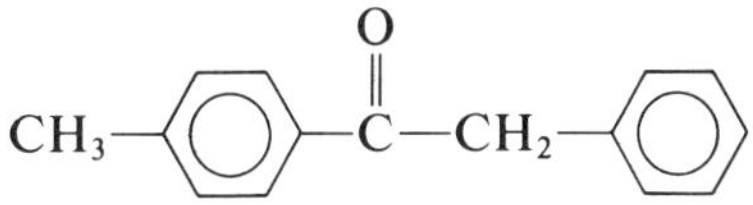
   CH_3—   —$\overset{\overset{\displaystyle O}{\|}}{\text{C}}$—$\text{CH}_2$—

   e. $(\text{CH}_3)_2\text{CHCH}_2\text{CHO}$

   f.   HO $\diagdown$ $\diagup$ CN
   CH_3—$\overset{}{\text{C}}$—CH_3

   g. 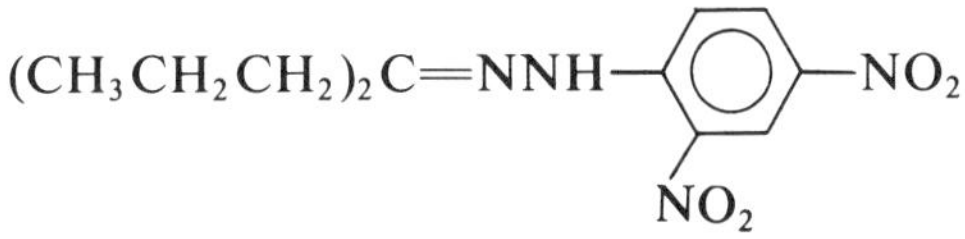 $(\text{CH}_3\text{CH}_2\text{CH}_2)_2\text{C}=\text{NNH}$—   —$\text{NO}_2$
   NO_2

   h.  $\text{CH}_3\text{CHCH}=\text{NOH}$

   i. 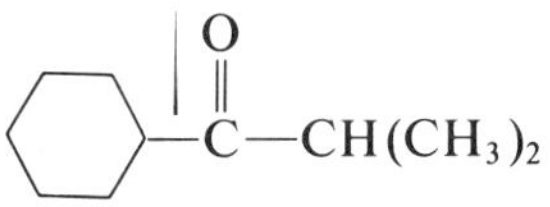   —$\overset{\overset{\displaystyle O}{\|}}{\text{C}}$—$\text{CH}(\text{CH}_3)_2$

   j. $\text{OHCCH}_2\text{CH}_2\text{CHO}$

2. Draw structures for each of the following compounds:
   a. propiophenone oxime
   b. diisobutyl ketone
   c. 3-iodobenzaldehyde
   d. octanal
   e. 3-phenyl-2-pentenal
   f. methyl vinyl ketone
   g. 2,4-hexadione
   h. α-methylbutyraldehyde 2,4-dinitrophenylhydrazone
   i. (di)p-propylphenyl ketone
   j. 2,3-difluorobutanal

3. Complete the following reactions:

   a. $CH_3\overset{\overset{\displaystyle O}{\|}}{C}H + CH_3MgBr \xrightarrow[\text{ether}]{\text{dry}}$

   b.  $\langle\bigcirc\rangle-\overset{\overset{\displaystyle O}{\|}}{C}CH_3 + LiAlH_4 \xrightarrow[\text{(2) } H_2O]{\text{(1) absolute ether}}$

   c. $2\,CH_3CH_2CHO + Na^{+\ -}OCH_2CH_3 \rightarrow$

   d. $(CH_3)_2CHOH + KMnO_4 \rightarrow$

   e. 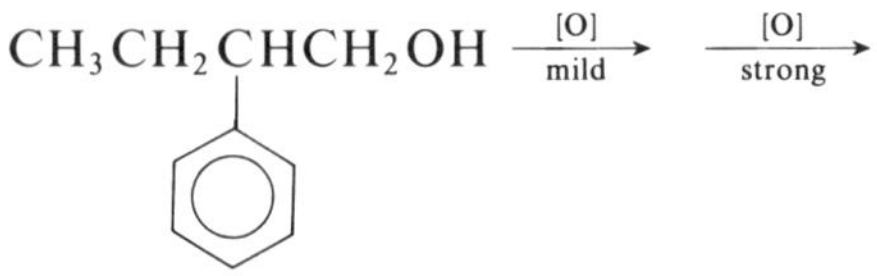 $CH_3CH_2CHCH_2OH \xrightarrow[\text{mild}]{\text{[O]}} \xrightarrow[\text{strong}]{\text{[O]}}$

   f. 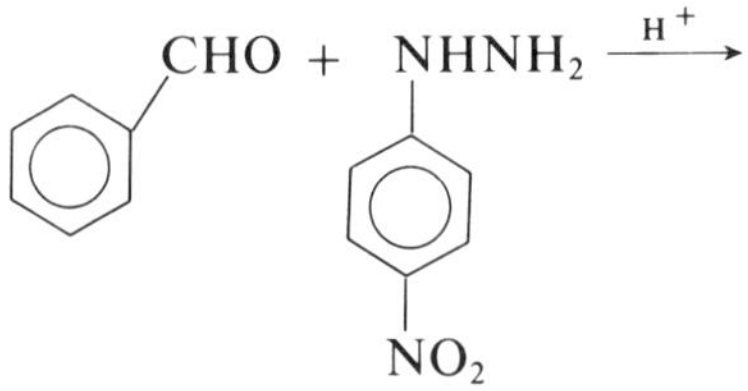 $\langle\text{phenyl}\rangle CHO + NHNH_2 \xrightarrow{H^+}$ (2,4-dinitrophenylhydrazine with NO_2)

   g. $HC{\equiv}CH + H_2O \xrightarrow[H^+]{HgSO_4}$

   h. $CH_3CH_2\overset{\overset{\displaystyle O}{\|}}{C}CH_3 + NaOI \rightarrow$

   i. 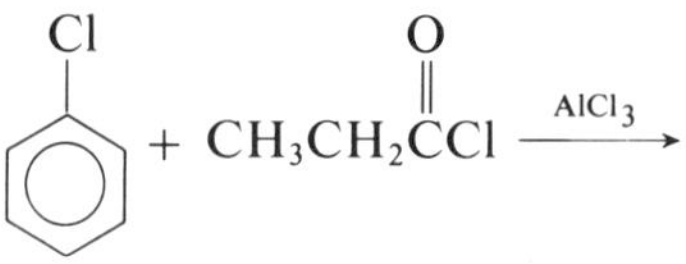 $\langle\text{Cl-phenyl}\rangle + CH_3CH_2\overset{\overset{\displaystyle O}{\|}}{C}Cl \xrightarrow{AlCl_3}$

j.

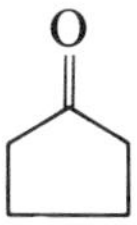

$$\text{(cyclopentanone)} + CH_3CH_2MgCl \xrightarrow[\text{ether}]{\text{dry}}$$

4. Complete the following reactions if one occurs under the conditions given:

　a. $CH_3CH_2CO_2CH_2CH_3 + NaOH \xrightarrow{H_2O}$

　b. $CH_3CH_2CH_2CH_2OH + SOCl_2 \rightarrow$

　c. $CH_3CH_2\overset{\displaystyle O}{\overset{\displaystyle \|}{C}}CH_3 + CH_3CH_2CH_2MgBr \xrightarrow[\text{ether}]{\text{absolute}}$

　d. $CH_3\overset{\displaystyle OH}{\underset{\displaystyle |}{C}}HC_6H_5 + KMnO_4 \xrightarrow{H_2O}$

　e. $CH_3CH_2O^-Na^+ + (CH_3)_2CHCH_2Cl \rightarrow$

　f. $CH_3CH=C(C_6H_5)_2 + K_2Cr_2O_7 \xrightarrow{H_2O}$

　g. $(CH_3)_2CH\overset{\displaystyle O}{\overset{\displaystyle \|}{C}}CH_3 \xrightarrow{NaOI}$

　h. 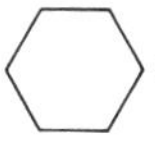 $\text{(cyclohexane ring)}=O + HONH_2 \rightarrow$

　i. $C_6H_5\overset{\displaystyle O}{\overset{\displaystyle \|}{C}}CH_3 + C_6H_5MgI \xrightarrow[\text{ether}]{\text{absolute}}$

　j. $CH_3\overset{\displaystyle O}{\overset{\displaystyle \|}{C}}C_6H_5 + NaBH_4 \xrightarrow{H_2O}$

　k. $CH_3\overset{\displaystyle O}{\overset{\displaystyle \|}{C}}CH_3 + Na^+{}^-HSO_3 \rightarrow$

5. Using a series of standard tests or reactions, how would you distinguish among the following compounds?

　a. $CH_3CH_2CH_2\overset{\displaystyle O}{\overset{\displaystyle \|}{C}}CH_3 \qquad CH_3CH_2CH_2CH_2CHO$

　　$CH_3CH_2\overset{\displaystyle O}{\overset{\displaystyle \|}{C}}CH_2CH_3$

b.

$$\underset{\underset{CH_2CH_3}{\bigcirc}}{\overset{\overset{O}{\parallel}}{C}CH_3} \qquad \underset{\underset{CH_3}{\bigcirc}}{\overset{\overset{O}{\parallel}}{C}CH_2CH_3} \qquad \underset{\bigcirc}{\overset{\overset{O}{\parallel}}{C}CH_2CH_2CH_3}$$

c. CH_2=$CHCH_2CHO$ $\qquad CH_2$=$CH\overset{\overset{O}{\parallel}}{C}CH_3$

HC≡CCH_2CH_2OH

Draw structural formulas and name all organic compounds in questions 6–17.

6. A five-carbon hydrocarbon can add water to produce two ketones, one of which gives a positive iodoform reaction.

7. A compound (A), $C_{14}H_{14}O$, on mild oxidation gives (B), $C_{14}H_{12}O$. Compound (B) reacts with 2,4-dinitrophenylhydrazine to give (C). When (A) is treated with H_2SO_4, (D)—$C_{14}C_{12}$—is produced. When (D) is strongly oxidized, (E), $C_7H_6O_2$, is the sole organic product.

8. Compound (A) had a neutralization equivalent of 103 ± 1. It gave a negative test with phenylhydrazine. Treatment with H_2SO_4 gave (B), which decolorized bromine solutions and $KMnO_4$. Compound (B) had a neutralization equivalent of 87 ± 1. When treated with NaOI, (A) gave (C), which had a neutralization equivalent of 52 ± 1.

9. An acid (A) has a neutralization equivalent of 73 ± 1. It was treated with $Ca(OH)_2$ and the resulting calcium salt heated to yield (B), C_5H_6O. Compound (B) reacted positively with phenylhydrazine, but did not react with Tollens' reagent.

10. A compound (A), C_3H_6O, on treatment with methylmagnesium bromide and subsequent hydrolysis, yields an alcohol, $C_4H_{10}O$, which is not readily oxidizable, but which when drastically oxidized yields only acetic acid and CO_2.

11.

$$C_5H_{10}O_2 + CH_3COCl \qquad \rightarrow C_7H_{12}O_3$$

$$C_5H_{10}O_2 \qquad \xrightarrow{[O]} C_5H_8O_3$$

$$C_5H_{10}O_2 + C_6H_5NHNH_2 \qquad \rightarrow C_{11}H_{16}ON_2$$

$$C_5H_{10}O_2 + NaOI \qquad \rightarrow CHI_3$$

$$C_5H_{10}O_2 + Tollens' \; test \qquad \rightarrow no \; reaction$$

12. A certain compound has the formula $C_5H_8O_2$. On complete reduction, it gives *n*-pentane. With phenylhydrazine, a derivative containing 17 carbons is produced, and with NaOH and I_2 it gives iodoform. On mild oxidation, a substance $C_5H_8O_3$ is formed, which reacts with phenylhydrazine to give a derivative containing 11 carbons. The original substance is unstable to Fehling's solution.

13. An acid (A) was found to react with phenylhydrazine and to give iodoform when treated with NaOI. Titration of 0.29 g of (A) required 25 ml of 0.1 N NaOH. The carbon chain of (A) was shown to contain no branching.

14. Compound (A), $C_{10}H_{10}O_2$, gave positive tests with Tollens', Fehling's and iodoform reagents. The hydrocarbon $C_{10}H_{14}$, resulting from appropriate reduction of (A), yielded only a single monobromo substitution product when treated with bromine in the presence of iron.

15. An unknown compound (A), $C_6H_{12}O$, reacted with hydroxylamine but not with $NaHSO_3$ or Fehling's solution. On catalytic hydrogenation, (A) gave (B), $C_6H_{14}O$. When (B) was treated with concentrated H_2SO_4, (C) was produced. Compound (C) had a formula C_6H_{12}, and, on oxidation under the proper conditions, produced two new compounds: (D) and (E). The former gave a negative Tollens' test and a positive iodoform reaction. The latter gave a positive Tollens' test and a negative iodoform reaction.

16. A compound (A), C_3H_6O, reacts positively with phenylhydrazine and Tollens' reagent. When treated with dilute base, (B), $C_6H_{12}O_2$, was formed. Compound (B) reacted with acetyl chloride. When (B) was oxidized, (C), $C_6H_{10}O_3$, was formed, which reacted with phenylhydrazine, but not with Tollens' reagent. Compound (C) had a neutralization equivalent of 130 ± 1.

17. A compound (A), $C_{11}H_{12}O_5$, reacts with acetyl chloride but not with phenylhydrazine. It has a neutralization equivalent of 112 ± 1. It reacts with NaOI to form iodoform and a new compound (F), $C_{10}H_8O_6$, with a neutralization equivalent of 75 ± 2. When (A) is treated with H_2SO_4, (B)—$C_{11}H_{10}O_4$—is formed, having a neutralization equivalent of 103 ± 1. Compound (B) is oxidized to form (C), $C_9H_6O_6$, with a neutralization equivalent of 70 ± 2, and (D), $C_2H_4O_2$, with a neutralization equivalent of 60 ± 2. Compound (C) can be dehydrated to form (E), $C_9H_4O_5$, with a neutralization equivalent of 192 ± 1.

18. Using standard organic reactions and inorganic chemicals, how

would you prepare the following compounds from the given starting material?

a. propyne (methylacetylene) from propanal

b. 2-butenal from ethanal

c. 2-propanol from acetic acid

d. 2-methyl-1-propanol from 3-methyl-2-butanone

e. 4-methyl-1,3-pentadiene from acetone

f . benzophenone from benzoic acid

g. *p*-nitrobenzyl alcohol from toluene

h. 3-nitro-4′-methylbenzophenone from toluene

19. What is wrong with the following reaction sequences? Can you propose an alternative route that avoids the difficulties?

a. $\underset{\underset{}{\overset{\overset{OH}{|}}{}}}{CH_2{=}CHCHCH_3}$ $\xrightarrow{K_2Cr_2O_7}$ $\underset{\underset{}{\overset{\overset{O}{\|}}{}}}{CH_2{=}CHCCH_3}$ $\xrightarrow{HBr}$

$\underset{\underset{}{\overset{\overset{O}{\|}}{}}}{BrCHCH_2CCH_3}$ $\xrightarrow{\underset{Pt}{H_2}}$ $\underset{\underset{}{\overset{\overset{OH}{|}}{}}}{BrCH_2CH_2CHCH_3}$

b. $\underset{\underset{}{\overset{\overset{O}{\|}}{}}}{CH_3CCH_2CH_2Cl}$ $\xrightarrow[\text{dry ether}]{Mg}$ $\underset{\underset{}{\overset{\overset{O}{\|}}{}}}{CH_3CCH_2CH_2MgCl}$ $\xrightarrow[(2)\ H^+]{(1)\ CO_2}$

$\underset{\underset{}{\overset{\overset{O}{\|}}{}}}{CH_3CCH_2CH_2CO_2H}$

c. $\underset{\underset{}{\overset{\overset{O}{\|}}{}}}{(CH_3)_3CCH}$ $\xrightarrow[(2)\ H^+]{(1)\ CH_3CH_2MgBr}$ $\underset{\underset{}{\overset{\overset{OH}{|}}{}}}{(CH_3)_3CCHCH_2CH_3}$ $\xrightarrow[(2)\ H^+]{(1)\ NaOI}$

$\underset{\underset{}{\overset{\overset{O}{\|}}{}}}{(CH_3)_3CCOH}$

20. The very useful Grignard reagent is best known for its reaction with carbonyl compounds. In each of the following, using acetylene and methanol as the only organic starting materials, suggest methods for preparing the required alcohol both with and without a Grignard reagent.

    a. 3-hexanol

    b. 1-butanol

    c. 2-methyl-2-butanol

Actually, several different combinations of Grignard reagents will work for each of the above compounds. What are they?

10

The Chemicals
and Chemistry
of Organisms

10.1
INTRODUCTION

Some of the organic chemicals we have discussed are found in plants and animals; however, a number of classes of these and related compounds are very closely associated with the chemistry of living cells. The ways in which such materials function in living matter are properly the subject of **biochemistry**, and our purpose here is to provide a transition to this topic by introducing the organic chemistry of certain major types. Just as in the preceding chapters, we shall have to be ruthless in our selection of topics. It is better for you to understand well a few important topics as a basis for future study than to skim over a long series of ideas in very little detail.

The first thing that strikes someone in reading about natural products is the size of the molecules. Many of the simplest structural units are big molecules, and some of the most important are natural polymers with molecular weights in the tens and hundreds of thousands. Closely related to this factor is the fact that most of the important natural products contain more than one functional group. Thus, the chemistry we are about to examine is complicated for both chemical and physical reasons. For example, if a reaction of one function is desired, it is always necessary to consider the effect of the reagent on other groups. The isolation and purification of either a reaction product or the natural product itself is made more difficult by the size and complexity of the molecules and their environment.

Despite these problems, you can still learn a number of very interesting and useful things about natural products, for much of the chemistry involved is exactly the same as that which you have learned for simple, monofunctional compounds. Each of the following sections will attempt to present certain key chemical reactions (both synthetic and analytical) that are clearly related to those with which you are familiar. We shall then discuss some of the biochemical significance of that class of compounds. With each class of compounds, we shall point out some of the special difficulties encountered in their study along with solutions that have proved effective. One point to be noted now pertains to nomenclature. The IUPAC names for such large molecules would be very cumbersome; therefore, the common or trivial names are used much more often.

Courtesy of the Edgar Fahs Smith Memorial Collection.

Louis Pasteur *(French, 1822–1895). Probably the most generally known scientist in the world, Pasteur is best remembered for his work as a biochemist and bacteriologist and for his contributions to medicine. His studies of optical isomers have had a far-reaching influence on organic chemistry, especially in natural products and mechanisms. A student of J. B. A. Dumas, he taught chemistry and physics for a few years before devoting himself to research.*

10.2A   General Structural Features

You may often think of the **sugars** as representing this class of natural products. In fact, there are a great number of complex sugars and related polymeric materials, such as **starch** and **cellulose**, which can be hydrolyzed to simple sugars. These two extremes are referred to as **mono-** and **polysaccharides**, respectively. The monosaccharides, which cannot be hydrolyzed to simpler sugars, are polyhydroxy aldehydes or ketones, and many of them have molecular formulas that can be written $C_x(H_2O)_y$. This fact accounts for the origin of the term carbohydrate, but it does not properly indicate the structure or chemistry of these compounds.

Table 10.1 gives the open-chain structures and names for a few monosaccharides. Even from these flat (Fischer) projections, you should be able to see that there is a great deal of stereochemistry involved in the sugars. Note that $D(+)$-glucose has four different asymmetric carbon atoms, and, from the van't Hoff

TABLE 10.1   PROJECTION STRUCTURES OF SOME COMMON SUGARS

$$
\begin{array}{ccc}
\text{CHO} & \text{CHO} & \text{CHO} \\
| & | & | \\
\text{H---C---OH} & \text{H---C---OH} & \text{HO---C---H} \\
| & | & | \\
\text{CH}_2\text{OH} & \text{H---C---OH} & \text{H---C---OH} \\
& | & | \\
& \text{CH}_2\text{OH} & \text{CH}_2\text{OH} \\
\text{D(+)-glyceraldehyde} & \text{D(--)-erythrose} & \text{D(--)-threose}
\end{array}
$$

$$
\begin{array}{cccc}
\text{CHO} & \text{CHO} & \text{CHO} & \text{CH}_2\text{OH} \\
| & | & | & | \\
\text{H---C---OH} & \text{HO---C---H} & \text{H---C---OH} & \text{C}=\text{O} \\
| & | & | & | \\
\text{HO---C---H} & \text{HO---C---H} & \text{H---C---OH} & \text{HO---C---H} \\
| & | & | & | \\
\text{H---C---OH} & \text{H---C---OH} & \text{H---C---OH} & \text{H---C---OH} \\
| & | & | & | \\
\text{H---C---OH} & \text{H---C---OH} & \text{CH}_2\text{OH} & \text{H---C---OH} \\
| & | & & | \\
\text{CH}_2\text{OH} & \text{CH}_2\text{OH} & & \text{CH}_2\text{OH} \\
\text{D(+)-glucose} & \text{D(+)-mannose} & \text{D(--)-ribose} & \text{D(--)-fructose}
\end{array}
$$

Rule (p. 37), it should be one of 2^4 stereomers. In fact, all 16 of these aldohexose sugars are known by either synthesis or isolation from natural sources. One of these stereomers is D(+)-mannose, which is a diastereomer of D(+)-glucose. The carbon adjacent to the aldehyde group in D(+)-mannose has the opposite configuration (i.e., is the mirror image), and the other three asymmetric atoms are identical to the corresponding carbons of D(+)-glucose.

The simplest possible "sugar," glyceraldehyde, should recall another aspect of stereochemistry—relative configuration (p. 36). In this system, the configuration shown was *assumed* and designated D, and any compound that could be related to it must also have had the D arrangement. In the case of sugars, it involves the position of groups about the asymmetric center farthest from the carbonyl group. Inspection of Table 10.1 shows that the hydrogen and hydroxyl groups at the carbon atom in question are all arranged the same way; hence, all are D sugars. An enantiomeric set of sugars could be drawn that would be related to L(−)-glyceraldehyde.

$$
\begin{array}{c}
\text{CHO} \\
|\\
\text{HO}-\text{C}-\text{H} \\
|\\
\text{CH}_2\text{OH}
\end{array}
$$

L(−)-glyceraldehyde

It is important to recall that the plus or minus sign only indicates the direction of rotation of plane-polarized light and has no simple relationship to the arrangement of atoms in space, that is, configuration. Thus, D-fructose, which has the D-glyceraldehyde configuration, is levorotatory. Now that the R configuration has been shown to be that of D-glyceraldehyde by x-ray diffraction and other evidence, it is possible to state the absolute configuration of many sugars.

10.2B The Chemistry of Sugars

Inasmuch as glucose is the most abundant of the monosaccharides, we shall use it to illustrate certain aspects of the entire class of compounds. Keep in mind our earlier comment that much of the chemistry we have discussed for simple molecules will be useful in studying the more complicated natural products. The sugars contain both hydroxyl and carbonyl groups; therefore, we may expect esterification, reduction, addition, and oxidation aldehyde) to be among the observed reactions.

1. *Esterification.* An experiment useful in determining the structure of glucose was its reaction with acetic anhydride to form a pentaacetate.

$$
\begin{array}{llll}
\text{CHO} & & \text{CHO} & \\
| & & | & \\
\text{HCOH} & \text{O} & \text{HCO}_2\text{CCH}_3 & \text{O} \\
| & \parallel & | & \parallel \\
\text{HOCH} + 5\ (\text{CH}_3\text{C})_2\text{O} \rightarrow & \text{CH}_3\text{CO}_2\text{CH} & + 5\ \text{CH}_3\text{COH} \\
| & & | & \\
\text{HCOH} & & \text{HCO}_2\text{CCH}_3 & \\
| & & | & \\
\text{HCOH} & & \text{HCO}_2\text{CCH}_3 & \\
| & & | & \\
\text{CH}_2\text{OH} & & \text{CH}_2\text{O}_2\text{CCH}_3 &
\end{array}
$$

As you will see later in this section, the reaction is not really as we have drawn it but the conclusion reached (that glucose has five hydroxyl groups) is correct. The preparation of a very important class of plastics, the cellulose acetates, is obviously related to this aspect of sugar chemistry, inasmuch as the complete hydrolysis of cellulose yields only glucose.

2. *Reduction.* A number of different reducing agents have been employed to convert glucose into the corresponding polyalcohol, sorbitol. These include sodium amalgam (Na-Hg), catalytic hydrogenation, and electrolytic reduction. An early

$$
\begin{array}{lll}
\text{CHO} & & \text{CH}_2\text{OH} \\
| & & | \\
\text{HCOH} & & \text{HCOH} \\
| & & | \\
\text{HOCH} & \xrightarrow{[\text{H}]} & \text{HOCH} \\
| & & | \\
\text{HCOH} & & \text{HCOH} \\
| & & | \\
\text{HCOH} & & \text{HCOH} \\
| & & | \\
\text{CH}_2\text{OH} & & \text{CH}_2\text{OH}
\end{array}
$$

experiment, which demonstrated the carbon skeleton of glucose, was its vigorous reduction with HI to a mixture of 1- and 2-iodohexane.

$$
\text{glucose} \xrightarrow{\text{HI}} \overset{\overset{\displaystyle \text{I}}{|}}{\text{CH}_2}\text{CH}_2\text{CH}_2\text{CH}_2\text{CH}_2\text{CH}_3 + \text{CH}_3\overset{\overset{\displaystyle \text{I}}{|}}{\text{CH}}\text{CH}_2\text{CH}_2\text{CH}_2\text{CH}_3
$$

3. *Oxidation.* The tests useful in distinguishing between simple aldehydes and ketones (p. 232) were actually developed through sugar chemistry research. Fehling's, Benedict's, and Tollens' reagents are all mild oxidizing agents that are reduced by glucose and other **reducing sugars**. Unlike the simple

carbonyl compounds, the readily oxidized α-ketol group (α-hydroxyl carbonyl) present in simple sugars prevents these tests from distinguishing aldoses such as glucose from ketoses such as fructose.

$$
\begin{array}{l}
\text{CHO} \\
| \\
\text{HCOH} \\
| \\
\text{HOCH} \\
| \\
\text{HCOH} \\
| \\
\text{HCOH} \\
| \\
\text{CH}_2\text{OH}
\end{array}
\quad
\begin{array}{l}
\xrightarrow[\text{OH}^-]{\text{Ag}^+} \text{Ag}^\circ \\
\\
\\
\\
\xrightarrow[\text{OH}^-]{\text{Cu}^{+2}} \text{Cu}_2\text{O}
\end{array}
\quad
\left. \right\}
\begin{array}{l}
\text{complex mixture} \\
\text{of oxidation} \\
\text{products}
\end{array}
$$

Other oxidizing agents have been useful in determining the structure of glucose. For example, aqueous bromine will convert the aldehyde to a carboxylic acid. A stronger reagent, nitric acid, also oxidizes the primary alcohol so that a dicarboxylic acid results.

$$
\begin{array}{l}
\text{CHO} \\
| \\
\text{HCOH} \\
| \\
\text{HOCH} \\
| \\
\text{HCOH} \\
| \\
\text{HCOH} \\
| \\
\text{CH}_2\text{OH} \\
\text{D-glucose}
\end{array}
\xrightarrow[\text{H}_2\text{O}]{\text{Br}_2}
\begin{array}{l}
\text{CO}_2\text{H} \\
| \\
\text{HCOH} \\
| \\
\text{HOCH} \\
| \\
\text{HCOH} \\
| \\
\text{HCOH} \\
| \\
\text{CH}_2\text{OH} \\
\text{D-gluconic acid}
\end{array}
\xrightarrow{\text{HNO}_3}
\begin{array}{l}
\text{CO}_2\text{H} \\
| \\
\text{HCOH} \\
| \\
\text{HOCH} \\
| \\
\text{HCOH} \\
| \\
\text{HCOH} \\
| \\
\text{CO}_2\text{H} \\
\text{D-glucaric acid} \\
\text{(a saccharic acid)}
\end{array}
$$

4. Addition. The presence of a carbonyl group in glucose (and other simple sugars) provides a site for addition reactions similar to those studied earlier (p. 227). The formation of a cyanohydrin (addition of HCN) has been especially useful in studying the structure of sugars. This **Kiliani-Fischer synthesis** (p. 249) allows sugars to be built up systematically from small molecules of known structure—for example, D-glyceraldehyde. Therefore, it is very useful in determining the configuration of asymmetric centers. Several points concerning the method are of special interest. First, two sugars are formed—in this case glucose and mannose—because the cyanide ion creates a new asymmetric center when it adds to the carbonyl group and it may add to either side of the $\diagdown$C=O plane. Second, it follows that

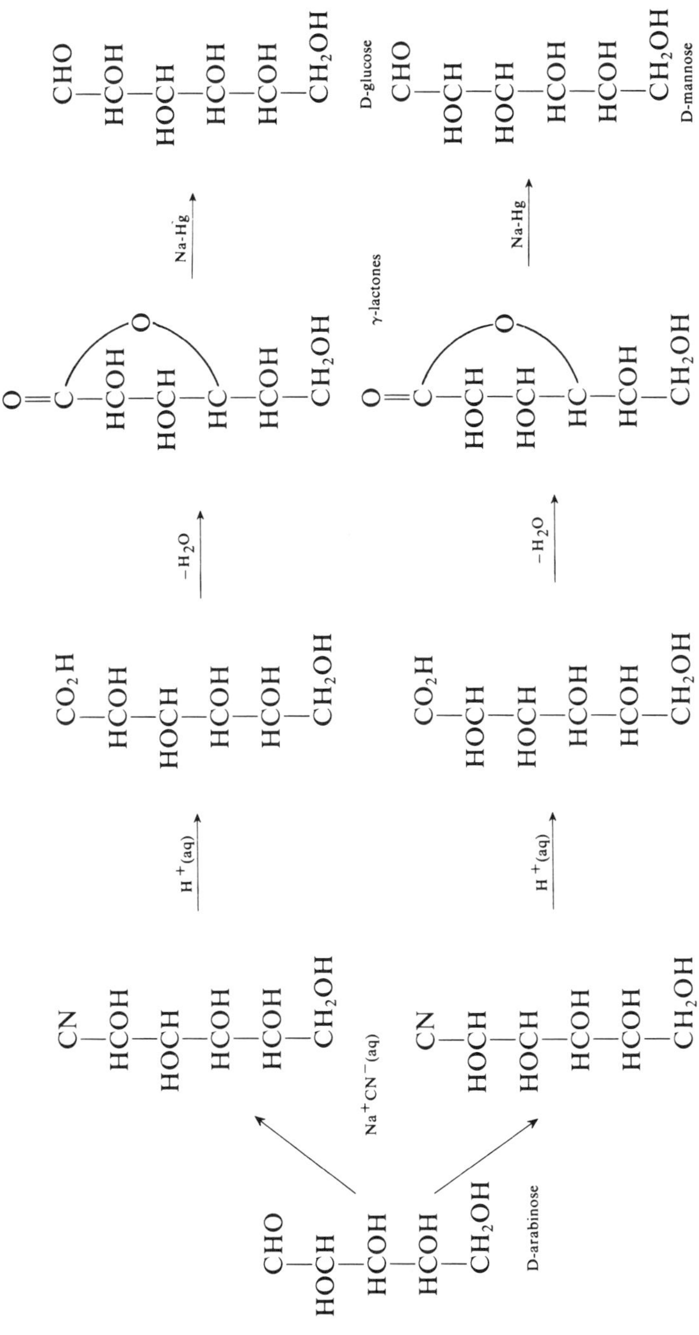

$$\begin{array}{l} \text{CHO} \\ \text{HCOH} \\ \text{HOCH} \\ \text{HCOH} \\ \text{HCOH} \\ \text{CH}_2\text{OH} \end{array}\ \text{D-glucose}$$

$$\begin{array}{l} \text{CHO} \\ \text{HOCH} \\ \text{HOCH} \\ \text{HCOH} \\ \text{HCOH} \\ \text{CH}_2\text{OH} \end{array}\ \text{D-mannose}$$

Na-Hg

γ-lactones

Na-Hg

$$\text{O}=\text{C}\ \begin{array}{l} \text{HCOH} \\ \text{HOCH} \\ \text{HC} \\ \text{HCOH} \\ \text{CH}_2\text{OH} \end{array}$$

$$\text{O}=\text{C}\ \begin{array}{l} \text{HOCH} \\ \text{HOCH} \\ \text{HC} \\ \text{HCOH} \\ \text{CH}_2\text{OH} \end{array}$$

$-H_2O$

$-H_2O$

$$\begin{array}{l} \text{CO}_2\text{H} \\ \text{HCOH} \\ \text{HOCH} \\ \text{HCOH} \\ \text{HCOH} \\ \text{CH}_2\text{OH} \end{array}$$

$$\begin{array}{l} \text{CO}_2\text{H} \\ \text{HOCH} \\ \text{HOCH} \\ \text{HCOH} \\ \text{HCOH} \\ \text{CH}_2\text{OH} \end{array}$$

H^+(aq)

H^+(aq)

$$\begin{array}{l} \text{CN} \\ \text{HCOH} \\ \text{HOCH} \\ \text{HCOH} \\ \text{HCOH} \\ \text{CH}_2\text{OH} \end{array}$$

$$\begin{array}{l} \text{CN} \\ \text{HOCH} \\ \text{HOCH} \\ \text{HCOH} \\ \text{HCOH} \\ \text{CH}_2\text{OH} \end{array}$$

Na^+CN^-(aq)

$$\begin{array}{l} \text{CHO} \\ \text{HOCH} \\ \text{HCOH} \\ \text{HCOH} \\ \text{CH}_2\text{OH} \end{array}\ \text{D-arabinose}$$

glucose and mannose differ only in their configuration at the carbon adjacent to the carbonyl group, and that the other three active centers have the same configuration as D-arabinose. Third, an intramolecular ester, called a **lactone**, is formed after hydrolysis of the cyanohydrin to a hydroxylic acid. In the presence of acid, lactones form very easily if a relatively unstrained five- or six-membered ring results. The prefix γ- indicates that the hydroxyl group on the fourth carbon is involved. Fourth, the amounts of the two cyanohydrins (hence, the sugars) formed will not be equal, the result of **asymmetric induction**. Qualitatively, if a new asymmetric center is formed in an enantiomer of an optically active compound, the configuration of the centers already present will not allow equal probability of the reactions leading to the two new diastereomers.

$$
\begin{array}{c}
\text{O} \\
\parallel \\
\text{C}-\text{H} \\
\nearrow \quad | \quad \nwarrow \\
\text{CN}^- \quad \text{R*} \quad \text{CN}^-
\end{array}
$$

The reverse process of reducing the chain length of sugars is known as the **Wohl degradation**, and it also begins with a familiar carbonyl addition reaction—oxime formation.

$$
\begin{array}{ccc}
\text{CHO} & & \text{CH}{=}\text{NOH} \\
| & & | \\
\text{HCOH} & & \text{HCOH} \\
| & \xrightarrow[{-\text{H}_2\text{O}}]{\text{NH}_2\text{OH}} & | \\
\text{HOCH} & & \text{HOCH} \\
| & & | \quad \xrightarrow{-\text{H}_2\text{O}} \\
\text{HCOH} & & \text{HCOH} \\
| & & | \\
\text{HCOH} & & \text{HCOH} \\
| & & | \\
\text{CH}_2\text{OH} & & \text{CH}_2\text{OH}
\end{array}
$$

$$
\begin{array}{ccc}
\text{CN} & & \\
| & & \\
\text{HCOH} & & \text{CHO} \\
| & & | \\
\text{HOCH} & \xrightarrow[{\text{Ag(NH}_3)_2^+}]{-\text{HCN}} & \text{HOCH} \\
| & & | \\
\text{HCOH} & & \text{HCOH} \\
| & & | \\
\text{HCOH} & & \text{HCOH} \\
| & & | \\
\text{CH}_2\text{OH} & & \text{CH}_2\text{OH} \\
& & \text{D-arabinose}
\end{array}
$$

An example of an addition reaction useful in both structure determination and qualitative identification of sugars is that with phenylhydrazine. Once again, the polyfunctional sugar molecule makes the reaction more complex than with the simple carbonyl compounds. With unsubstituted phenylhydrazine, only mannose gives the phenylhydrazone analogous to simple aldehydes.

$$
\begin{array}{ccc}
\text{CHO} & & \text{CH}\!\!=\!\!\text{NNH}\!-\!\!\bigcirc \\
| & & | \\
\text{HOCH} & & \text{HOCH} \\
| & \bigcirc\!-\!\text{NHNH}_2 & | \\
\text{HOCH} & \xrightarrow{-\text{H}_2\text{O}} & \text{HOCH} \\
| & & | \\
\text{HCOH} & & \text{HCOH} \\
| & & | \\
\text{HCOH} & & \text{HCOH} \\
| & & | \\
\text{CH}_2\text{OH} & & \text{CH}_2\text{OH} \\
\text{mannose} & & \text{mannose phenylhydrazone}
\end{array}
$$

This fact appears to be related to the solubility of the hydrazone, and substituted phenylhydrazines (e.g., bromo- and nitro-) can be used to form the mono- addition product in some other sugars. Under certain conditions, mannose can be made to react like other sugars.

With a water-soluble phenylhydrazone and excess phenyl-hydrazine, an oxidation of the secondary alcohol adjacent to the carbonyl and addition of a second phenylhydrazine take place. The result is a water-insoluble **osazone**. The osazones frequently show sharp melting points, a great aid in identification of the sugars (sugars usually melt with decomposition). The crystalline form of the osazone make it easy to purify and identify.

It is interesting that in fructose the second addition takes place at the 1-carbon and that glucosazone is the product. There-fore, these two sugars, as well as mannose—which also yields glucosazone—must have the same configuration at carbon atoms 3, 4, and 5. The disastereomeric sugars glucose and mannose are called **epimers**. See structures at the top of p. 252.

10.2C   Detailed Carbohydrate Structure

The straight line projections of open-chain monosaccharides are, in fact, inadequate representations of their structure. This fact became obvious very early in the study of their chemistry, when it was found that the carbonyl group did not show all of the ex-pected properties. For example, it does not form a bisulfite addi-tion product, and the infrared spectra show essentially no

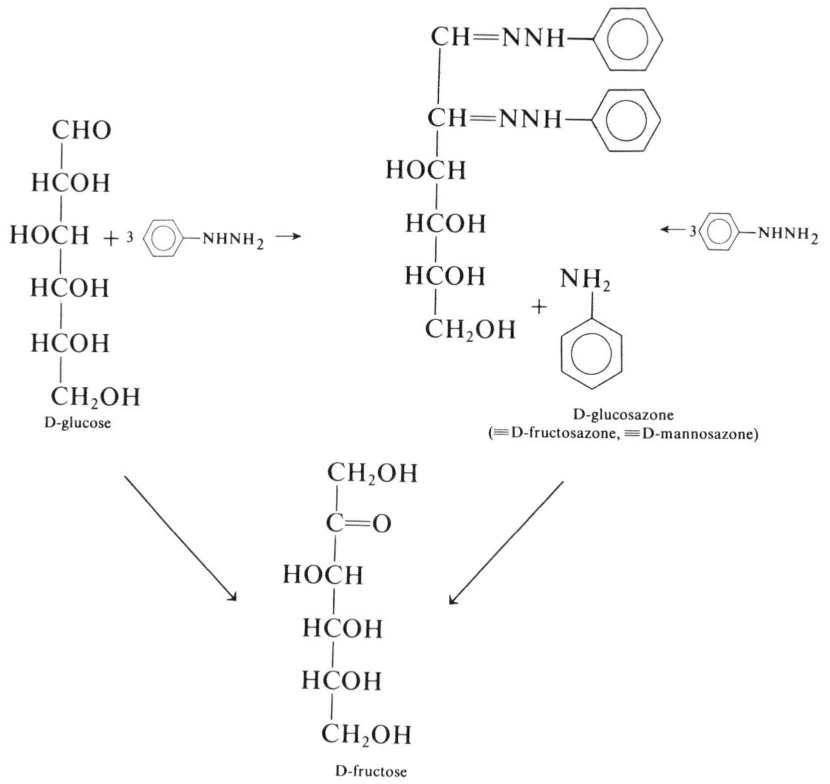

$$\begin{array}{c} CH{=}NNH{-}\bigcirc \\ | \\ CH{=}NNH{-}\bigcirc \\ | \\ HOCH \\ | \\ HCOH \\ | \\ HCOH \\ | \\ CH_2OH \end{array}$$

$$\begin{array}{c} CHO \\ | \\ HCOH \\ | \\ HOCH \ \ +\ 3\ \bigcirc{-}NHNH_2 \rightarrow \\ | \\ HCOH \\ | \\ HCOH \\ | \\ CH_2OH \end{array}$$

D-glucose

$$\leftarrow 3\ \bigcirc{-}NHNH_2$$

$$+\ \begin{array}{c} NH_2 \\ \bigcirc \end{array}$$

D-glucosazone
($\equiv$ D-fructosazone, $\equiv$ D-mannosazone)

$$\begin{array}{c} CH_2OH \\ | \\ C{=}O \\ | \\ HOCH \\ | \\ HCOH \\ | \\ HCOH \\ | \\ CH_2OH \end{array}$$

D-fructose

$C{=}O$ absorption. The most important experiment related to the structure of glucose involves an addition reaction between aldehydes and alcohols that has not been discussed before— **acetal formation**.

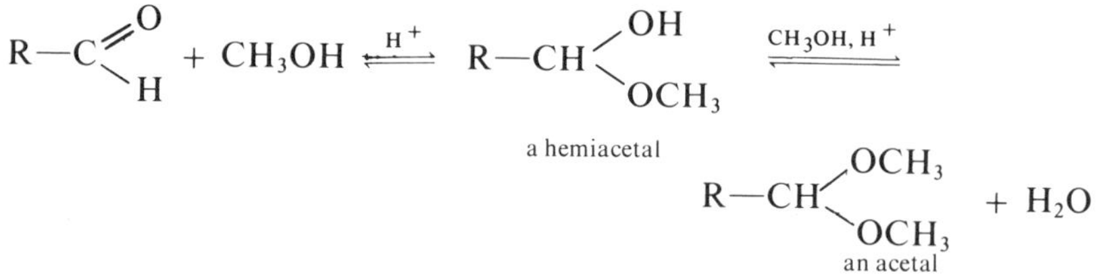

$$R{-}C\overset{O}{\underset{H}{\diagup}} + CH_3OH \underset{}{\overset{H^+}{\rightleftharpoons}} R{-}CH\overset{OH}{\underset{OCH_3}{\diagdown}} \quad \overset{CH_3OH,\ H^+}{\rightleftharpoons}$$

a hemiacetal

$$R{-}CH\overset{OCH_3}{\underset{OCH_3}{\diagdown}} + H_2O$$

an acetal

When this reaction is carried out with glucose, only *one* equivalent of methanol is consumed and *two* stereoisomeric products are formed. These facts indicate that glucose itself must exist as a cyclic hemiacetal. By a method to be discussed, it was found that the hydroxyl group at carbon 5 is involved, which is reasonable inasmuch as a six-membered ring similar to cyclohexane would be produced.

If glucose exists as a cyclohexane type of oxide ring, then the proper structural formula would be as follows:

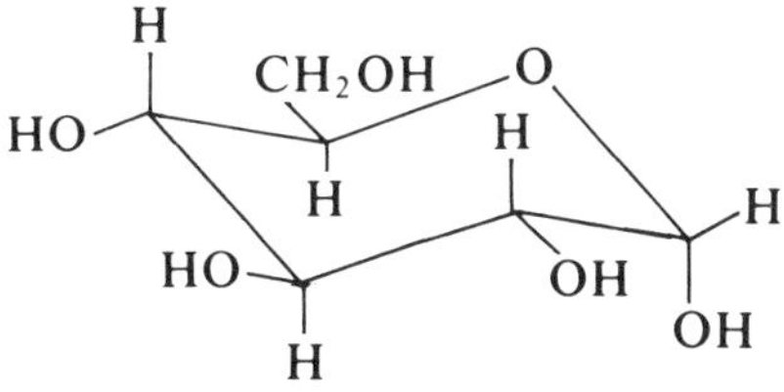

α-D-glucose 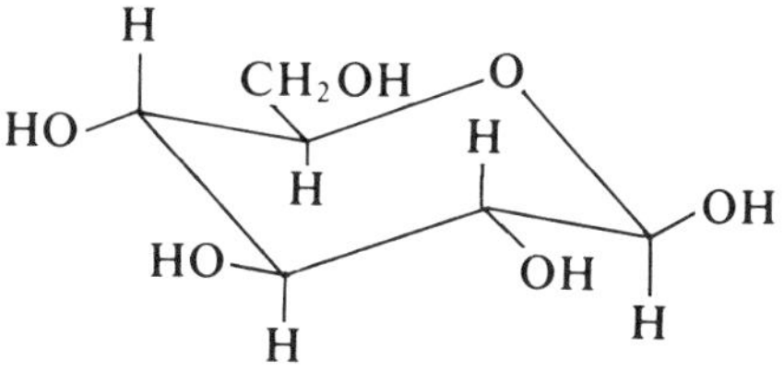   β-D-glucose

The α and β forms of glucose (called **anomers**) are diastereomers, inasmuch as a new asymmetric center is formed at the carbonyl carbon (lower right-hand carbons in the preceding structures). The cyclic structures are frequently referred to as **pyranose** forms from their formal similarity to pyran. Analogous five-membered cyclic sugars are known and called **furanose** (recall THF, p. 174).

pyran    furan

The experiment described earlier between glucose and methanol resulted in the formation of acetals (**glucosides**), which can also be α or β.

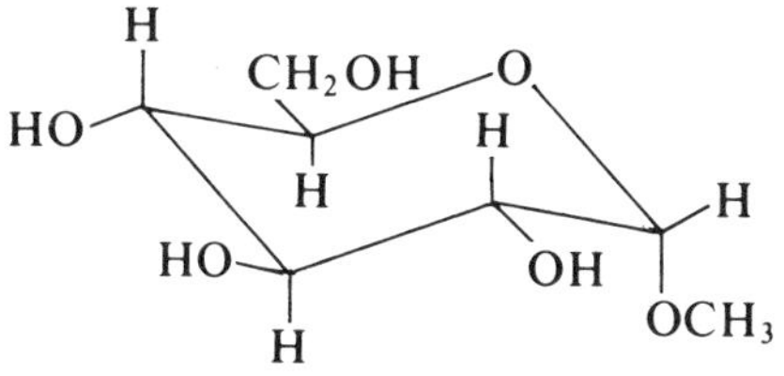

methyl α-D-glucoside

D-glucose + CH_3OH $\overset{H^+}{\rightleftharpoons}$

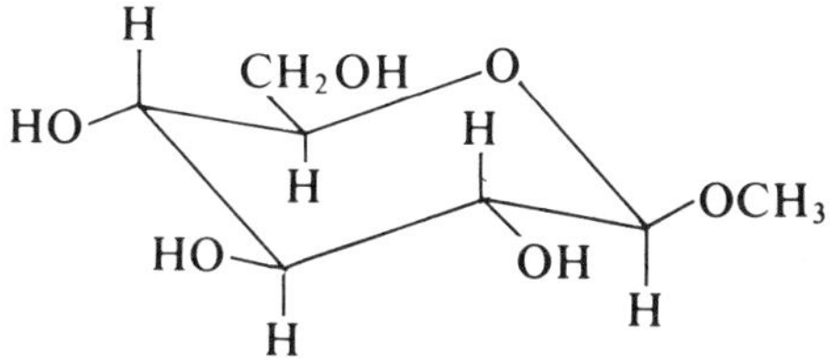

methyl β-D-glucoside

All the carbonyl-like reactions of glucose can be understood as resulting from the two cyclic ethers being in **tautomeric equilibrium** with the open-chain aldehyde.

$[\alpha] = +112°$ aldehyde form

$[\alpha] = +18.7°$

Both α- and β-D-glucose are stable crystalline materials, but in solution the small concentration of aldehyde form (0.024 mole percent at neutrality) allows them to be interconverted (i.e., in equilibrium). An examination of the α and β forms reveals that the difference lies in the fact that α-glucose has the newly formed hydroxyl group in the axial position. It follows that β-glucose (hydroxyl equatorial) should be more stable and favored in the equilibrium. All these facts serve to explain the phenomenon of **mutarotation**. It has been observed that when either α- or β-glucose is dissolved, the optical rotation changes (from +112 or +18.7°, respectively) to an equilibrium value of +52.5°, representing a mixture of 63% β-glucose and 37% α-glucose.

The final point to be discussed in connection with the detailed structure of glucose is the determination of the size of the cyclic oxide ring. This topic involves the use of another oxidizing agent of general interest, but of special importance in sugar chemistry. When **periodate** (IO_4^-) reacts with *vic*-glycols, the number of moles of (1) reagent consumed, (2) formaldehyde formed, and (3) formic acid formed, is indicative of the structure of the oxide ring. First, the basic reactions are

$$\begin{array}{c} R \\ | \\ CHOH \\ | \\ CH_2OH \end{array} \xrightarrow{Na^+IO_4^-} \begin{array}{c} R \\ | \\ CHO \\ + \\ CH_2O \end{array} \qquad \begin{array}{c} R \\ | \\ CHOH \\ | \\ CHOH \\ | \\ R \end{array} \xrightarrow{Na^+IO_4^-} \begin{array}{c} R \\ | \\ CHO \\ + \\ CHO \\ | \\ R \end{array}$$

$$\begin{array}{c} R \\ | \\ CHOH \\ | \\ CHOH \\ | \\ CHOH \\ | \\ R \end{array} \xrightarrow{2\,Na^+IO_4^-} \begin{array}{c} R \\ | \\ CHO \\ + \\ HCO_2H \\ + \\ CHO \\ | \\ R \end{array}$$

Suppose that this reagent is applied to the methyl glucoside in both the furanose and pyranose form (cleavage occurs between *vic*-carbinol groups, as shown):

	Moles of IO_4^- consumed	Moles of HCO_2H formed	Moles of CH_2O formed
	2	0	1
	2	1	0

From these, as well as other earlier experiments, it became evident that a six-membered oxide ring was generally present.

10.2D Higher Saccharides

The importance of the di- and polysaccharides in our lives makes it desirable to examine briefly their structure and chemistry. In general, the disaccharides should chemically resemble the monosaccharides from which they are made. The principal difference will be associated with the manner in which they are joined.

Probably the most familiar of all sugars is **sucrose** or common table sugar. It is not a reducing sugar, does not react with phenylhydrazine, and does not show mutarotation. These facts all indicate that the monosaccharides must be connected by bonds involving both potential carbonyl groups—that is, the arrangement must be analogous to that of a methyl glucoside for both parts of the molecule. Complete hydrolysis of sucrose gives equal amounts of glucose and fructose. Oxidation experiments, of the types described for monosaccharides, indicate that gluco-pyranose and fructofuranose are the ring structures involved.

The final question deals with the stereochemical configuration of each sugar—that is, α or β. This question would be extremely difficult to answer if it were not for complex natural materials called **enzymes**. Their chemistry will be discussed later in the text (pp. 295–298); for now, it is enough to know that they are capable of very specifically catalyzing chemical reactions. If sucrose is treated with enzymes that promote either the hydroly-sis of α-glucosides or β-fructosides, or both, the hydrolysis is greatly facilitated. It is therefore reasonable to assume that such configurations are present and that the structure of sucrose may be represented as

By similar experiments and reasoning, the structure of other common disaccharides have been determined. **Maltose** and

maltose (α)

cellobiose (β)

cellobiose represent some interesting aspects of disaccharide structure. They are both made of two glucose units with the glucosidic linkage between the same carbon atoms. The difference lies in the stereochemistry of the glucosidic bonds; maltose is an α-glucoside, whereas cellobiose is a β-glucoside. Both are reducing sugars, which means that one glucose unit is in the hemiacetal form. As indicated, the glucosidic linkage involves the hydroxyl group at carbon 4 of the second glucose unit. Inasmuch as this glucose is free to participate in the tautomeric equilibrium described earlier, both the α and β forms will be present, with the β form (as shown for cellobiose) predominating.

Maltose and cellobiose are the enzymatic hydrolysis products of starch and cellulose, respectively. Thus, both these familiar materials are made up of the same basic unit—glucose. The great importance of enzymes is evident in the fact that although starch provides man with an important source of food, cellulose is indigestible to him. We can understand this fact on the basis of our lack of enzymes that hydrolyze the β-glucosidic linkage. On the other hand, enzymes are present in our digestive system for the hydrolysis of α-glucosides, such as those present in starch.

The molecular weight of the macromolecules present in polymers such as starch and cellulose varies over a fairly wide range. The source of the material is also important in determining the average length of the chains. For example, cellulose has been shown to have molecular weights of around 300,000 to 500,000, or over 2000 glucose units. Some cotton may have 3000 glucose units. These units are usually arranged in a linear fashion, and it is not surprising that useful fibrous materials, such as cotton, wood, flax, hemp, and so on, result. The chains can interact with one another to form hydrogen bonds that add greatly to the strength of the fibers and also decrease their water solubility.

Starch is made up of both a straight-chain polymer (**amylose**) and a branched-chain polymer (**amylopectin**). Amylose is of much lower molecular weight than cellulose (of the order of

100,000 or less), whereas amylopectin is much higher (up to 1 million). Because of the short chains in amylose and the frequent branching in amylopectin, neither form of starch provides strong fibers and the former is water soluble.

Very little starch is dissolved by cold water, but when the outer membrane of the granules is broken by mechanical means, the amylose dissolves. It can also be extracted through the membrane by warm water. The water causes the starch granules to swell because of the highly branched structure of amylopectin. As the temperature is raised, the swelling becomes more rapid until the granules burst. These processes allow the fractions of different molecular weight ranges and structures to be separated. Partial hydrolysis provides a means of obtaining lower weight polymers having a wide variety of uses. The polysaccharides—cellulose and starch—are of very great importance in our daily lives for clothing and food.

10.2E   Carbohydrate Biochemistry

The synthesis of carbohydrates in man is of very limited importance; we obtain nearly all this energy source from green plants. **Chlorophyll-*a***, a pigment present in green plants, can be activated by sunlight to oxidize water and reduce carbon dioxide. The details of this process of **photosynthesis** are not yet completely understood, but much has been learned. Some compound related to D-glyceric acid is probably produced as the first step toward carbohydrates. Much of the detail of the enzyme-catalyzed reactions has been worked out.

$$x\,CO_2 + y\,H_2O \xrightarrow[h\nu]{\text{chlorophyll-}a} \underset{\text{D-glyceric acid}}{H-\overset{\displaystyle CO_2H}{\underset{\displaystyle CH_2OH}{C}}-OH} \xrightarrow[\text{reactions}]{\text{enzymatic}} (CH_2O)_x + x\,O_2$$

A great deal more is known about the use the body makes of the carbohydrates. It will be apparent as we study other important natural products that these uses are very closely interrelated, but for now we shall attempt to restrict our discussion to the carbohydrates. The first step after **ingestion** or eating the di- and polysaccharides is hydrolysis, chiefly to glucose, by enzymes in the digestive tract. After being passed through the intestinal wall and transported to the cell, the glucose enters the process of **glycolysis**.

Before we can talk about the metabolic reactions, it is necessary for us to fix our attention on the central reason for these reactions and to form at least a qualitative picture of the mechanism by which they are accomplished. The degradation (**metabolism**) of carbohydrates and other foods in the body shows the close relationship of energy and chemistry. Although we wish to discuss the chemical changes that have been demonstrated, we should not lose sight of the importance of energy considerations. A molecule of fundamental importance in energy transfer during metabolism is a complex sugar called **adenosine**.

adenine   D-ribose

Such combinations of a heterocyclic base and a sugar are called **nucleosides**, and we shall treat them in more detail in protein chemistry (pp. 282–284). The primary hydroxyl group of the D-ribose can be esterified with 1,2, or 3 phosphoric acids to form the **nucleotides** adenosine mono-, di-, or triphosphate, usually written AMP, ADP, and ATP, respectively. These are the "energy-rich" compounds that play a vital role in cell metabolism.

AMP   ADP   ATP

The first reaction of glucose in the process of glycolysis is with ATP, and it results in the formation of glucose-6-phosphate and ADP.

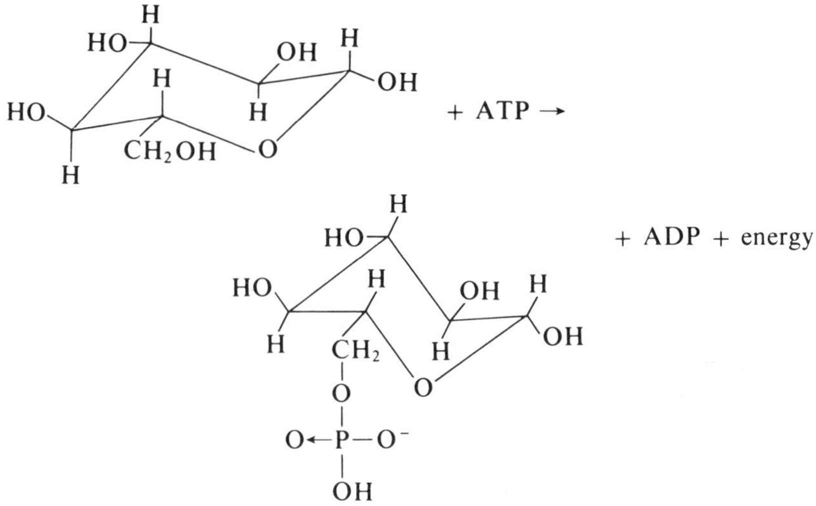

$$+ ATP \rightarrow$$

$$+ ADP + energy$$

The various intermediates in the glycolytic process are phosphorylated, and the overall reaction is the conversion of 1 mole of glucose to 2 moles of pyruvic acid. In the process, a net gain of 2 moles of ATP is made and energy is released (i.e., it is **exothermic**), about half of which is stored in the ATP. A few of the key steps are shown on the following scheme. Remember that each of the relatively simple reactions is taking place under conditions of temperature, pH, and so on, of the living body—that is, **physiological conditions**. For this process to occur, the highly specific enzyme catalysts are essential.

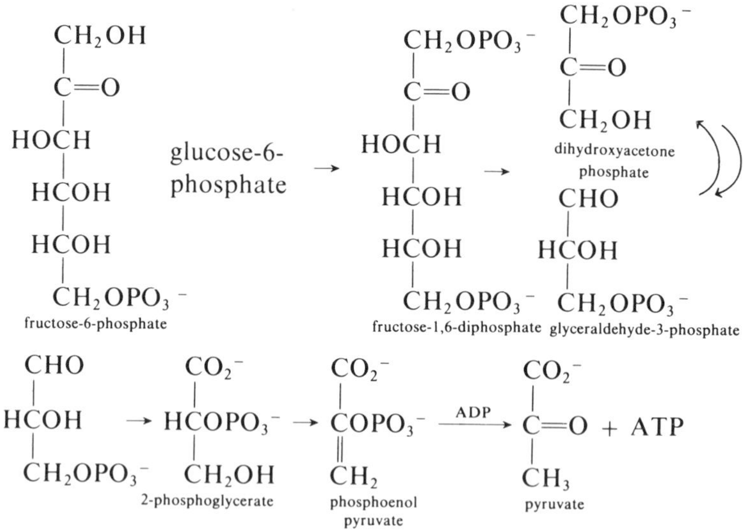

fructose-6-phosphate

glucose-6-phosphate

dihydroxyacetone phosphate

fructose-1,6-diphosphate

glyceraldehyde-3-phosphate

2-phosphoglycerate

phosphoenol pyruvate

pyruvate

Carboxyl and phosphoric acid groups are written as anions, because at physiological pH they exist chiefly in the ionized form.

Glycolysis, often called the **Embden-Meyerhof-Parnas Scheme**, releases only a small part of the energy available in a mole of glucose (26 kcal, as compared to 686 kcal). The pyruvic acid formed can enter the **tricarboxylic acid cycle**, which is usually known as the **Krebs cycle** after its developer. However, pyruvic acid does not enter the Krebs cycle directly. It is first converted to an "active" form by a **coenzyme**. The coenzymes are rather complicated organic molecules that perform a variety of tasks related to the enzymes. The particular coenzyme of interest here is called **coenzyme A (CoA)**. It contains a **thiol** or **mercaptan** group (-SH) analogous to an alcohol, and, as a **thioester**, it plays an important part in the metabolism of the body.

$$\underset{\displaystyle \overset{\displaystyle |}{CH_3}}{\overset{\displaystyle \overset{\displaystyle CO_2^-}{|}}{C}}\!=\!O \; + \; CoASH \; \rightarrow \; CoAS\overset{\displaystyle O}{\overset{\displaystyle \|}{C}}CH_3 \; + \; CO_2$$

acetyl CoA

The overall effect of the Krebs cycle is to oxidize 1 mole of pyruvate to carbon dioxide, water, and energy, as shown in the following equation:

$$CH_3\overset{\displaystyle O}{\overset{\displaystyle \|}{C}}CO_2^- \; + \; 5\,O \; \rightarrow \; 3\,CO_2 \; + \; 2\,H_2O \; + \; 273\,\text{kcal}$$

An interesting fact is that the ADP-ATP system we have discussed is not directly involved in the Krebs cycle. There exists a poorly understood system of oxidative phosphorylation, which is driven by the cycle and converts 15 moles of ADP to ATP for every mole of pyruvate consumed.

$$15\,ADP \; + \; 15\,H_3PO_4 \; + \; 180\,\text{kcal} \; \rightarrow \; 15\,ATP$$

Because of the **endothermic** (energy-consuming) nature of the reaction, the Krebs cycle and its related phosphorylations store about two-thirds of the energy as ATP for future use.

The following chart outlines some key intermediates in the Krebs cycle.

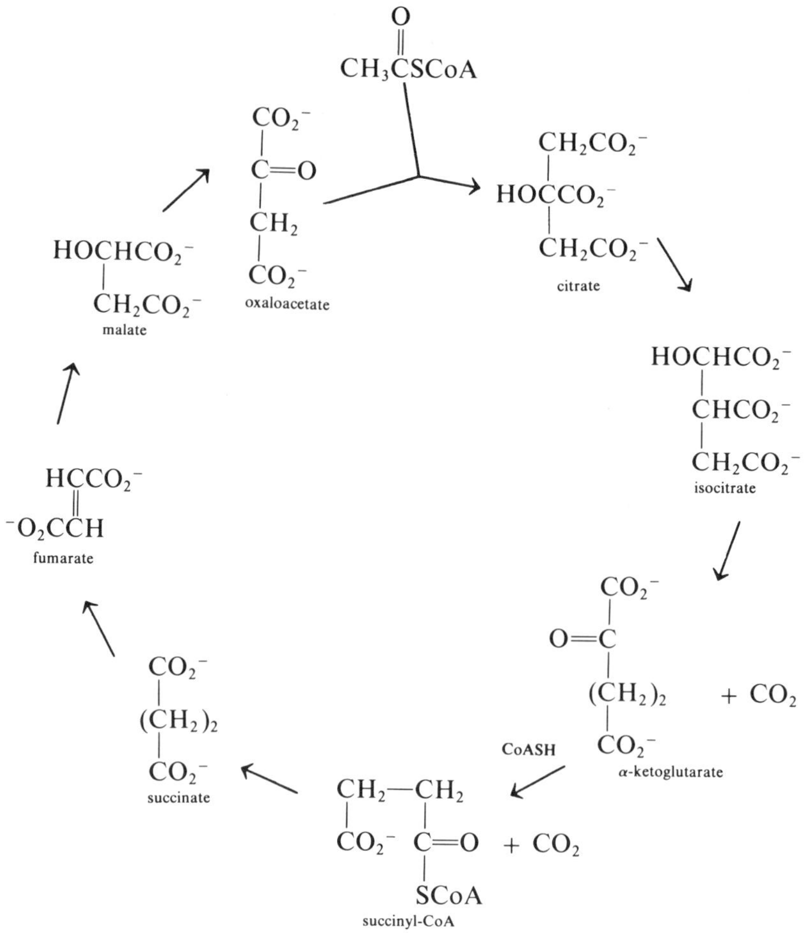

Two points should be especially emphasized before we leave the Krebs cycle and the carbohydrates. First, this cycle and acetyl coenzyme A are of central importance in the body's use of food to supply materials and energy. We shall meet this pathway again with the lipids and proteins. Second, only the barest of outlines has been presented in the discussion. A great deal more is known about the intermediates, the energetics, and especially the enzymes required to bring about the transformations. This additional understanding is available to you in the Suggested Additional Readings.

10.3A General Structural Features

The most common types of lipids (from the Greek, *lipos*, fat) are the **fats** and **oils**. They are the water-insoluble fractions obtained from plants or animals that are usually quite soluble in ether or hydrocarbons. Structurally, they are esters of long-chain carboxylic acids and the triol, glycerol. These esters are referred to as **glycerides**.

a glyceride

An arbitrary distinction is made between fats and oils on the basis of their usual physical state—that is, the former are solids, the latter liquids.

The acids involved may be the same (a simple glyceride) or different (a mixed glyceride), and a typical natural fat or oil will contain a number of different acids. Some acids often found in fats are given in Table 10.2.

TABLE 10.2 ACIDS COMMONLY OBTAINED FROM FATS AND OILS

Name	Structure	Melting point, °C
Lauric	$CH_3(CH_2)_{10}CO_2H$	44
Myristic	$CH_3(CH_2)_{12}CO_2H$	58
Palmitic	$CH_3(CH_2)_{14}CO_2H$	64
Stearic	$CH_3(CH_2)_{16}CO_2H$	70
Palmitoleic	$CH_3(CH_2)_5CH{=}CH(CH_2)_7CO_2H$ (*cis*)	1
Oleic	$CH_3(CH_2)_7CH{=}CH(CH_2)_7CO_2H$ (*cis*)	14
Linoleic	$CH_3(CH_2)_4CH{=}CHCH_2CH{=}CH(CH_2)_7CO_2H$ (*cis, cis*)	−11
Linolenic	$CH_3CH_2CH({=}CHCH_2CH)_2{=}CH(CH_2)_7CO_2H$ (*cis, cis, cis*)	−5

It can be seen from the table that unsaturation lowers the melting point of the acid. This fact agrees with the observation that the oils are usually unsaturated whereas the fats are usually saturated. In fact, the solid household cooking fats are often made by hydrogenation of vegetable oils.

The simple glycerides may be named in the same way as ordinary esters, but a short form is often used; for example,

$$
\begin{array}{ll}
\text{CH}_2\text{O}_2\text{C(CH}_2)_{14}\text{CH}_3 & \text{CH}_2\text{O}_2\text{C(CH}_2)_{12}\text{CH}_3 \\
| & | \\
\text{CHO}_2\text{C(CH}_2)_{14}\text{CH}_3 & \text{CHO}_2\text{C(CH}_2)_{12}\text{CH}_3 \\
| & | \\
\text{CH}_2\text{O}_2\text{C(CH}_2)_{14}\text{CH}_3 & \text{CH}_2\text{O}_2\text{C(CH}_2)_{12}\text{CH}_3
\end{array}
$$

glyceryl tripalmitate (palmitin)   glyceryl trimyristate (myristin)

Naming the mixed glycerides requires some means of indicating the arrangement of the acids. Usually, the carbons of glycerol are given the Greek letters α, β, and γ. For example,

$$
\begin{array}{lll}
\alpha & \text{CH}_2\text{O}_2\text{C(CH}_2)_{16}\text{CH}_3 & \text{CH}_2\text{O}_2\text{C(CH}_2)_{14}\text{CH}_3 \\
 & | & | \\
\beta & \text{CHO}_2\text{C(CH}_2)_{2}\text{CH}_3 & \text{CHO}_2\text{C(CH}_2)_{16}\text{CH}_3 \\
 & | & | \\
\gamma & \text{CH}_2\text{O}_2\text{C(CH}_2)_{14}\text{CH}_3 & \text{CH}_2\text{O}_2\text{C(CH}_2)_{14}\text{CH}_3
\end{array}
$$

β-butyro-γ-palmito-α-stearin β-stearo-α, γ-dipalmitin

Two alternatives are shown in the following example:

$$
\begin{array}{lll}
\alpha & 1 & \text{CH}_2\text{O}_2\text{C(CH}_2)_{14}\text{CH}_3 \\
 & & | \\
\beta & 2 & \text{CHO}_2\text{C(CH}_2)_{7}\text{CH}{=}\text{CH(CH}_2)_{7}\text{CH}_3 \ (cis) \\
 & & | \\
\alpha' & 3 & \text{CH}_2\text{O}_2\text{C(CH}_2)_{14}\text{CH}_3
\end{array}
$$

2(or β)-oleo-1,3 (or α,α')-dipalmitin

10.3B The Chemistry of the Lipids

Inasmuch as naturally occurring fats and oils are usually complex mixtures of glycerides—for example, olive oil contains at least 5 important fatty acids and butter at least 14—it will be most useful for us to consider reactions in general terms. In practice, the individual pure components are only separated for detailed analysis and structure proofs.

1. *Hydrolysis.* Glycerides, like simple esters, react with aqueous bases to produce an alcohol (glycerol) and acid salts.

$$
\begin{array}{l}
\text{CH}_2\text{O}_2\text{CR} \\
| \\
\text{CHO}_2\text{CR} \; + \; \text{Na}^+\text{OH}^- \quad \xrightarrow[\text{heat}]{\text{H}_2\text{O}} \\
| \\
\text{CH}_2\text{O}_2\text{CR}
\end{array}
\qquad
\begin{array}{l}
\text{CH}_2\text{OH} \\
| \\
\text{CHOH} \; + \; \text{R(R' or R'')}{-}\text{CO}_2^-\text{Na}^+ \\
| \\
\text{CH}_2\text{OH}
\end{array}
$$

glycerol   soap

The manufacture of soap is one of the oldest chemical industries and was once a part of every family's life. The simplest explanation of how soaps clean reveals some interesting facts about the physical properties of organic molecules.

A soap molecule is made up of a **hydrophilic** (from the Greek, *hydra-*, water, and *-philos*, loving) portion and a **hydrophobic** (from the Greek, *-phobia*, fear of) portion, as shown in the diagram.

$$\underbrace{CH_3(CH_2)_{10-16}}_{\text{water ``fearing''}}\overset{\overset{\displaystyle O}{\|}}{\underbrace{C-O^-Na^+}_{\text{water ``loving''}}}$$

Most water-insoluble dirt is also oily or hydrophobic, and the addition of soap can form an **emulsion** or mixture of small, but polymolecular, drops suspended in the water. This condition results quite naturally from the "fatlike tails" of the soap dissolving in the oil and the polar carboxylate ends dissolving in the water (see Figure 10.1).

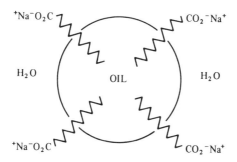

FIGURE 10.1. Fatty Acid Soap Emulsion.

2. Saponification Number. In principle, this analytical technique is exactly like the saponification equivalent discussed earlier (p. 188) for the simple esters. Back titration of the base remaining after complete hydrolysis of a measured amount of fat by a measured excess of standard base should lead to the equivalent weight of the sample. However, inasmuch as the natural glycerides are all complex mixtures and, in fact, vary in composition even from a single source, the determination does not lead to a unique structure or even a small number of isomeric possibilities. Still, the saponification numbers for a large number of fats and oils have been obtained, and the ranges are narrow enough and show sufficient variation between different natural materials that the method is useful to the practicing chemist. The usual units are milligrams of KOH per gram of fat.

3. *Hydrogenation.* Like the manufacture of soaps, the reduction of the unsaturated glycerides, often found in oils, is a very large chemical industry. The alkene linkages are reactive sites for oxidation, and the lower molecular weight acids produced cause the unpleasant odor and taste associated with rancidity. With hydrogen and a finely divided nickel catalyst, the amount of unsaturation can be lowered until the desired physical and chemical properties are obtained; for example,

$$
\begin{array}{c}
\text{CH}_2\text{O}_2\text{C(CH}_2)_7\text{CH}\!=\!\text{CH(CH}_2)_7\text{CH}_3 \\
|\\
\text{CHO}_2\text{C(CH}_2)_7\text{CH}\!=\!\text{CH(CH}_2)_7\text{CH}_3 \\
|\\
\text{CH}_2\text{O}_2\text{C(CH}_2)_7\text{CH}\!=\!\text{CH(CH}_2)_7\text{CH}_3
\end{array}
\xrightarrow[\text{Ni}]{3\,\text{H}_2}
\begin{array}{c}
\text{CH}_2\text{O}_2\text{C(CH}_2)_{16}\text{CH}_3 \\
|\\
\text{CHO}_2\text{C(CH}_2)_{16}\text{CH}_3 \\
|\\
\text{CH}_2\text{O}_2\text{C(CH}_2)_{16}\text{CH}_3
\end{array}
$$

olein   stearin

Stearin and other completely saturated fats are too hard to be attractive to the housewife, and such products as Crisco and Spry are left partially unsaturated.

4. *Hydrogenolysis.* The reduction process may be carried beyond the addition of hydrogen to unsaturated centers by the use of higher pressure and a copper chromite catalyst. This reaction takes place at the ester linkages, and the products are glycerol and long-chain primary alcohols.

$$
\begin{array}{c}
\text{CH}_2\text{O}_2\text{CR} \\
|\\
\text{CHO}_2\text{CR}' \\
|\\
\text{CH}_2\text{O}_2\text{CR}''
\end{array}
\xrightarrow[\substack{\text{copper}\\\text{chromite}}]{6\,\text{H}_2}
\begin{array}{c}
\text{CH}_2\text{OH} + \text{RCH}_2\text{OH} \\
|\\
\text{CHOH} + \text{R}'\text{CH}_2\text{OH} \\
|\\
\text{CH}_2\text{OH} + \text{R}''\text{CH}_2\text{OH}
\end{array}
$$

The actual mixture of alcohols formed will be even more complex than indicated in the equation because of the large range of acids found in typical natural fats. The range of molecular weights can be reduced by physical methods, such as distillation, and the products frequently have important industrial uses. One interesting use of the intermediate chain lengths, such as lauryl alcohol or dodecanol, is in the preparation of acid esters of sulfuric acid.

$$
\text{CH}_3(\text{CH}_2)_{11}\text{OH} \xrightarrow{\text{H}_2\text{SO}_4} \text{CH}_3(\text{CH}_2)_{11}\text{OSO}_3\text{H} \xrightarrow{\text{Na}^+\text{OH}^-}
$$

$$
\text{CH}_3(\text{CH}_2)_{11}\text{OSO}_3^-\text{Na}^+
$$

lauryl hydrogen   sodium lauryl
sulfate   sulfate

The salts of these half-esters are the **detergents** that are, to a large extent, used in place of soaps for certain cleaning processes. Their combination of a polar and nonpolar portion causes them to clean in much the same way as a soap, but they have the advantage of not forming precipitates with calcium, magnesium, and ferric ions. Thus, the detergents can be used in both hard and soft water. This very desirable property rapidly led to a demand that could be satisfied economically only by synthetic detergents. The process used, polymerization of alkenes, gave branched chains that were not degraded by bacteria during sewage disposal, and the detergents appeared to be increasingly contaminating fresh water supplies. Biodegradable detergents are now being produced.

One final note about hydrogenolysis is in order. It is possible to obtain long-chain unsaturated alcohols by this process. It requires the use of a catalyst that is specific for the ester linkage and does not reduce the double bonds.

$CH_2O_2C(CH_2)_7CH{=}CH(CH_2)_7CH_3$
$|$
$CHO_2C(CH_2)_7CH{=}CH(CH_2)_7CH_3 \quad \xrightarrow[\text{zinc}\ \text{chromite}]{6\,H_2}$
$|$
$CHO_2C(CH_2)_7CH{=}CH(CH_2)_7CH_3$

CH_2OH
$|$
$CHOH \quad + \ 3\,CH_3(CH_2)_7CH{=}CH(CH_2)_7CH_2OH$
$|$
CH_2OH

5. *Iodine Number.* The analysis of a fat can be extremely difficult, but some insight about its chemical nature can be obtained fairly readily—for example, the saponification number (p. 265). In the case of fats containing unsaturation, an estimate of the amount of unsaturation can be of great practical importance. The addition of halogen to the alkene linkage provides a convenient method of estimating relative unsaturation.

$CH_2O_2C(CH_2)_{12}CH_3$
$|$
$CHO_2C(CH_2)_7CH{=}CH(CH_2)_7CH_3 \quad \xrightarrow{I{-}X}$
$|$
$CH_2O_2C(CH_2)_{14}CH_3$

$CH_2O_2C(CH_2)_{12}CH_3$
$|$
$CHO_2C(CH_2)_7CH{-}CH(CH_2)_7CH_3$
$| \qquad\qquad\ \ I{-}\ \ X{-}$
$CH_2O_2C(CH_2)_{14}CH_3$

As indicated, the mixed halogens (ICl or IBr) are used because I_2 does not add easily, but the results are expressed as centigrams of iodine per gram of fat (or grams of $I_2/100$ grams of fat).

10.3C Lipid Biochemistry

The lipids are very widely distributed in nature, and they serve a variety of biochemical needs. Because the fats can be stored and have a high energy content, they constitute an important reserve within the body. Inasmuch as fats are poor conductors and are soft, pliable materials, they are important in reducing thermal and mechanical shocks. The body not only consumes fats as an energy source, but it synthesizes them as well. The routes by which these two processes are accomplished are now fairly well understood which represents a most significant achievement.

The first steps in the utilization of fats in the body is their partial hydrolysis in the small intestine, transport across the cell membranes, and movement through the lymphatic and blood systems. Some reesterification takes place and small amounts of free glycerol may enter the carbohydrate cycles during the process of moving the fatty acids to the cells where they are to be oxidized. The overall process may be represented as follows, but it is the intermediate steps and their discovery that is most interesting.

$$RCO_2H \xrightarrow{\ O_2\ } x\,CO_2 + y\,H_2O + \text{energy}$$

A classic experiment, at the turn of the century, provided some insight concerning the intermediate steps. Franz Knoop fed fatty acids with a terminal phenyl group (in the ω position) to animals and found in their wastes benzoic or phenylacetic acids, depending on the number of carbons in the acid they ate.

$$\langle\bigcirc\rangle\text{--}(CH_2)_5CO_2H \xrightarrow[\text{oxidation}]{\text{metabolic}} \langle\bigcirc\rangle\text{--}CH_2CO_2H$$

$$\langle\bigcirc\rangle\text{--}(CH_2)_4CO_2H \xrightarrow[\text{oxidation}]{\text{metabolic}} \langle\bigcirc\rangle\text{--}CO_2H$$

The even number of carbons produced phenylacetic acid, whereas the odd number of carbons gave benzoic acid. From this experiment, Knoop concluded that the acids are degraded two carbons at a time. This very clever experiment is an early example of labeling, and, in principle, it is analogous to the O^{18}

experiments discussed in the synthesis of esters (pp. 183–184). Inasmuch as the loss of two carbon fragments requires the breaking of the α, β bond and oxidation of the β carbon, the concept is usually referred to as the β-**oxidation theory**.

Fifty years later, Fritz Lipmann discovered coenzyme A, which we discussed in connection with the Krebs cycle in carbohydrate metabolism (p. 261). The significant structural feature of CoA was that the sulfur functional group corresponds to an alcohol—that is, -SH a thiol or mercaptan. This group reacts with the carboxyl group to form a thioester, which is the active form for metabolic oxidation of the fatty acids.

$$RCH_2CH_2CO_2H + \underset{\text{coenzyme A}}{CoASH} \xrightarrow{-H_2O} \underset{\text{a thioester}}{RCH_2CH_2\overset{\displaystyle O}{\overset{\|}{C}}SCoA} \xrightarrow{-2H}$$

$$RCH{=}CH\overset{\displaystyle O}{\overset{\|}{C}}SCoA \xrightarrow{H_2O} RCH\overset{OH}{\underset{}{|}}CH_2\overset{\displaystyle O}{\overset{\|}{C}}SCoA \xrightarrow{-2H} \underset{\text{a }\beta\text{-ketoester}}{R\overset{\displaystyle O}{\overset{\|}{C}}CH_2\overset{\displaystyle O}{\overset{\|}{C}}SCoA}$$

$$\xrightarrow{CoASH} \underset{\substack{\text{shortened}\\\text{acid as thioester}\\\text{of CoA}}}{R\overset{\displaystyle O}{\overset{\|}{C}}SCoA} + \underset{\text{acetyl CoA}}{CH_3\overset{\displaystyle O}{\overset{\|}{C}}SCoA}$$

The new thioester is ready to participate in the cycle again, and thus, in time, will be completely degraded with the loss (to the body) of energy from all of the exothermic, enzyme-catalyzed reactions shown. The active acetate, in the form of the acetyl CoA, enters the Krebs cycle (p. 262), or can be used in the synthesis of fatty acids.

The means by which the body produces fatty acids is not simply the reversal of the degradation scheme shown, but an independent pathway. It allows the organism to regulate the oxidation and synthesis process. It also explains the experimental fact that living body components are in a dynamic state, that is, they are always building up and tearing down materials even though the net effect may indicate a static condition.

Acetyl CoA can react with carbon dioxide to produce the half-CoA-ester of malonic acid, which starts the synthetic route to fatty acids.

$$CH_3\overset{O}{\underset{\|}{C}}SCoA + CO_2 \rightarrow HO_2C(CH_2)_2\overset{O}{\underset{\|}{C}}SCoA \xrightarrow{R\overset{O}{\underset{\|}{C}}SCoA}$$

$$\underset{RC\underset{\underset{O}{\|}}{}}{HO_2C}\diagdown_{CH_2\overset{O}{\underset{\|}{C}}SCoA + HSCoA}$$

$$\searrow_{CO_2} \quad RC\overset{O}{\underset{\|}{C}}CH_2\overset{O}{\underset{\|}{C}}SCoA \xrightarrow[\substack{(2) \ -H_2O \\ (3) \ 2\,H}]{(1) \ 2\,H} RCH_2CH_2\overset{O}{\underset{\|}{C}}SCoA$$

Once again, this cycle is one which is enzyme catalyzed and can be repeated to build up acids of the required length. The details of how all these facts were experimentally determined form an exciting story for your further reading.

10.3D The Compound Lipids

In addition to the glycerides or simple lipids, which are made up of glycerol and fatty acids, there are a large number of similar materials that also contain other structural features. The most common of these compound lipids are the **phospholipids**, which contain a phosphoric acid residue and a nitrogen base—for example, the **α-lecithins**, which on hydrolysis yield **choline**.

$$\begin{array}{l} CH_2O_2CR \\ | \\ CHO_2CR' \\ | \\ \quad O \\ \quad \uparrow \\ CH_2OPOCH_2CH_2N^+(CH_3)_3 \\ \quad | \\ \quad O^- \end{array} \xrightarrow[H^+]{5\,H_2O} \begin{array}{c} glycerol \\ + \\ RCO_2H \\ + \\ R'CO_2H \end{array} + \begin{array}{c} O \\ \uparrow \\ HOPOH \\ | \\ OH \end{array}$$

$$+ \ [HOCH_2CH_2N(CH_3)_3]^+OH^-$$
choline (salt form)

Another compound lipid frequently encountered is the **glycolipid**. In addition to a fatty acid, the glycolipid will contain a carbohydrate (galactose or glucose) and the nitrogen base **sphingosine**.

The functions of the compound lipids are not well understood. It seems clear, however, that they are very important, because the bulk of the lipids found in the brain, nerve tissue, and vital organs—such as the heart, kidney, liver, and so on—

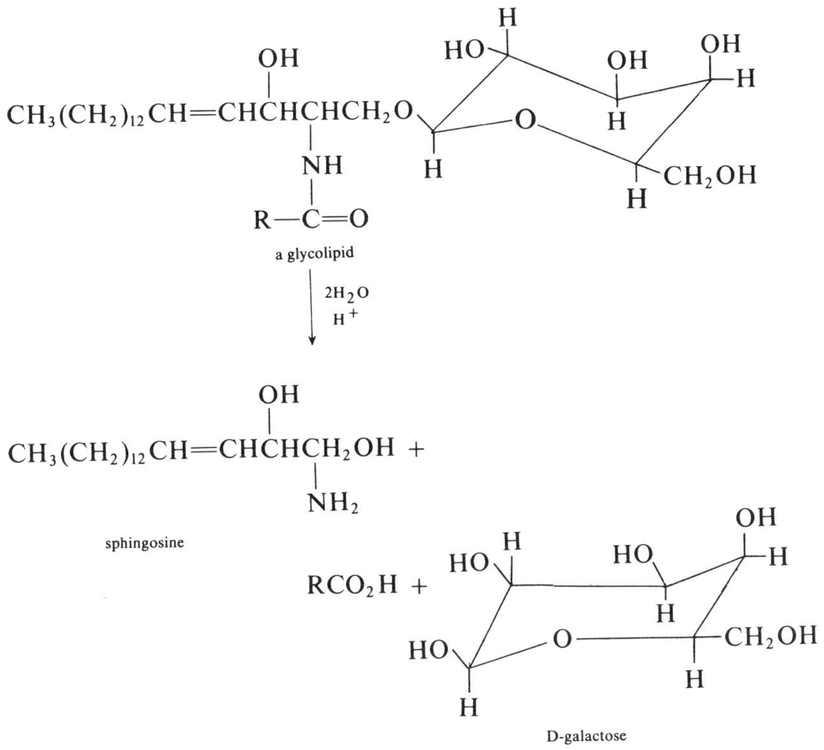

$$CH_3(CH_2)_{12}CH=CHCHCHCH_2O\text{—}$$

with OH and NH—R—C=O substituents

a glycolipid

$$\xrightarrow[H^+]{2H_2O}$$

$$CH_3(CH_2)_{12}CH=CHCHCH_2OH +$$

with OH and NH$_2$ substituents

sphingosine

$$RCO_2H +$$

D-galactose

are of the complex type. The fact that they have both polar and nonpolar sites suggests roles as surface-active agents. Some evidence has been found that the phospholipids work in the transport of fats.

10.4
THE AMINO ACIDS AND PROTEINS

It might not seem at first that the simple combination of an amino and a carboxyl group in a molecule would be a particularly complicated or important topic. Yet, as we shall see, the chemistry of the α-amino acids (especially of the L or S configuration) is involved in the very basis of life itself. The complete hydrolysis of **proteins** (from the Greek, *proteios*, first) always gives a mixture of relatively few α-amino acids. A few of these, along with their common names (which are almost always used), are given in Table 10.3. The structures as drawn in the table are misleading, because the presence of both an acidic and

**TABLE 10.3   STRUCTURE AND NAMES OF
SOME α-AMINO ACIDS**

Name	*Structure*

Glycine $H_2NCH_2CO_2H$

Alanine H_2NCHCO_2H
$$|$$
$$CH_3$$

Valine H_2NCHCO_2H
$$|$$
$$CHCH_3$$
$$|$$
$$CH_3$$

Leucine $(CH_3)_2CHCH_2CHCO_2H$
$$|$$
$$NH_2$$

Serine H_2NCHCO_2H
$$|$$
$$CH_2OH$$

Cysteine H_2NCHCO_2H
$$|$$
$$CH_2SH$$

Phenylalanine H_2NCHCO_2H
$$|$$
$$CH_2$$

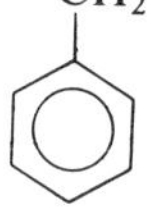

Proline $HN\!\!-\!\!-\!\!-CO_2H$ (ring structure)

Aspartic acid H_2NCHCO_2H
$$|$$
$$CH_2$$
$$|$$
$$CO_2H$$

Lysine H_2NCHCO_2H
$$|$$
$$(CH_2)_4$$
$$|$$
$$NH_2$$

a basic group leads to a dipolar ion structure. Thus chemical and physical evidence (e.g., solubility, melting points, acidity, and basicity) indicates that glycine exists in neutral solution as a **Zwitterion** (from the German, *Zwitter*, hybrid).

$$\overset{+}{H_3N}CH_2CO_2^{-}$$

From the table, we see that a variety of structural types exist— for example, acyclic, aromatic rings, other substituents, and so forth. You should note that extra carboxyl and amino groups can be present, giving acidic and basic amino acids, respectively.

10.4A   The Syntheses and Reactions of Amino Acids

The methods by which chemists and biochemists prepare α-amino acids for further protein studies are not especially unusual, but they do give us an opportunity to present a few new reactions. In the study of amines (pp. 203–204), we discussed the direct reaction of alkyl halides with excess ammonia. This method, and certain modifications of it, is the most general of the numerous syntheses that have been developed. The first problem is that of obtaining the α-halo acid; it can be solved either by the **Hell-Volhard-Zelinsky halogenation** or by a modification of the **malonic ester synthesis.**

$$RCH_2CO_2H \xrightarrow[P]{X_2} RCHCO_2H$$
$$\underset{X}{|}$$

$$\begin{array}{ccccc} CO_2H & & CO_2H & & \\ | & & | & & \\ RCH & \xrightarrow[ether]{X_2} & RC\!-\!X & \xrightarrow{heat} & RCHCO_2H + CO_2 \\ | & & | & & | \\ CO_2H & & CO_2H & & X \end{array}$$

$X_2 = Br_2$ and Cl_2

Emil Fischer *(German, 1852–1919). A student of Kekulé and Baeyer, Fischer is one of the giants of organic chemistry. His best-known contributions are in carbohydrate and protein chemistry, especially structural problems. Actually he did important work in a broad area of organic chemistry. Fischer developed the aqueous acid hydrolysis of proteins as well as several synthetic methods. While the techniques have been improved by later scientists, many of his findings have proved to be correct. He discovered phenylhydrazine and applied it to the field of carbohydrate chemistry with great success. Fischer received the second Nobel prize in chemistry in 1902.*

Courtesy of the Edgar Fahs Smith Memorial Collection.

In the Hell-Volhard-Zelinsky (H-V-Z) method, the phosphorus converts some of the acid into the corresponding acid halide, which is halogenated in the α position and then reacts with more acid to repeat the cycle.

$$3 \, X_2 + 2 \, P \rightarrow 2 \, PX_3$$

$$RCH_2CO_2H + PX_3 \rightarrow RCH_2COX$$

$$RCH_2COX + X_2 \rightarrow \underset{\underset{X}{|}}{R}CHCOX + HX$$

$$\underset{\underset{X}{|}}{R}CHCOX + RCH_2CO_2H \rightarrow \underset{\underset{X}{|}}{R}CHCO_2H + RCH_2COX$$

All the α hydrogens can be replaced by halogens, but it is possible, in practice, to limit the extent of the reaction.

The malonic ester method is especially useful for complex acids, inasmuch as the nature of the R shown in the preceding equation can be varied widely.

$$\underset{\underset{CO_2R}{|}}{\overset{CO_2R}{\overset{|}{CH_2}}} \xrightarrow{C_2H_5O^-Na^+} \underset{\underset{CO_2R}{|}}{\overset{CO_2R}{\overset{|}{CH^-Na^+}}} \xrightarrow{RX} \underset{\underset{CO_2R}{|}}{\overset{CO_2R}{\overset{|}{CHR}}} \xrightarrow{hydrolysis} \underset{\underset{CO_2H}{|}}{\overset{CO_2H}{\overset{|}{CHR}}} + Na^+X^-$$

From either reaction sequence, the α-halo acid is treated with a large excess of ammonia.

$$\underset{\underset{X}{|}}{R}CHCO_2H \xrightarrow[\text{excess}]{NH_3} \underset{\underset{NH_2}{|}}{R}CHCO_2H$$

a racemic α-amino acid

As indicated, the product is a mixture of enantiomers (except for glycine) and must be resolved (pp. 330–401) before the synthetic acid can be compared with the isolated natural material or, in most cases, before it can be used in further synthesis.

A clever synthesis of amino acids that avoids further reaction of the primary amino group with more halo acid is the **Gabriel phthalimide synthesis**.

A combination of the phthalimide and the malonic ester syntheses can also be used to good advantage in some cases.

The reactions of α-amino acids are those which we have
studied for carboxylic acids and for amines. A few of these are
of special importance at this time and should be reviewed here.

The formation of liquid esters was very important in the early
studies as a method of obtaining pure samples of the amino
acids. The body makes use of amide formation at the α-amino

group to protect itself from undesirable organic acids. Amide formation at the carboxyl and amino groups is the basis of protein structure, as we shall see shortly.

An additional reaction of primary amino groups, which is of special importance in protein studies, is that with nitrous acid.

$$\underset{\underset{NH_2}{|}}{RCHCO_2H} + HONO \rightarrow \underset{\underset{OH}{|}}{RCHCO_2H} + N_2\uparrow + H_2O$$

By measuring the amount of nitrogen produced from a given sample weight of protein, it is possible to determine the number of free primary amino groups present.

10.4B   The Degradation and Synthesis of Peptides

When the amino and carboxyl groups involved in an amide both come from amino acids, we have the formation of a **peptide**—the first step on the long path to the proteins.

$$\underset{\underset{NH_2}{|}}{RCHCO_2H} + \underset{\underset{HO_2CCHR'}{|}}{NH_2} \rightarrow \rightarrow \rightarrow \underset{\underset{NH_2 \quad R'}{|}}{RCH\overset{\overset{O}{\|}}{C}NHCHCO_2H} \quad \text{(not directly)}$$
a dipeptide

It is generally accepted that we talk about peptides up to a molecular weight of 10,000; above that, the polymeric amides are considered proteins. With 20 to 25 different α-amino acids commonly found (on hydrolysis) and with a typical protein containing hundreds or even thousands of these acids, the possibilities for variation in protein structure begin to approach the infinite.

Despite the enormous problems involved in the understanding of protein structure, some of which we have not yet even suggested, progress is being made. In our little book, we can not hope to do more than entice you to read further, but it will be worthwhile to examine the approaches that have shown promise. The first task is to establish the number and kind of amino acids present. As you will see, other molecules may also be present, but for now, let us consider simple proteins, that is, those containing only amino acids. We have already introduced some of the required tools for dealing with these questions. The complete hydrolysis of a "pure" protein and the comparison of the amino acids with authentic samples should tell us what and how much is present. A popular tool has been paper chromatography. More recently, gas and thin-layer chromatography of the methyl esters is being used. Other instrumental methods, such as the amino acid analyzer, speed up the work. There are two major difficulties in this work: the protein's (1) purity and (2) molecular weight.

Just as the structure of proteins is a difficult problem, so, too, are the tasks of obtaining a homogeneous material and of measuring its molecular weight. The huge number of different proteins possible is illustrated by the complex mixtures found in living material. In addition, there is the problem of **denaturation**. When a protein is removed from its natural environment, even very mild methods can cause physical and chemical changes that are irreversible and that render certain kinds of further study useless. The study of the proteins in a fried egg will give us only limited information about their natural condition. Inasmuch as the usual techniques of recrystallization, distillation, melting points, and boiling points are futile, new ones must be found. Some conventional forms of chromatography are useful, especially those on gels and other natural and synthetic polymers. The migration of ions under the influence of applied electric fields, either in solution or on substrates such as cellulose or starch, is known as **electrophoresis** and is important both for separation and as a criterion of purity. The transport of material across membranes is called **osmosis** and is also frequently used. Very high-speed centrifugation in an **ultracentrifuge** can cause selective sedimentation and thus purification. These techniques also give information about the relative molecular weights of the proteins being studied. **Countercurrent distribution** is particularly useful as a mild method of obtaining homogeneous samples from natural materials.

A still more difficult problem remains—that of determining the order or sequence of the amino acids in the protein amide chain. It can easily be shown that a polypeptide made up of just 10 different amino acids, each taken only once, can have 3,628,800 different sequences. This very "simple" molecule illustrates the job of fitting together, say, 15 amino acids each taken three or four times. A most significant type of information is the structure of the amino acid residue at each end of the chain. In the simplest, and fortunately the most common, case, there will be a free amino group on one end of the peptide and a free carboxyl group on the other. A common method of discovering the structure of the **N-terminal residue** is to react the peptide with 2,4-dinitrofluorobenzene. The two nitro groups activate the molecule so that a nucleophilic displacement of the halogen by the amine takes place.

a DNP peptide

When the peptide, which has now been labeled, is hydrolyzed, the terminal amino acid can be separated because of its different physical properties and identified by comparison with an authentic sample. The chemical determination of the **C-terminal residue** (i.e., the free carboxyl end) has not been so successful, and an enzymatic method is usually used. The enzyme **carboxypeptidase** has the property of catalyzing the hydrolysis of only the amide (peptide) linkage adjacent to a free carboxyl group. Once again, the free amino acid can be separated from the shortened peptide and identified. In principle, it would be possible to repeat this process, and other methods of N-terminal analysis as well, and to remove the acids one at a time for determination of the sequence. In actual practice, this extremely tedious process is replaced by a partial hydrolysis followed by studies of the resulting smaller peptides. When enough di-, tri-, and so on, peptides have been identified, it is possible to fit them together as in a jigsaw puzzle. The amount of effort required for such a study is measured in man-years and accounts for the small number of proteins whose amino acid sequence has been completely worked out.

The next step in understanding the structure of a peptide is its synthesis. The major difficulty is the fact that when an attempt is made to form an amide between two different amino acids, four products are possible.

$$H_2N-A-CO_2H + H_2N-B-CO_2H$$

$$\begin{array}{c} O \\ \parallel \\ H_2N-A-CNH-B-CO_2H \end{array}$$

$$\begin{array}{c} O \\ \parallel \\ H_2N-B-CNH-A-CO_2H \end{array}$$

$$\begin{array}{c} O \\ \parallel \\ H_2N-A-CNH-A-CO_2H \end{array}$$

$$\begin{array}{c} O \\ \parallel \\ H_2N-B-CNH-B-CO_2H \end{array}$$

Part of the problem is taken care of by the fact that an acid derivative (e.g., the acid chloride) rather than the free acid is used, but it does not prevent the acid derivative from reacting with another molecule like itself.

$$\begin{array}{c} O \\ \parallel \\ H_2NCH_2CCl \end{array} + \begin{array}{c} H_2NCHCO_2H \\ | \\ CHCH_3 \\ | \\ CH_3 \end{array}$$

$$\begin{array}{c} O \\ \parallel \\ H_2NCH_2CNHCHCO_2H \\ | \\ CHCH_3 \\ | \\ CH_3 \end{array}$$
glycylvaline

$$\begin{array}{c} O \\ \parallel \\ H_2NCH_2CNHCH_2COCl \end{array}$$
glycylglycine (acid chloride)

You have seen the use of protective groups before (pp. 157 and 207–208), but here we have the additional problem of needing one that can be removed under mild conditions which do not break the new peptide linkage. One of the most useful of the protective groups is acylation by **benzyl chlorocarbonate** (carbobenzoxy chloride).

$$\text{C}_6\text{H}_5\text{CH}_2\text{OH} + \underset{\text{phosgene}}{\text{Cl}-\overset{\overset{\text{O}}{\|}}{\text{C}}-\text{Cl}} \longrightarrow \underset{\text{benzyl chlorocarbonate}}{\text{C}_6\text{H}_5\text{CH}_2\text{O}\overset{\overset{\text{O}}{\|}}{\text{C}}\text{Cl}}$$

$$\text{C}_6\text{H}_5-\text{CH}_2\text{O}_2\text{CCl} + \text{H}_2\text{NCH}_2\text{CO}_2\text{H} \longrightarrow$$

$$\text{C}_6\text{H}_5-\text{CH}_2\text{O}_2\text{CNHCH}_2\text{CO}_2\text{H} \xrightarrow{\text{SOCl}_2}$$

$$\text{C}_6\text{H}_5-\text{CH}_2\text{O}_2\text{CNHCH}_2\overset{\overset{\text{O}}{\|}}{\text{C}}\text{Cl} + \underset{\underset{\text{CH}_3}{|}}{\underset{\text{CHCH}_3}{|}}{\text{H}_2\text{NCHCO}_2\text{H}} \longrightarrow$$

$$\text{C}_6\text{H}_5-\text{CH}_2\text{O}_2\text{CNHCH}_2\overset{\overset{\text{O}}{\|}}{\text{C}}\text{NHCHCO}_2\text{H} \xrightarrow[\text{Pd}]{\text{H}_2}$$
$$\underset{\underset{\text{CH}_3}{|}}{\underset{\text{CHCH}_3}{|}}$$

$$\text{C}_6\text{H}_5\text{CH}_3 + \text{CO}_2 + \text{H}_2\text{NCH}_2\overset{\overset{\text{O}}{\|}}{\text{C}}\text{NHCHCO}_2\text{H}$$
$$\underset{\underset{\text{CH}_3}{|}}{\underset{\text{CHCH}_3}{|}}$$

glycylvaline

The final step of removing the protective group by catalytic hydrogenation is especially important, because it does not affect the peptide bond and because the by-products (toluene and carbon dioxide) are easily removed.

10.4C   The Detailed Structure of Proteins

On the basis of our discussion of the degradation and synthesis of proteins, it might seem that the structure of the proteins has already been presented. In the classical organic chemistry sense it has been; we know the number and kind of amino acids present and how they are joined, which is called the **primary structure**. We have discussed conformation in simple molecules, such as ethane and cyclohexane (pp. 28–30 and 77–79), and found that these spatial arrangements can have important physical and chemical effects. For the long polymeric chain of amide linkages of a protein, even greater energy differences between conformations might be expected, and these, in turn, should produce marked changes in properties. Such structural considerations are known as the **secondary structure**, which is thought to be largely responsible for the very specific properties of proteins— for example, the catalytic effects of the enzymes.

Two approaches have been especially useful in the study of secondary structure: first, the synthesis and study of simple polypeptides containing only one kind of amino acid; second, the method of study called **x-ray diffraction**. Unlike the techniques of infrared and ultraviolet spectroscopy (see Appendix II), structure analysis using X rays is far from routine. Even using high-speed computers, years of effort are required to determine the structure of a complex molecule, but progress is being made. There is now ample evidence that an **alpha helix** (in the **right-handed** sense) is the preferred conformation of many natural polypeptides and proteins (see Figure 10.2). Perhaps the most

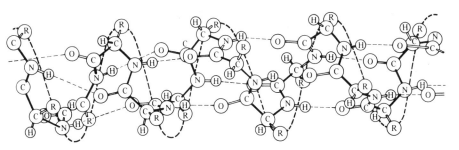

FIGURE 10.2.   Segment of a Peptide Showing α Helix.

important consequence of the α helix is the fact that distances and angles between atoms are about right to allow hydrogen bonding between amide hydrogen and carbonyl oxygen of amino acids several peptide linkages apart. These forces play an important role in maintaining the structure of the protein, and they strongly influence its properties. We should note in this qualitative picture that the right-hand "thread" of the α helix is required by the S (or L) configuration of the natural amino acids. This fact, too, must be related to the great specificity of protein functions. The process of denaturation (p. 277) seems to be related to the uncoiling of the α helix.

Still more refined descriptions of protein structure are possible, and a great deal of active research is being carried out. The **tertiary structure** of proteins is concerned with the manner in which the α helix is folded, and therefore with the interaction of atoms in more or less remote parts of the chain. The questions of hydration are also closely related to tertiary structure. Another problem, which is beginning to be referred to as **quaternary structure**, deals with the forces that hold groups of α helices together. For example, it has been suggested that in some cases the α helix itself is coiled in a superhelix, and that these superhelices are, in turn, woven together much like a stranded rope or cable. As the detail we seek grows, so do the difficulties, and only a limited amount of insight has yet been obtained on these last two structural levels.

10.4D   The Nucleic Acids—Synthesis and Heredity

The importance of the proteins, with their great variety of structures and functions, to the survival of the human organism is obvious. The questions of paramount importance are the why and how of the synthesis of these remarkable natural products— **biosynthesis**. There exist in the body **nucleoproteins**, which are proteins associated with other natural polymers called **nucleic acids**. We have already met one example of the basic units in a nucleic acid—the nucleotide—adenosine (p. 259). In addition to adenine and D-ribose, other heterocyclic nitrogen bases and one other sugar are important in the nucleic acids.

guanine   cytosine   thymine   uracil

D-2-deoxyribose

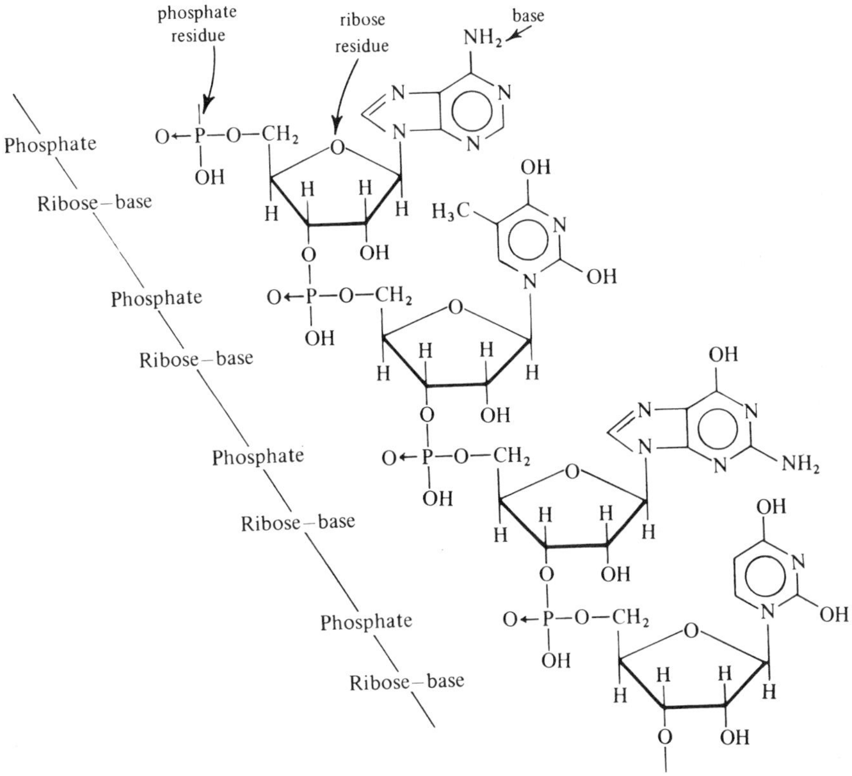

FIGURE 10.3.   Partial Structure of a Polynucleotide.

The polymeric chains of the nucleic acids are made up of a series of nucleosides (i.e., a sugar-base pair) linked together as polyphosphate esters. Thus, they may be described as **polynucleotides** (see Figure 10.3), which we can represent schematically as follows:

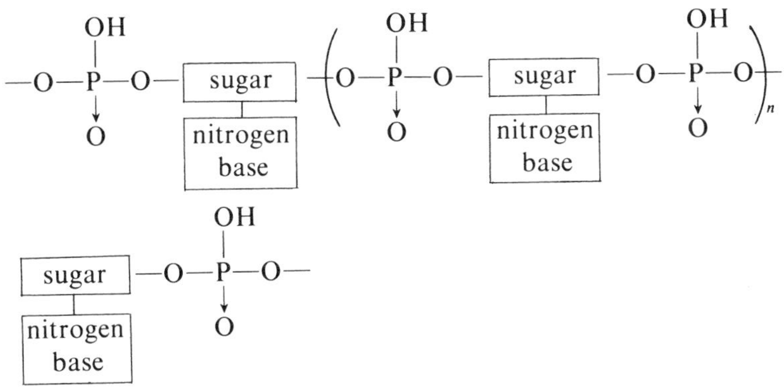

The value of n in typical nucleic acids is very large and shows a great deal of variation depending on the source from which it is obtained. Molecular weights of 1 million to 1 billion are known. Very little detailed information can be given about a nucleic acid unless the source is specified, but a general description of two general classes is of interest. **Deoxyribonucleic acids (DNA)** make up the chromosomes found in plant and animal cell nuclei and are known to contain the genetic information controlling the biosynthesis of proteins. In other words, these are the molecules that form the basis of heredity. As in the proteins, the nucleic acids are wound in the form of a helix. The form of DNA has been described as a double helix with the two strands forming a complementary structure. Such a model allows the most favorable arrangement of the hydrogen bonds maintaining the desired positions of the various components. The sequence of the bases (adenine, thymine, guanine, and cytosine are involved in DNA) has not been determined and certainly varies for different DNA's, as does the overall percentage composition of the bases. It is this sequence of bases, called the **genetic code**, that carries the hereditary information.

The exact mechanism by which DNA causes the synthesis of a desired protein has not been worked out. A promising theory is that it serves as a template on which a protein is built. A difficulty with this theory is the fact that although most protein synthesis takes place outside the cell nucleus, DNA is not found there. The obvious solution is that DNA passes its information on to some intermediate, which carries it to the site of protein synthesis. The best information now available suggests that **ribonucleic acids (RNA)** play this role. RNA is similar to DNA, except that D-ribose replaces D-2-deoxyribose, and uracil replaces thymine. The base sequence in RNA is not generally known for naturally occurring materials, and the regularities in the proportion of bases observed in DNA's are not found. RNA seems to exist as a single helix, and the bulk of it is found outside the nucleus. Different RNA's fulfill different tasks; one type has been called **messenger RNA**. It is this type that appears to convey the directive influence of the DNA to the protein being synthesized.

10.4E   The Metabolism of Protein

The pathways by which the body obtains and uses the energy of the proteins begin at a common point—their breakdown to

α-amino acids by enzymes. However, the story becomes much more difficult to follow for the individual amino acids, because their degradations appear to be as different as their structures. We shall simply discuss a few representative examples to place the proteins in the overall metabolic process.

One very significant first step in the metabolism of amino acids is transamination.

$$
\begin{array}{c}
CO_2^- \\
| \\
RCHCO_2^- + \overset{|}{C}=O \\
| \\
{}_+NH_3 \quad\quad (CH_2)_2 \\
| \\
CO_2^-
\end{array}
\rightarrow
\begin{array}{c}
CO_2^- \\
| \\
RCCO_2^- \\
\| \\
O
\end{array}
+
\begin{array}{c}
\overset{+}{C}O_2^- \\
| \\
H_3NCH \\
| \\
(CH_2)_2 \\
| \\
CO_2^-
\end{array}
\rightarrow
\begin{array}{c}
CO_2^- \\
| \\
C=O \\
| \\
(CH_2)_2 \\
| \\
CO_2^-
\end{array}
+ NH_3
$$

α-ketoglutarate   an α-keto acid   glutamate

At first glance, this little cycle may not seem to be accomplishing very much; in fact, it is of great importance. The α-keto acid is just the kind of structure most suitable for entering the Krebs cycle (after further degradation). Indeed, if we started with alanine, we have produced pyruvate (pp. 260–261)!

$$
\begin{array}{c}
CH_3CHCO_2^- \\
| \\
NH_3^+
\end{array}
\rightarrow
\begin{array}{c}
CH_3CCO_2^- \\
\| \\
O
\end{array}
+ NH_3
$$

The required α-ketoglutarate is available because it is an intermediate in the Krebs cycle. The ammonia is converted to the waste product urea.

Certain amino acids, after transamination, can enter the fatty acid scheme; for example, isoleucine.

$$
\begin{array}{c}
CH_3 \\
| \\
CH_3CH_2CHCHCO_2^- \\
| \\
NH_3^+
\end{array}
\rightarrow
\begin{array}{c}
CH_3 \;\; O \\
| \quad \| \\
CH_3CH_2CH-CSCoA
\end{array}
\rightarrow
\begin{array}{c}
O \quad\;\; O \\
\| \quad\quad \| \\
CH_3CCHC-SCoA \\
| \\
CH_3
\end{array}
$$

$$\downarrow \text{CoA}$$

$$
\begin{array}{c}
O \\
\| \\
CH_3CSCoA
\end{array}
+
\begin{array}{c}
O \\
\| \\
CH_3CH_2CSCoA
\end{array}
$$

The acetyl CoA is the vital starting material for not only the Krebs cycle, but also the synthesis of a wide variety of materials. The three-carbon ester is converted by reaction with carbon dioxide to succinyl CoA, which is also an intermediate in the Krebs cycle.

It should be clear from even our limited discussion of the metabolism of the carbohydrates, lipids, and proteins that these processes are related by a number of common intermediates and that the Krebs cycle is of central importance. These facts allow the various food materials essential for survival to be interconverted to a large extent. As was pointed out earlier, the body is a dynamic rather than a static organism, one aspect of which is the common pool of metabolic intermediates.

SUGGESTED ADDITIONAL READINGS

Biochemistry in General

J. M. Sturtevant, "Biochemistry in the Introductory College Chemistry Course," *J. Chem. Educ.*, **44,** 184 (1967).

W. R. Roderick, "Structural Variety of Natural Products," *J. Chem. Educ.*, **39,** 2 (1962).

R. O'Connor, "Natural Product Chemistry," *J. Chem. Educ.*, **42,** 492 (1965).

Carbohydrates

Cason, Chapters 23–24.
Cram and Hammond, Chapter 27.
Karlson, Chapters 15, and 17–18.
Mahler and Cordes, Chapters 10 and 13.
Morrison and Boyd, Chapters 33–34.
Nussenbaum, Chapter 15.
Roberts and Caserio, Chapter 18.
Steiner, Chapters 12–13.

R. L. Horecker, "Pathways of Carbohydrate Metabolism and Their Physiological Significance," *J. Chem. Educ.*, **42,** 244 (1965).

P. Oesper, "Error and Trial: The Story of the Oxidative Reactions of Glycolysis," *J. Chem. Educ.*, **45,** 607 (1968).

Photosynthesis

Karlson, Chapter 16.
Mahler and Cordes, Chapter 11.

E. I. Rabinowitch and Govindjee, "The Role of Chlorophyll in Photosynthesis," *Sci. Am.*, **213** (1), 74 (1965).

Lipids

Karlson, Chapters 12 and 18.
Mahler and Cordes, Chapters 12 and 15.
Nussenbaum, Chapter 16.

D. M. Gibson, "The Biosynthesis of Fatty Acids," *J. Chem. Educ.*, **42,** 236 (1965).

M. J. R. Dawkins and D. Hall, "The Production of Heat by Fats," *Sci. Am.*, **213** (2), 62 (1965).

Amino Acids and Proteins

Cason, Chapter 25.
Cram and Hammond, Chapter 26.
Karlson, Chapters 2–4, 7–8, and 18.
Mahler and Cordes, Chapters 2–3, 16, and 18.
Morrison and Boyd, Chapter 37.
Nussenbaum, Chapter 17.
Roberts and Caserio, Chapter 20.
Steiner, Chapters 2–6.

A. L. McClellan, "The Significance of Hydrogen Bonds in Biological Structures," *J. Chem. Educ.*, **44,** 547 (1967).

B. F. C. Clark and K. A. Marcker, "How Proteins Start," *Sci. Am.*, **218** (1), 36 (1968).

R. R. Merrifield, "The Automatic Synthesis of Proteins," *Sci. Am.*, **218** (3), 56 (1968).

Nucleic Acids

Karlson, Chapter 7.
Mahler and Cordes, Chapters 4, and 17–18.
Steiner, Chapters 8–11.

J. S. Roth, "Ribonucleic Acids and Protein Synthesis," *J. Chem. Educ.*, **38,** 217 (1961).

B. Axelrod and L. E. Trachtman, "The World's Smallest Chemical Factory," *Chemistry*, **37** (5), 14 (1964).

R. W. Holley, "The Nucleotide Sequence of a Nucleic Acid," *Sci. Am.*, **214** (2), 30 (1966).

D. R. Davies, "X-ray Diffraction and Nucleic Acids," *Chemistry*, **40** (2), 8 (1967).

A. Kornberg, "The Synthesis of DNA," *Sci. Am.*, **219** (4), 64 (1968).

The Genetic Code

M. H. Nirenberg, "The Genetic Code: II," *Sci. Am.*, **208** (3), 80 (1963).

F. H. C. Crick, "The Genetic Code: III," *Sci. Am.*, **215** (4), 55 (1966).

SUMMARY

1. Many of the organic compounds that make up living organisms are high molecular weight, polymeric, polyfunctional molecules. The study of their chemistry is the work of the biochemist.

2. Starch and sugar are carbohydrates or polyhydroxylic aldehydes or ketones.

3. The hydroxyl and carbonyl groups of the carbohydrates show many of the reactions of these groups in simpler compounds, for example, esterification, addition, reduction, and oxidation.

4. There are numerous stereochemical questions associated with the carbohydrates (and the proteins), and these have profound effects on their chemistry especially in living systems.

5. Carbohydrates are found to exist as five- or six-member cyclic oxides. These hemiacetals are in equilibrium with the open chain compound, and this accounts for their ability to show some of the carbonyl reactions.

6. The higher saccharides are made up of two or more simple carbohydrates linked together as glucosides.

7. The production of carbohydrates in nature is the process of photosynthesis, and much of the detail of the reactions involved has been learned.

8. The carbohydrates supply much of the energy the body requires. The process by which the energy is released and stored is now reasonably well understood.

9. Reactions taking place under physiological conditions require highly specific catalysts called enzymes.

10. The Krebs cycle is of central importance in the interconversion of food materials in the body. Connected with this is the balance of material and energy which must be maintained.

11. The esters of long-chain fatty acids and glycerol are the fats and oils known as lipids.

12. On saponification the fats yield salts of the acids and these are soaps. The interaction of the polar and nonpolar parts of the soap with oil and water explains their usefulness as cleaning agents.

13. Many of the reactions of the fats are similar to the simple esters, for example, saponification, hydrogenation, hydrogenolysis, and addition. Saponification and addition can be semiquantitative for identification purposes.

14. The idea of β oxidation is important in understanding the metabolism of fats and how they supply energy to the body.

15. The lipids can be synthesized by the body, and this leads to a dynamic steady state in the living organism.

16. Numerous amide or peptide bonds between α-amino acids form the polymeric proteins.

17. A number of generally useful reactions have been employed in the synthesis of α-amino acids.

$$RCH_2CO_2H \xrightarrow[P]{X_2} \underset{X}{RCHCO_2H} \xrightarrow{NH_3} \underset{NH_2}{RCHCO_2H}$$

$$\underset{\substack{| \\ CH_2 \\ | \\ CO_2H}}{CO_2H} \xrightarrow{X_2} \underset{\substack{| \\ CHX \\ | \\ CO_2H}}{CO_2H} \xrightarrow{heat} \underset{X}{CH_2CO_2H}$$

$$X = Br_2 \text{ and } Cl_2$$

$$\text{(phthalimide)}N^-K^+ + \underset{X}{RCHCO_2R} \rightarrow$$

$$\text{(phthalimido)}N-\underset{R}{CHCO_2R} \xrightarrow{H^+ \text{(aq)}} \underset{NH_2}{RCHCO_2H}$$

18. Some reactions of amino acids are as follows:

$$RCHCO_2H \begin{cases} + R'OH \rightleftharpoons RCHCO_2R' \\ \qquad\qquad\quad NH_2 \\ \\ + \text{[benzene]} COCl \rightarrow RCHCO_2H \\ \qquad\qquad\qquad\qquad NHCO-\text{[benzene]} \\ \\ + HONO \rightarrow RCHCO_2H + N_2 + H_2O \\ \qquad\qquad\qquad OH \end{cases}$$

(with NH_2 on the left $RCHCO_2H$)

19. The structure of a protein is only determined with great difficulty. After a homogeneous sample has been obtained, its composition is determined by complete hydrolysis and its sequence or constitution by partial hydrolysis. After this primary structure has been determined, other more difficult questions of configuration arise.

20. Various instrumental techniques such as mass spectrometry and X-ray diffraction have become important for discovering the primary and secondary structure of proteins.

21. In the synthesis of peptides care must be used so that the proper amino acid is introduced in the sequence and that complex mixtures of products are avoided. Of the various protective groups used, carbobenzoxy chloride has proved to be one of the best.

22. Combinations of certain nitrogen heterocycles and sugars as polyphosphate esters are known as polynucleotides. These polymeric materials are known to contain the genetic information of heredity.

23. The metabolism of proteins is more complex than that of the carbohydrates and lipids, but it is known that all three are related, and that the Krebs cycle is of central importance.

24. Coenzyme A, especially acetyl CoA, is an intermediate in the metabolism of all three food materials we have discussed. The importance of its role in maintaining the proper metabolic balance is difficult to overstate.

PROBLEMS

1. A useful method of locating the various sugars after they have been separated by paper or thin-layer chromatography is to spray the sheet with ammoniacal silver nitrate solution. Why is it useful

in terms of chemical reactions, and what should be observed? Suppose that a mixture of glucose, fructose, and gluconic acid is chromatographed under conditions known to separate all three; it is then sprayed with $Ag(NH_3)_2^+$. What should you observe?   If any of the compounds do not show up, suggest another useful spray.

2. Starting with α-hydroxyacetaldehyde, outline a suitable route for preparing each aldotetrose. Consider the question of the resolution of racemic mixtures and indicate when these should be carried out. Are there other points in your synthesis when pure enantiomers could have been obtained? Why did you select the ones you did?

3. Write the reaction of D-ribose with each of the following:

a. HIO_4
b. Br_2/H_2O
c. H_2/Ni
d. HNO_3

e. $(CH_3CO)_2O$
f. $CH_3OH + H^+$
g. HCN
h. $C_6H_5NHNH_2$

4. In question 3, part e, calculate the number of grams of acetic anhydride required to react completely with 1 g of D-ribose.

5. A monosaccharide (A) melted with decomposition at 167 to 168°. It was soluble in water and gave negative tests for nitrogen, halogens, sulfur, and metals. It also reacted with acetyl chloride, decolorized permanganate solution, and reduced Fehling's and Tollens' reagents. When (A) reacted with phenylhydrazine, (B) was produced, with a melting point of from 199 to 201°d. If (A) was warmed with HNO_3, a vigorous oxidation took place and (C) was formed after cooling. Compound (C) was soluble in dilute base but not in water; its neutralization equivalent was 104 ± 1. Treatment of (C) with acetyl chloride produced a new compound, but (C) did not react with phenylhydrazine. If (C) was kept above its decomposition point (212 to 213°) for a short time, it was converted into (D), which was soluble in dilute sodium bicarbonate solution. The neutralization equivalent of (D) was 111 ± 1. Treatment of (D) with p-bromophenacyl bromide gave a derivative (E), melting at 137 to 138°. Compound (A) was optically active with a specific rotation of +81°, but (B), (C), (D), and (E) were optically inactive. By reference to suitable tables, draw structures for all of the compounds and complete all of the reactions described.

6. Draw the structure and name a glyceride containing fatty acids labeled as in Knoop's experiments. Describe the β-oxidation process for your glyceride showing why Knoop drew the conclusions he did.

7. Twenty-five grams of a certain fat reacts with 23.8 g of iodine.

Calculate the average number of double bonds per molecule if the fat has a molecular weight of 800. Why is this figure an average number? Suggest a specific glyceride that fits these facts.

8. A naturally occurring fat reacts with each of the following reagents:
   a. $NaOH/H_2O$ c. ICl
   b. H_2/Ni d. H_2/copper chromite (heat and pressure)
   Draw the structure of a glyceride that would show these reactions, and give it a suitable name. Using the same fatty acids, draw other fats that would show all the above reactions.

9. Select one of your answers to question 8 and calculate (a) its iodine number, (b) its saponification equivalent, and (c) its saponification number.

10. Suggest more than one synthetic route from benzene and three-carbon alcohols to each of the following amino acids:

    a. CH_3CHCO_2H c. $CH_3CHCH_2CHCO_2H$
         | | |
        NH_2 CH_3 NH_2

    b. CH_2CHCO_2H d. $\langle\bigcirc\rangle$—CH_2CHCO_2H
       | | |
      OH NH_2 NH_2

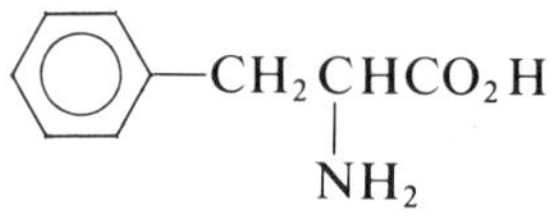

    Name all the organic compounds involved and discuss the advantages of each route.

11. Phenylalanine will react with each of the following chemicals:
    a. ammonia/P_2O_5 d. nitrous acid
    b. methanol/H^+ e. benzoyl chloride
    c. acetic anhydride   f. $SOCl_2$
    Write the equations for each reaction and name all compounds.

12. A heptapeptide was allowed to react with 2,4-dinitrofluoro-benzene and was then subjected to complete hydrolysis. Thin-layer chromatography (quantitative) showed the following amino acids and their relative amounts: 1 mole of dinitrophenylglycine (DNP-glycine), 1 mole of serine, 1 mole of valine, 2 moles of glycine, and 2 moles of leucine. The peptide was partially hydrolyzed and five fragments were obtained. The di- and tripeptides were treated with dinitrofluorobenzene, completely hydrolyzed, and the following amino acids were found:
    1. DNP-leucine, glycine, and serine
    2. DNP-glycine, glycine, and leucine
    3. DNP-serine, valine, and glycine

4. DNP-leucine and leucine

5. DNP-glycine and valine

On the basis of these facts, deduce the structure of the heptapeptide and draw it.

13. Propose a method for preparing the tripeptides actually found in **1**, 2, and 3 of question 12.

14. A linear polypeptide is treated with excess nitrous acid. It is found that 54.0 mg of peptide gives 2.58 ml of N_2 at STP. If glycine, lysine, and phenylalanine, in the molar ratio 6:1:1, make up the chain, what is the molecular weight of the polypeptide?

11

Natural Products
of Health and Disease

11.1
INTRODUCTION

In Chapter 10, we discussed the general classes of compounds that make up and nourish the human body. Of equal importance are the substances that control and regulate the body and those that fight disease, either naturally occurring or man-made. With topics as broad and complex as these, it is all but impossible to place the various materials in separate compartments; therefore, we shall find some overlap. For example, the nucleoproteins were arbitrarily placed in Chapter 10, but they are clearly vital in the control of the body processes. The enzymes and coenzymes that were frequently cited as being vital constituents of cellular reactions will be discussed in this chapter. Whatever the difficulties, the unifying and essential fact remains that these vital materials are all basically organic compounds and as such deserve at least a brief treatment in this text. As was the case in Chapter 10, the account will have to be rather qualitative and incomplete; the structures and reactions are frequently complex, and the present state of our understanding is far less perfect than we might wish. The Suggested Additional Readings will help the first shortcoming. Improvement in the latter must come from the numerous research laboratories where many of the problems we are discussing are under study.

11.2
ENZYME CATALYSIS

Once again, we must begin by talking about energy—not just the energy the body obtains from metabolism, but a more fundamental question of the energy considerations of individual reactions. All chemical reactions are reversible and many (e.g., esterifications, pp. 181–183) show measurable equilibrium constants. It is also true that most organic reactions show a measurable activation energy. That is, they require some input of energy before reaction can take place. This energy requirement in biochemical reactions is often supplied by ATP, which we have found stores some of the energy obtained from the metabolism of foods (pp. 259–262). Whatever the source of the energy, there must always be a balance of energy for reactions to take place. The question of real importance in our present discussion is the rate at which the equilibrium is reached. For it to be a practically useful rate, it is frequently necessary to introduce a large amount of energy. An alternative is to use a **catalyst** that serves to lower effectively the energy of activation or the **energy barrier**, as it is often called. We have encountered catalysts before—for example, the reduction of alkynes (p. 81).

In biochemical systems, the catalysts are the **enzymes**, which are proteins as far as is presently known. You will recall that for many of the reactions in Chapter 10 we said that a particular enzyme was required. Quite a large number of enzymes have been obtained in crystalline form, but only a limited amount of detailed structural data is available. One enzyme, ribonuclease, has had its amino acid sequence worked out. The question of nomenclature is both simple and difficult. Inasmuch as little is known about the chemical composition of enzymes, they cannot be named as organic compounds. Such names would be useless in any case because of their length. The usual procedure is to add the suffix **-ase** to a brief description of the type of activity in which the enzyme takes part. Thus, proteases are enzymes involved in cleaving proteins, esterases deal with the cleavage of esters, methyltransferases assist in reactions requiring the interchange of a methyl group, and so on. More specific names are made by including the chemical name of the substrate; for example, lactate dehydrogenase catalyzes the removal of hydrogen from the lactic acid anion, and glucose 6-phosphatase catalyzes the hydrolysis of the phosphoric acid ester at the 6-carbon of glucose. As in all organic chemistry, some of the older enzymes have common names that are less descriptive; for example, pepsin catalyzes the hydrolysis of peptide linkages, and emulsin catalyzes the hydrolysis of β-glycosides (p. 256–257).

The most remarkable aspect of enzyme catalytic activity is its great specificity. You have seen many examples of the fact that even for simple organic reactants several courses of reaction are possible. In most organic reactions, it is only possible to minimize the yields of by-products; rarely can they be eliminated. The body cannot afford this inefficiency nor the production of the foreign by-products. Thus, the enzyme catalysts not only have to change the energy requirement of reaction, but they must make this change only for the desired reaction. They do so with remarkable success. For example, the enzyme emulsin will affect only the hydrolysis of β-glycosides, whereas maltase affects only those with the α arrangement. It would seem that this state of affairs would essentially solve many of the problems of organic synthesis. There are technical difficulties, but *in vitro* biosynthetic routes are being developed for many difficult or nearly impossible organic preparations. You should recall that such a process has been in use for centuries in the fermentation of glucose to ethanol.

Another aspect of enzyme specificity has to do with optical activity. We have already pointed out that nearly all the naturally occurring α-amino acids have the S configuration; thus, the enzymes are optically active with many asymmetric centers. In their catalytic activities, the enzymes are highly stereospecific with respect to the degradation and synthesis of compounds. For example, photosynthesis produces only R-glucose and S-glucose is not used in animal metabolism. This fact also suggests an immediate practical application by the organic chemist—the resolution of racemic mixtures. In fact, it has been used with remarkable success; for example, a penicillin mold is known that reacts more rapidly with 2(R),3(R)-(+)-tartaric acid than 2(S),3(S)-(−)-tartaric acid, and nearly pure levorotatory acid can be obtained from the racemate.

$$
\underset{\text{racemic mixture}}{
\begin{array}{c}
CO_2H \\
| \\
HCOH \\
| \\
HOCH \\
| \\
CO_2H
\end{array}
\quad + \quad
\begin{array}{c}
CO_2H \\
| \\
HOCH \\
| \\
HCOH \\
| \\
CO_2H
\end{array}
}
\quad \xrightarrow{\text{mold}} \quad
\underset{(-)\text{-tartaric acid}}{
\begin{array}{c}
CO_2H \\
| \\
HCOH \\
| \\
HOCH \\
| \\
CO_2H
\end{array}
}
$$

A great deal remains to be learned about the reasons for the specificity of enzyme action, but it will be worthwhile to outline the most likely current mechanism. There is ample evidence that the enzyme and the substrate first form a complex in which the nature of the bonding is specific both for the substrate and for the reactions to follow. Such a complex is formed reversibly, and the bonding is certainly more like electrostatic or dipolar attractions than normal covalent bonds. Recently, direct evidence of the intermediate complex has become available. This theory helps to explain the substrate specificity of enzymes, especially that observed for optically active compounds. Another attractive aspect of the enzyme-substrate complex theory is the explanation it offers for **inhibitors** or substrates that decrease the catalytic activity of enzymes. A classic example is the inhibition of succinate dehydrogenase by malonate.

$$
\begin{array}{c}
CO_2^- \\
| \\
CH_2 \\
| \\
CH_2 \\
| \\
CO_2^-
\end{array}
\quad \xrightarrow[\text{dehydrogenase}]{\text{succinate}} \quad
[\text{succinate-enzyme}] \rightarrow
\underset{\text{fumarate}}{
\begin{array}{c}
H \qquad\quad CO_2^- \\
\diagdown \; C \; \diagup \\
\| \\
\diagup \; C \; \diagdown \\
{}^-O_2C \qquad\quad H
\end{array}
}
$$

(complexes)

$$
\begin{array}{c}
CO_2^- \\
| \\
CH_2 \\
| \\
CO_2^-
\end{array}
\qquad\qquad
[\text{malonate-enzyme}] \quad \rightarrow \text{ no reaction}
$$

This model of enzyme action has led to the development of methods for treating the kinetics of enzyme-catalyzed reactions, which have, in turn, provided a great deal of insight into the mechanisms of these vital processes.

One final point should be made about the general nature of enzyme action. Like other catalysts, enzymes change the rate at which equilibrium is reached (or approached), but they do not change the point of equilibrium—that is, the value of the equilibrium constant under a specific set of conditions, such as temperature and so on. Thus, it would seem that with all of these specific catalysts available the body should come to equilibrium rapidly. Earlier in our discussion of metabolism (pp. 269 and 286), we carefully pointed out that the body is a dynamic rather than a static organism. These two seemingly contradictory facts can be understood as a result of the body being an **open** rather than a **closed system**. In such a system, energy and material are being lost to, and gained from, "outside," and equilibrium is *never* reached. This fact has a very important consequence for the enzymes. It is their purpose to maintain a steady state of energy and material by tending *toward* equilibrium. In this way, the enzymes can regulate the system, or, in other words, they can act to overcome disturbances.

11.3
THE COENZYMES AND VITAMINS

Some of the enzymatic reactions require the participation of another, generally nonprotein, substance called a **coenzyme**. In Chapter 10, we frequently employed coenzyme A for the degradation and synthesis of materials. Although CoA is a rather complex molecule ($C_{21}H_{36}O_{16}N_7P_3S$), most coenzymes are fairly simple organic compounds. Because they can be studied by the usual methods of organic chemistry, their structure has been known for some time. Most of the coenzymes are related structurally to the nucleotides (p. 283), and many of them are **vitamins**. They cannot be synthesized by the body and must be ingested in the food supply—hence, the need for vitamin pills and a balanced diet, which includes foods containing adequate amounts of required vitamins.

You have all heard that **niacin** is an important member of the **B-vitamins**. This compound is the simple substituted pyridine, nicotinic acid or 3-carboxypyridine. In the form of its pyridinium salt, the corresponding amide is a part of the coenzyme **nicotinamide-adenine nucleotide (NAD$^+$)**.

niacin   nicotinamide

The processes of oxidation and reduction are obviously of great importance in the body, and NAD^+ works with alcohol dehydrogenase to accomplish the oxidation of primary and secondary alcohols. After the coenzyme (in the reduced form) has left the dehydrogenase, it is reoxidized in combination with another enzyme.

$$CH_3CH_2OH \rightleftharpoons \text{NADH} + CH_3CH + H^+$$

In these and similar paths, we find a molecular level understanding of such vital questions as why we must breathe the oxygen in the air. Not a great deal of detailed information is available about the way in which the enzyme and coenzyme are bound together, but one interesting observation is the complete stereospecificity of the hydrogen (actually the hydride ion, $H:^-$) transfer. Ethanol, which has one deuterium on the methylene group, exists as an enantiomeric pair. If the mirror image compounds are resolved and used in separate experiments with NAD^+ and alcohol dehydrogenase, one will transfer only hydrogen and one will transfer only deuterium.

$$NAD^+ + CH_3CHDOH \quad \begin{array}{c} \nearrow \text{NADH} + CH_3C{\overset{O}{\underset{D}{\parallel}}} + H^+ \\ \searrow \text{NADD} + CH_3C{\overset{O}{\underset{H}{\parallel}}} + H^+ \end{array}$$

This experiment can be understood if the coenzyme is assumed to lie "flat" on the enzyme surface and if the alcohol must approach the nicotinamide ring in a specific orientation.

Another familiar vitamin is **thiamine** or **vitamin B$_1$**. The sulfur in one ring accounts for the name.

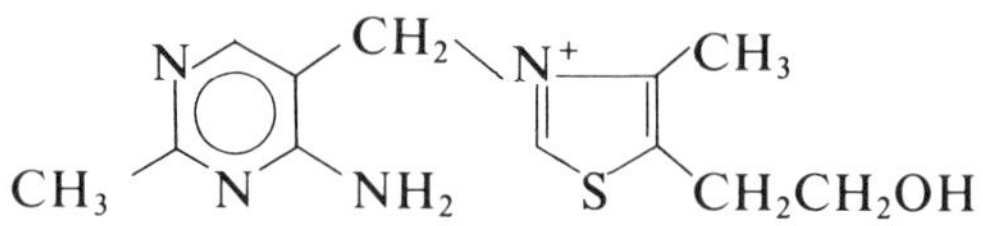

thiamine

Two phosphoric acid groups attached to the ethyl alcohol residue give thiamine pyrophosphate, which acts with a decarboxylase to accomplish the important task of splitting off CO_2 from α-keto acids. The reaction appears to involve the ionization of one of C-H bonds in the sulfur-containing ring. In the case of pyruvic acid, the acetyl group is attached to this position in the thiamine and is transferred to an oxidizing agent.

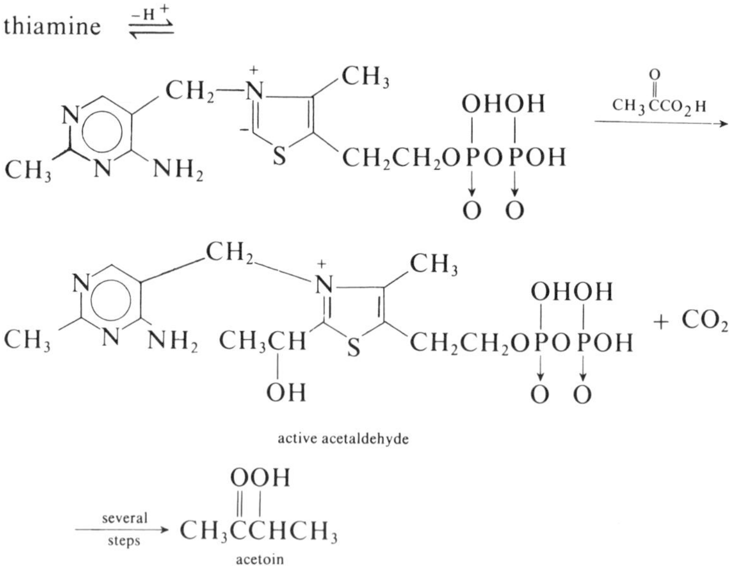

thiamine $\xrightleftharpoons{-H^+}$

active acetaldehyde

acetoin

Before we leave the coenzymes, we should make several concluding points. First, the nonvitamin adenosine triphosphate or ATP (pp. 259–261) is not only an energy storage molecule but also a transfer coenzyme. Second, certain lower molecular

weight ribonucleic acids (about 25,000), although large molecules, can be reasonably called coenzymes because they are involved in the activation of amino acids for protein synthesis
(pp. 282–284). Finally, although we completely ignored the more
usual aspects of vitamin actions—that is, the prevention of
diseases—it should be clear from their chemistry and biochemistry that we are beginning to understand at least a little about
the reasons behind these empirical observations.

11.4
DRUGS—THEIR TYPES AND CHEMISTRY

The subject of drugs and their effect on the human organism
is a very broad one. Not only are the biochemical reactions and
mechanisms diverse, complex, and poorly understood, but the
drugs themselves represent a variety of types of organic chemicals. Just as in the preceding sections, we shall have to be con-
tented with discussing a limited number of examples.

11.4A   Antibiotics

One class of drugs of great value and wide renown encompasses
the **antibiotics**, of which **penicillin** is one of the earliest developed
and most important. In general, the antibiotics are chemicals
(often produced by microorganisms) that destroy or greatly in-
hibit other microorganisms. Penicillin, which prevents the
growth of certain bacteria involved in several infectious diseases,
is, in fact, a whole family of antibiotic materials with the following general structure:

the penicillins

The structure of the R group can be varied chemically or by
changing the "food" given to the growing penicillin mold.
One of the most widely used drugs is penicillin G, where

$R = C_6H_5CH_2$. This variation is especially important because it provides drugs for fighting bacteria resistant to the natural penicillins; hopefully, structures will be found that will overcome the adverse reactions some people have to the drugs. The problem of synthesizing penicillin proved to be a difficult one, despite its relatively simple structure. The molecule is not very stable and even very mild conditions cause ring opening and rearrangement. For this reason, synthetic penicillins are formed in such poor yield that it is easier to "grow" them by a fermentation process. However, the knowledge gained from the synthesis has made possible the "unnatural" penicillins.

An earlier, but still useful, family of antibiotic compounds includes the **sulfa drugs**. Structurally, they are still simpler than the penicillins, and they consist of various amides of *p*-aminobenzenesulfonic acid (sulfanilic acid). The synthesis of the sulfa drugs is usually accomplished by the chlorosulfonation of an aniline. This route would not be useful if the free amino group were present to form sulfonamides with the sulfonyl chloride being introduced. The technique of a protective group is used once again (pp. 157 and 207).

John C. Sheehan (American, 1915–   ). *Sheehan's laboratory at MIT has done much work in fundamental organic chemistry on the structure and*

synthesis of natural products. Most of these compounds have been important because of their medicinal use, and they include steroids, alkaloids, and peptides. The structure of such antibiotics as Telomycin was determined by Sheehan's group, and some new "natural" amino acids were discovered, identified, and synthesized. Of all these accomplishments, the first total synthesis of a natural penicillin (in 1958) is certainly the most important. Sheehan's studies of Gramicidin S have also contributed greatly to our understanding of peptide analysis and synthesis.

Courtesy of Professor Sheehan

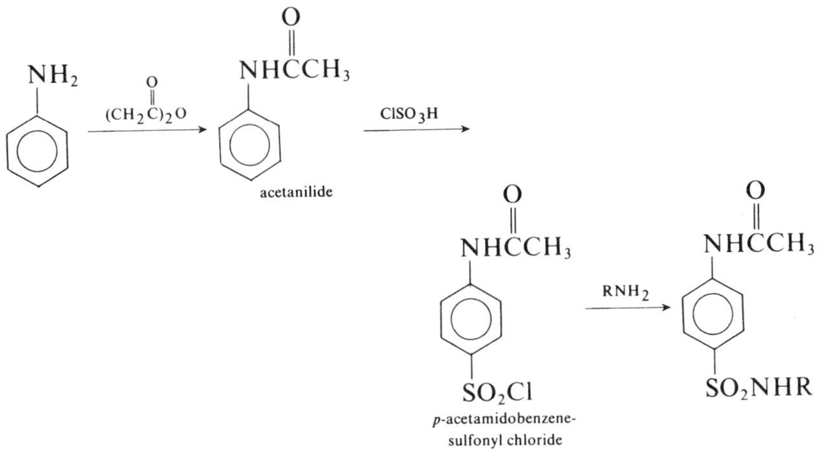
NH2
(CH2C)2O
NHCCH3
O
acetanilide
ClSO3H
SO2Cl
p-acetamidobenzene-
sulfonyl chloride
RNH2
SO2NHR

The use of the compound as a drug dictates the nature of the amine (i.e., the R) employed. It is necessary to have high anti-bacterial activity and low toxicity; of the hundreds of compounds tested, heterocyclic rings have proved the most useful.

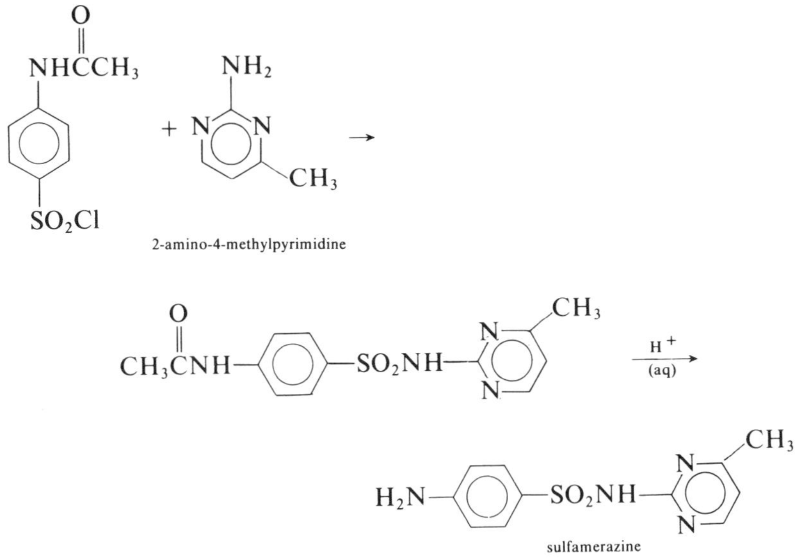
NHCCH3
O
SO2Cl
NH2
N
CH3
2-amino-4-methylpyrimidine
CH3CNH
SO2NH
H+
(aq)
H2N
sulfamerazine

The removal of the protecting acetyl group can be accomplished because the amides of carboxylic acids are more easily hydrolyzed than the sulfonamides.

The question of how the antibiotics work is related to the mechanism suggested for enzyme inhibition (p. 297). Many of these drugs resemble materials required for the growth of the undesirable organisms. In those we have discussed, amide groups similar to peptide linkage are present; in others, there are sugarlike residues. These groups allow the antibiotic to compete for specific sites in vital compounds of the growing organism, and, because they cannot be used, they slow down its rate of growth. For example, penicillin interferes with enzymes involved in building the bacterial cell walls.

11.4B   Steroids and Hormones

The steroids form a very large group of natural and synthetic materials, which are related by having the same complex fused ring system.

general steroid structure

Classing these compounds as drugs is arbitrary, inasmuch as many occur naturally and are both synthesized and metabolized in the body. They are discussed here to emphasize the great current interest in them for treating disease (especially heart and cancer) and regulating body functions (especially reproduction). The roles they play in these biochemical processes are only beginning to be understood, but a great deal is known about their chemistry.

The number of asymmetric carbon atoms (six in an unsubstituted system) and the possibility of *cis* or *trans* ring fusions makes the stereochemistry of the steroids very complex. Fortunately, only a few of the possible isomers exist naturally. Stereochemical changes in the basic ring system can have profound effects on the physiological action of the compound. Obviously, the problems posed by these alternative arrangements must be carefully considered in any proof of structure or synthesis. If all the rings are fused *trans* to one another, the following arrangement is found.

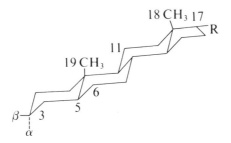

Cholesterol is perhaps the most studied and widely known steroid. It has a 3-hydroxyl group in the equatorial (above the plane of the ring system or β), a 5–6 double bond, and the following R side chain:

$$\underset{\overset{|}{-\mathrm{CHCH_2CH_2CH_2CH}}}{\mathrm{CH_3}}\overset{\diagup \mathrm{CH_3}}{\underset{\diagdown \mathrm{CH_3}}{}}$$

The proof of structure, the synthesis, and the biosynthesis of cholesterol make fascinating stories for your future reading. The fact that cholesterol can be synthesized from acetic acid in the liver with the assistance of CoA is evidence of the enzymes' ability to direct complex chemical operations.

Cholesterol has been the subject of extensive research and publicity because there is evidence that it is involved in the hardening of the arteries. This condition, which is related to heart disease, results in the buildup of deposits (high in cholesterol) in the arteries. The exact relationship is not yet known, but low cholesterol diets are often prescribed and the *in vivo* synthesis and metabolism of cholesterol are being studied in many laboratories. Because the body can synthesize cholesterol, limiting it in the diet is only of temporary and partial assistance. Inasmuch as acetyl-CoA is involved in cholesterol synthesis, any kind of diet can lead to its formation. Even the popular low-saturated fat diet appears to be of limited use. The problem is both vital and complex, not unlike many of the biochemical questions we have raised.

Another class of natural products significant for the proper functioning of the human body includes the **hormones**. Many of these are protein substances similar to the enzymes, but it is the steroid hormones with which we shall deal here. There are two major classes of steroid hormones: (1) **sex hormones** and (2) **adrenocorticoid hormones**. The following are typical examples:

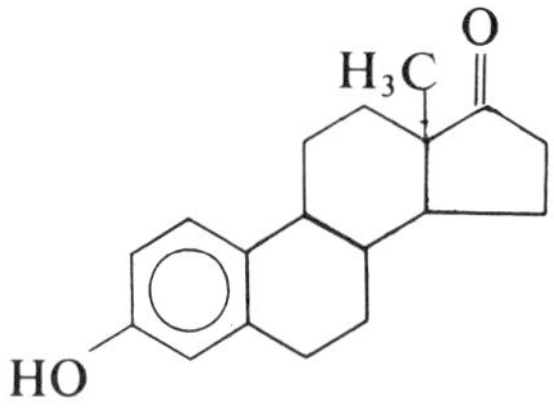

estrone

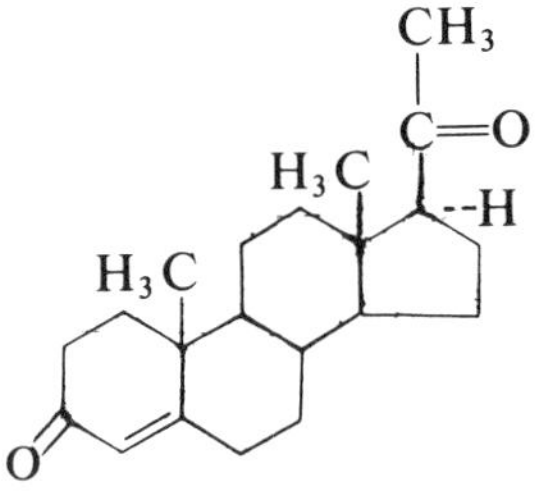

progesterone

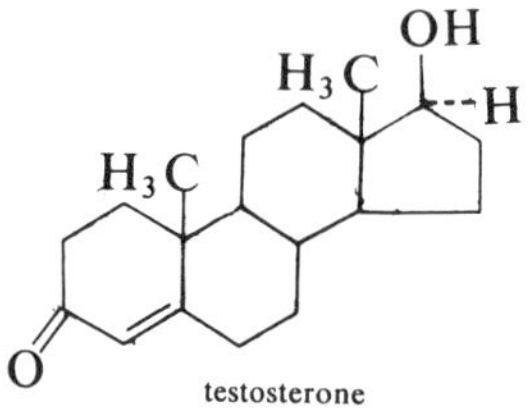

testosterone

Sex Hormones

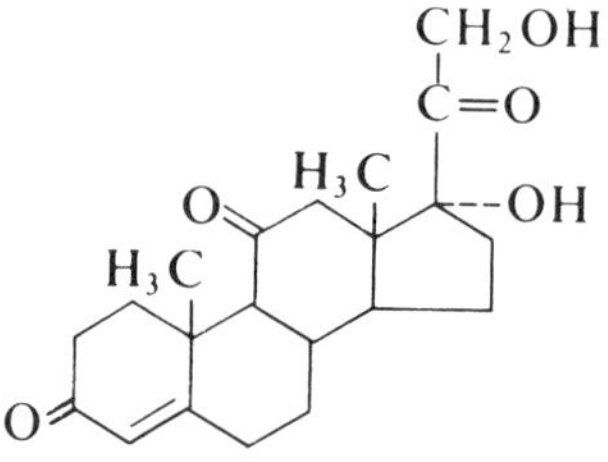

cortisone

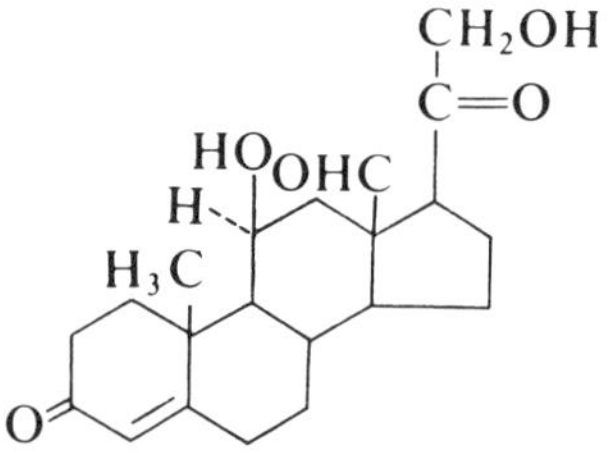

aldosterone

Adrenocorticoid Hormones

All the hormones are synthesized by the body and serve the general purpose of regulation. Their structures are closely related, as shown in the preceding examples, but their actions are very specific. Only small amounts are required to carry out their tasks, which made their relation and structure difficult to prove, inasmuch as huge quantities of material had to be processed to yield a few milligrams of pure steroid. Thousands of steroids are known, and a great many chemical transformations among them have been carried out. Most of these reactions and those used in total and partial synthesis of steroids are closely related to the reactions we have studied with smaller organic molecules. The chief difference arises from the rigid stereochemistry of the ring system. In many instances, this framework of known geometry has been useful for the study of the mechanism of an organic reaction. Because various groups can be held in a certain position relative to others, the details of their interactions during the course of a reaction can be more precisely defined.

Estrone and testosterone direct the sexual development of the female and male, respectively. When they are not being produced in sufficient quantity by the body, they can be administered, which represents one of their chief medical uses. The treatment of certain conditions other than deficiencies have proved successful. For example, estrogens will suppress lactation and prevent atrophy of the uterus and breast after the ovaries are removed. Androgens, such as testosterone, are used to enhance protein synthesis and are therefore useful in treating premature infants. Progestrogens play a role in preparing the female for conception. The timing of their administration with respect to the menstrual cycle can either promote or prevent pregnancy. This fact has affected a great deal of progestrogen research directed both toward helping people have children and toward controlling population.

Cortisone and related compounds control the synthesis, storage, and metabolism of glucose. It is especially important in the conversion of proteins to carbohydrates; therefore, it has an effect on the metabolic balance that the body must maintain. Aldosterone is one of the most important of the hormones controlling the electrolyte balance; it regulates the excretion of water and such ions as Na^+, K^+, Cl^-, HCO_3^-, and HPO_4^{-2}. This process is among the most vital of all body activities, inasmuch as a serious imbalance, such as excessive Na^+ excretion, can cause death in a few days. Treatment with hormones and their synthetic analogs can, in many cases, correct the conditions, a fact that has provided part of the stimulus for the research which has produced the large number of synthetic steroids. Some of these are effective in smaller amounts than the natural steroids and some show greater specificity in their effects. Such limitation of effect is one of the goals most sought for in all new drugs; it does little good to treat one condition successfully at the expense of upsetting another vital function.

We have said nothing about the mode of action of these substances because despite the vast amount of empirical knowledge, no coherent picture of the reason behind the effects has been advanced. The closer one gets to current research the more likely this fact is to be true.

11.4C The Alkaloids

One of the oldest, largest, and most extensively studied groups of drugs are the **alkaloids**. A wide variety of structural types are included, and they have the common features of having basic nitrogen and being of plant origin. Often, the nitrogen is part of a heterocyclic ring system, and the structure of this central part of the molecule provides the most common classification system. The following represent a few of these types:

indole   quinoline   tropane

In addition, there exist alkaloids based on pyridine—for example, niacin (p. 298), and purine bases similar to adenine (p. 282). The names of the alkaloids are nearly always common ones, often taken from the source, the discoverer, their physiological effect, or some related compound. We shall attempt to look briefly at the structure and physiological actions of a member of each aforementioned class, but it should be pointed out that, as in the steroids, a very large number of compounds are known. This fact is all the more impressive because the alkaloids are usually found in small (perhaps trace is a better word) amounts and in combination with a number of closely related structures. To obtain even enough pure alkaloid to characterize it, much less determine its structure, is a formidable task.

In addition to niacin, which we discussed earlier as a vitamin, a common member of the pyridine-based alkaloids is **nicotine**.

nicotine

Nicotine, of course, comes from the tobacco plant. It is one of the most poisonous of the alkaloids. The most important use of nicotine and related alkaloids is as insecticides.

Another very familiar alkaloid, **caffeine**, is obtained from tea leaves, coffee, and cocoa beans and contains a purine base.

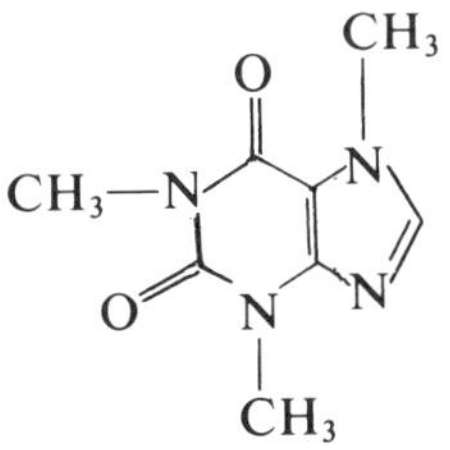

caffeine

This alkaloid is a heart stimulant and affects the central nervous system. A cup of coffee contains a rather large amount of caffeine (about 100 mg), which would be fatal with any of the really poisonous alkaloids.

The indole alkaloids are a very large group varying in structure from compounds related to the simple amino acids to very complex molecules of great scientific and practical importance. The general class is usually subdivided into groups of compounds with related structures and generally obtained from one family of plants. The Ergot fungus produces the Ergot alkaloids of which **lysergic acid** is the best known.

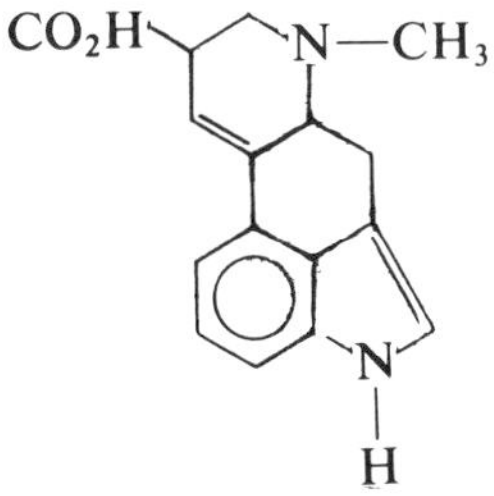

lysergic acid

The diethylamide of lysergic acid is not naturally occurring and has become widely known as LSD. These hallucinogenic drugs cause a psychological state resembling schizophrenia and may hold promise in the study and treatment of mental disorders. Other Ergot alkaloids are useful in the birth process because they stimulate the contractions of the uterus.

A member of another "popular" group of drugs, the tranquilizers, is **reserpine**, which is a Yohimbe alkaloid.

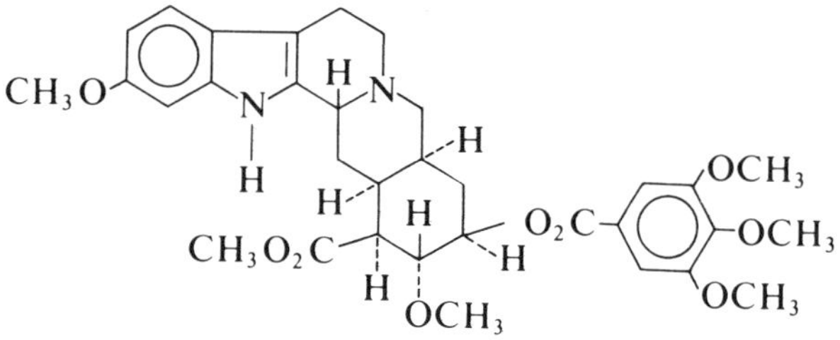

reserpine

In addition to its tranquilizing effect, which is useful in the treatment of the emotionally disturbed, reserpine is useful clinically in cases of high blood pressure.

Two Strychnos alkaloids having special chemical importance are **strychnine** and **brucine**. Both are deadly poisons.

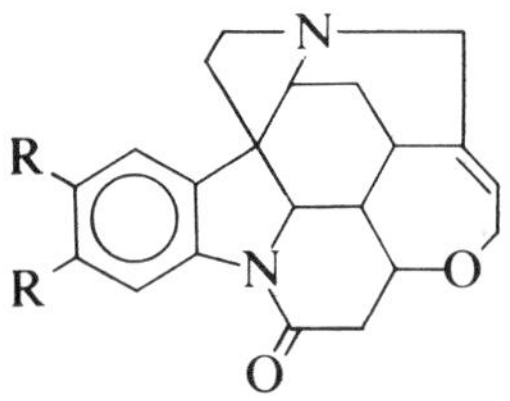

strychnine (R = H)   brucine (R = OCH₃)

The existence of these and many other alkaloids in optically active form and their ability to form crystalline diastereomeric salts with racemic acids have made them useful in the resolution of such mixtures. The details of such a separation are given in Chapter 12 (pp. 330 and 401).

A drug of first-rate importance is **quinine**, an alkaloid containing the quinoline ring system.

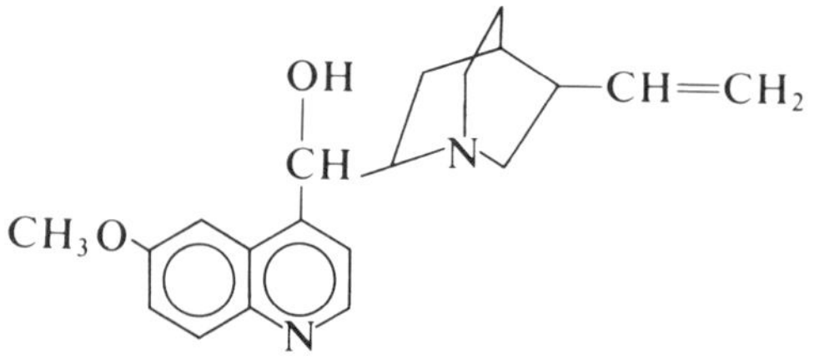

quinine

This compound is also used for the resolution of racemates, but it is far more important as an antimalarial. The pressures of short supply and jungle wars have made the quest for other effective compounds a large and intensive research problem for many years.

The balance between useful and dangerous doses of drugs is illustrated by alkaloids containing the tropane nucleus, such as **cocaine**.

cocaine

Despite the fact that cocaine is rather poisonous, it was widely used as a local anesthetic. Today, because the addictive property of these compounds is known, **novocaine** and related synthetic compounds have replaced cocaine for this use. Novocaine has some of the structural features of cocaine.

Another alkaloid with both beneficial and dangerous properties is **morphine**, and related alkaloids, from the opium poppy. This compound also has a complex ring structure and a nitrogen bridge.

Marshall D. Gates, Jr. (American, 1915–). A fine teacher and experimentalist in synthetic organic chemistry, Gates received his Ph.D. degree at Harvard in 1941 and has spent most of his professional career at the University of Rochester. His interests have been chiefly in the area of the synthesis of natural products, especially the analgesic drugs. The first synthesis of morphine was accomplished in his laboratory in 1952. Further studies on this alkaloid have been directed toward reducing its addictive properties. Gates has made a large contribution to the advancement of modern chemistry through his efforts as editor of the Journal of the American Chemical Society.

Courtesy of Professor Gates

morphine

Its medical importance lies in its **analgesic** or pain-killing properties. A great amount of effort has been expended in trying to find modifications of its structure that retain the desirable effects and reduce its addictive tendency. Some success has been achieved.

The complex structures of many of the alkaloids—for example, reserpine, strychnine, brucine, quinine, and morphine—have made their total synthesis of great interest to organic chemists; in addition, understanding their structure and chemical characteristics is of obvious practical importance. Some of the most brilliant recent history of organic chemistry is contained in the preparation of these and other natural products. In Chapter 12, we shall look at a simple example to point out some of the methods and difficulties.

SUGGESTED ADDITIONAL READINGS

Enzyme Catalysis

> Karlson, Chapter 5.
> Mahler and Cordes, Chapters 6–7.
> Roberts and Caserio, pp. 727–30.
> Steiner, Chapter 7.

H. Neurath, "Protein-Digesting Enzymes," *Sci. Am.*, **211** (6), 68 (1964).

J-P. Changeux, "The Control of Biochemical Reactions," *Sci. Am.*, **212** (4), 36 (1965).

I. Raw, "Enzymes—How They Operate," *Chemistry*, **40** (6), 8 (1967).

B. R. Baker, "Interactions of Enzymes and Inhibitors," *J. Chem. Educ.*, **44**, 610 (1967).

Coenzymes

> Karlson, Chapter 6.
> Mahler and Cordes, Chapter 8.
> Roberts and Caserio, pp. 730–32.

Vitamins

> Karlson, Chapter 22.
> Mahler and Cordes, pp. 348–69.
> Nussenbaum, pp. 478–80.

J. E. Dowling, "Night Blindness," *Sci. Am.*, **215** (4), 78 (1966).

Drugs

> Nussenbaum, pp. 317–21 and 474.

H. O. J. Collier, "Aspirin," *Sci. Am.*, **209** (5), 96 (1963).

F. Barron, M. E. Jarvik, and S. Bunnell, Jr., "The Hallucinogenic Drugs," *Sci. Am.*, **210** (4), 29 (1964).

U. V. Solmssen, "The Chemist and New Drugs," *Chemistry*, **40** (4), 22 (1967).

T. Watanabe, "Infectious Drug Resistance," *Sci. Am.*, **217** (6), 19 (1967).

Antibiotics

> Karlson, pp. 40–41.
> Nussenbaum, pp. 475–78.

L. Gorini, "Antibiotics and the Genetic Code," *Sci. Am.*, **214** (4), 102 (1966).

Steroids

> Karlson, Chapter 14.
> Mahler and Cordes, pp. 641–51.
> Nussenbaum, pp. 483–89.
> Roberts and Caserio, pp. 1149–71.

Hormones

> Karlson, Chapter 20.

C. H. Li, "The ACTH Molecule," *Sci. Am.*, **209** (1), 46 (1963).

E. H. Davidson, "Hormones and Genes," *Sci. Am.*, **212** (6), 36 (1965).

Alkaloids

> Nussenbaum, pp. 489–97.
> Roberts and Caserio, pp. 1019–24.

M. Gates, "Analgesic Drugs," *Sci. Am.*, **215** (5), 131 (1966).

SUMMARY

1. The enzymes are proteins that serve as highly specific catalysts to reduce the activation energy for some desirable reaction in the organism.

2. The dynamic system in the body is always tending toward equilibrium, but never reaches it. This allows the enzymes to control the system and to act to overcome undesirable disturbances.

3. The coenzymes and the vitamins are often associated with enzymes and are required for the proper functioning of the enzyme.

4. The term drug is very broad and includes any compound that can serve to maintain the balance or correct the imbalance of the body.

5. The antibiotics include the penicillins and the sulfa drugs. They frequently act by interfering with the growth of bacteria.

6. The steroids and hormones appear to be important in controlling the balance of specific functions in the biochemistry of the body. Thus, it is possible by attempting to prevent their synthesis or by administering them to influence the processes they regulate.

7. The alkaloids are a broad class of drugs having the common features of being derived from plants and having one or more basic nitrogen atoms.

8. Many of the alkaloids are poisonous and have addictive properties. In spite of this they are often useful medically once the proper dosages have been determined.

9. Much of the current research in alkaloids is directed toward retaining their beneficial properties and minimizing their undesirable attributes.

10. The alkaloids are frequently useful as resolving agents.

PROBLEMS

1. A vitamin, called pantothenic acid, is the amide formed by the reaction of 2,4-dihydroxy-3,3-dimethylbutanoic acid with 3-aminopropanoic acid. Draw its structure.

2. The pantothenic acid of question 1 is a significant part of coenzyme A in the form of a 2-mercaptoethylamide. Draw its structure.

3. The complete structure of coenzyme A consists of a diphosphate bridge from the 5-hydroxymethyl group of adenosine to the terminal

hydroxyl group of the answer to question 2 and another phosphate ester at the 3 position. Draw the structure of coenzyme A.

4. A sulfa drug with useful properties is succinoylsulfathiazole, which contains the heterocycle 2-aminothiazole

$$NH_2$$

$$N \diagdown S$$

. Draw the most likely structure of the drug and propose a synthesis starting from benzene, 2-aminothiazole, and 4 carbon or smaller alcohols.

5. Although the steroids are large polyfunctional compounds, their individual functional groups show most of the chemical properties we have studied with simpler compounds. Using cholesterol, estrone, and cortisone as examples, write the reactions (if any occur) with each of the following reagents:
   a. $(CH_3CO)_2O$ e. $KMnO_4(aq)$ (dilute)
   b. H_2/Ni f. $LiAlH_4$
   c. $HONH_2$ g. $NaOI (NaOH + I_2)$
   d. NBS/H_2O h. H^+

6. *Gramicidin S* is a polypeptide with important antibiotic properties. It also has some unusual structural features, including D-phenylalanine, the amino acid ornithine $(H_2NCH_2CH_2CH_2CHCO_2H)$,

$$NH_2$$

and an overall structure that will become apparent in the following problem. The complete hydrolysis products showed the empirical make up of *Gramicidin S* to be 1 mole each of leucine, ornithine, phenylalanine, proline, and valine. The molecular weight is approximately 1300. What is the molecular amino acid composition of *Gramicidin S*? When attempts were made to determine the terminal residues, the C or carboxyl determination proved negative and the N or amino determination gave only DNP-ornithine. Partial hydrolysis to di- and tripeptides showed that the following had been formed:
   (1) valylornithylleucine   (5) phenylalanylproline
   (2) prolylvalylornithine   (6) ornithylleucine
   (3) phenylalanylprolylvaline   (7) leucylphenylalanine
   (4) valylornithine
   Give the complete structure of *Gramicidin S* based on these data.

7. A degradation product of an alkaloid, hygrinic acid, can be prepared by the following series of reactions. Complete each step and use the solution in question 8.

$$BrCH_2CH_2CH_2Br + CH(CO_2C_2H_5)_2^- Na^+ \rightarrow C_{10}H_{17}BrO_4$$

$$C_{10}H_{17}BrO_4 + Br_2 \rightarrow C_{10}H_{16}Br_2O_4 \xrightarrow{\text{CH}_3\text{NH}_2} C_{11}H_{19}O_4N$$

$$C_{11}H_{19}O_4N \xrightarrow{\text{OH}^-} \xrightarrow{\text{H}^+} \xrightarrow{\text{heat}} \text{hygrinic acid}$$

8. An alkaloid of fairly simple structure, hygrine, comes from the cocoa plant. After completing question 7, it should be possible to propose a structure for hygrine on the basis of the following observations. Hygrine has the molecular formula $C_8H_{15}NO$ and is soluble in aqueous acid, but not base. It does not react with benzenesulfonyl chloride. It does react with 2,4-dinitrophenylhydrazine and sodium hypoiodite. The latter reaction gives a yellow crystalline solid and a carboxylic acid ($C_7H_{13}O_2N$). Strong oxidation of this acid produces hygrinic acid.

12

Classic Organic Problems
and Their Solution

In the preceding chapters, we have discussed a great deal of organic chemistry, and, to some extent, we have seen its application to the practical problems faced daily by the organic chemist. As a conclusion to this text, we should like to take you on a brief tour of a few carefully selected examples of real organic research problems. These will not be the artificial kind of problem necessarily used earlier because of our limited knowledge; rather, they will be taken from the chemical literature and will involve a very wide cross section of the chemistry you have learned.

There are at least three major classifications of organic research problems, and we shall attempt to present an example of each. First, there is the study of the mechanism of organic reactions. Second, there are the problems of new methods of preparing desirable organic molecules. Third, from the field of natural products, we raise the question of determining the exact structure of some new organic compound. As you begin this true-to-life summary, keep in mind the requirement of applying all the preceding information.

317

In 1930, there existed in the literature a very puzzling state of affairs regarding the addition of hydrogen bromide to 3-bromopropene or allyl bromide.

$$CH_2\!\!=\!\!CHCH_2Br + HBr \rightarrow \underset{\underset{Br}{|}}{CH_2}\underset{\underset{Br}{|}}{CH_2}CH_2 + \underset{\underset{Br}{|}\;\underset{Br}{|}}{CH_3CHCH_2}$$

The fact that both isomeric dibromides were reported was surprising in view of the prediction of Markownikoff's Rule, which most reactions of this type were then expected to follow very closely. However, the situation was even more complicated, for different laboratories had reported widely varying ratios of the two products.

Professor Kharasch and Frank Mayo, one of his graduate students, began a thorough study of this interesting, unexpected result. At first, the results showed the same kind of variable product composition as had been reported. Through a number of carefully conducted experiments, and especially by a very thoughtful review of the data, a pattern began to emerge. The surprising correlation was between the product composition and the age of the starting materials. If the allyl bromide was freshly distilled, the product was largely 1,2-dibromopropane, whereas older samples gave more 1,3-dibromopropane.

With this promising observation, the application of the scientific method required the formulation of a hypothesis. It is at this stage in the development of this problem that the true genius of Kharasch showed itself most clearly. It was his idea, based on the finding of peroxides in the older sample, that the older allyl bromide had a chance to react with atmospheric oxygen to form peroxides, which somehow promote the abnormal addition.

$$CH_2\!\!=\!\!CHCH_2Br + O_2 \rightarrow \text{traces of peroxides (i.e., molecules}$$
$$\text{containing an } —O—O— \text{ linkage)}$$

The next step in applying the scientific method involves the design of experiments to test the validity of the suggested hypothesis.

The particular case of anti-Markownikoff addition required the preparation of completely peroxide-free allyl bromide and then the use of it for the addition of hydrogen bromide alone and in the presence of added peroxide.

$$CH_2\!=\!CHCH_2Br + HBr \begin{cases} \xrightarrow{\text{peroxide free}} & CH_3\underset{\underset{Br}{|}}{C}H\underset{\underset{Br}{|}}{C}H_2 \\[2em] \xrightarrow{\text{added peroxide}} & CH_2\underset{\underset{Br}{|}}{C}H_2C\underset{\underset{Br}{|}}{}H_2 \end{cases}$$

As these reactions indicate, there is a complete reversal of the direction of addition. Thus, the hypothesis was shown to be a valid explanation of the observed results. On the other hand, it required many more carefully planned and executed experiments before the details of the mechanism of the process were understood.

These researches produced the following series of reactions, which are now accepted as describing the "peroxide effect" and

Morris S. Kharasch (Ukrainian-American, 1895–1957). *Kharasch received his Ph.D. degree from the University of Chicago in 1919 and except for four years*

spent his entire career there. Just before his death the University, indicating their high regard for him, created an Institute of Organic Chemistry for his direction. Kharasch's treatment of the peroxide effect was entirely typical of him; although he published the experimental observations at once, he waited for much additional data before describing the theory and mechanism. He and his students then developed a host of useful synthetic and mechanistically important free radical reactions. Some of his students have become leaders of organic chemistry today, e.g., H. C. Brown, F. H. Westheimer, and C. Walling.

Courtesy of The University of Chicago

the abnormal addition of HBr that it produces:

$$ROOR \xrightarrow[\text{light}]{\text{heat or}} 2\,RO\cdot$$
alkoxy radical

$$RO\cdot + HBr \rightarrow ROH + Br\cdot$$
bromine atom or radical

$$\left.\begin{array}{l}\end{array}\right\}\text{chain initiation}$$

$$Br\cdot + CH_2{=}CHCH_2Br \rightarrow BrCH_2\overset{\cdot}{C}HCH_2Br$$

$$BrCH_2\overset{\cdot}{C}HCH_2Br + HBr \rightarrow BrCH_2CH_2CH_2Br + Br\cdot$$

$$\left.\begin{array}{l}\end{array}\right\}\text{chain propagation}$$

As we learned in an earlier chapter, the secondary radical is more stable than the primary radical; this fact is consistent with the preceding reactions. Of greater importance is the chain nature of the process, which accounts for the fact that only a catalytic amount of peroxide is required.

$$2\,Br\cdot \rightarrow Br_2$$

$$BrCH_2\overset{\cdot}{C}HCH_2Br + Br\cdot \rightarrow BrCH_2\underset{\underset{Br}{|}}{C}HCH_2Br$$

$$2\,BrCH_2\overset{\cdot}{C}HCH_2Br \rightarrow BrCH_2\underset{\underset{BrH_2C}{|}}{C}H\underset{\underset{CH_2Br}{|}}{C}HCH_2Br$$

$$\left.\begin{array}{l}\end{array}\right\}\text{chain termination}$$

The final three independent reactions are those that end a radical chain, inasmuch as they do not result in the production of a new radical product. That they are, in fact, the actual termination reactions has been shown by the isolation of very small amounts of the required compounds from the reaction mixture. From this one well-documented example of a radical process, Kharasch and his students went on to discover and describe numerous useful radical reactions.

12.3
DO CARBON RINGS EXIST AND HOW DO WE MAKE THEM?

One of the very important aspects of the organic chemist's work is the synthesis of new compounds. The reasons for this vary all the way from simply wanting to see if such a molecule can exist to the need to cure a disease or defend a nation. Frequently, the story involves the lives and efforts of a number of men and has all of the interest and suspense of a good mystery story or football game. Such a tale is found in the attempts of chemists to prepare compounds containing carbon rings of various sizes.

In the second half of the ninteenth century, when the structural theory of organic chemistry was just beginning to show its great power, it was commonly believed that carbocyclic compounds either smaller or larger than six atoms were incapable of existence. There was no good reason to think otherwise, for no one had ever found any other ring size in nature and all attempts to prepare such a system had failed.

The first significant change in this state of affairs was made by a young Englishman, W. H. Perkin, when he was studying organic chemistry in the famous German laboratory of Adolf von Baeyer. Despite the generally discouraging prospects for this research problem, he was able, during a very short time, to synthesize three-, four-, and five-membered ring systems, using the following reaction:

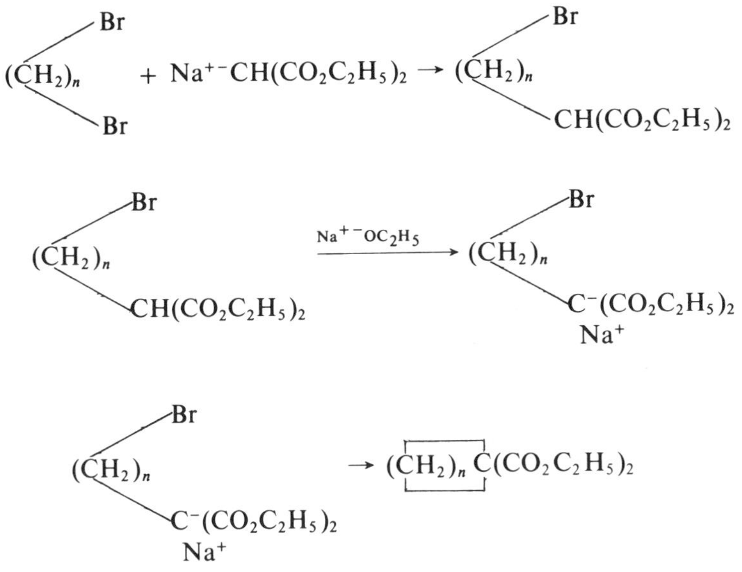

$$(CH_2)_n \overset{Br}{\underset{Br}{<}} \quad + \; Na^{+-}CH(CO_2C_2H_5)_2 \; \rightarrow \; (CH_2)_n \overset{Br}{\underset{CH(CO_2C_2H_5)_2}{<}}$$

$$(CH_2)_n \overset{Br}{\underset{CH(CO_2C_2H_5)_2}{<}} \quad \xrightarrow{Na^{+-}OC_2H_5} \quad (CH_2)_n \overset{Br}{\underset{\underset{Na^+}{C^-(CO_2C_2H_5)_2}}{<}}$$

$$(CH_2)_n \overset{Br}{\underset{\underset{Na^+}{C^-(CO_2C_2H_5)_2}}{<}} \quad \rightarrow \; (CH_2)_n\,C(CO_2C_2H_5)_2$$

$$n = 2 \text{ to } 4$$

For example,

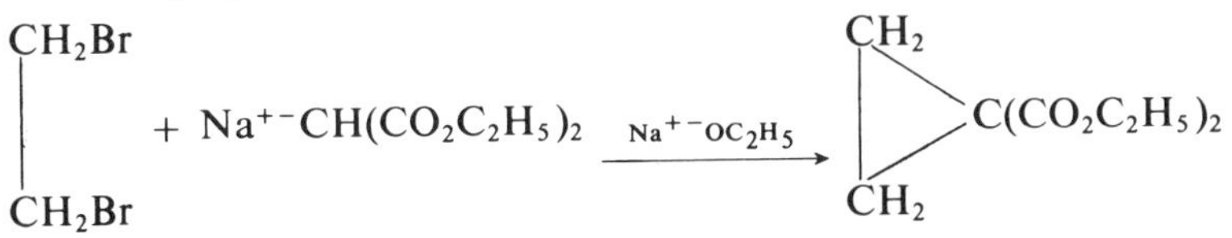

$$\begin{array}{l} CH_2Br \\ | \\ CH_2Br \end{array} + \; Na^{+-}CH(CO_2C_2H_5)_2 \quad \xrightarrow{Na^{+-}OC_2H_5} \quad \begin{array}{l} CH_2 \\ | \quad > C(CO_2C_2H_5)_2 \\ CH_2 \end{array}$$

These successes, and especially the chemical characteristics of the small ring compounds, led von Baeyer to propose, in 1885, his famous "ring strain theory," discussed earlier (pp. 99–100). You will recall that if the fundamental assumption of a planar ring were true, the rings of more than six carbons should become more strained and difficult to prepare. The story of how our present knowledge of them became available is very interesting, but we shall concentrate on only the most generally useful reaction for their preparation.

In 1947, two Swiss chemists quite independently published the results of their efforts to make large rings in high yield. These reports were the beginning of what has proved to be the best method for large rings (more than 12 carbons) and the only method of preparing medium rings (8 to 12 carbons).

The earliest synthesis of large-ring compounds resulted from the pyrolysis or strong heating of metal salts of long-chain dicarboxylic acids.

$$(CH_2)_n \underset{CO_2^-}{\overset{CO_2^-}{<}} \quad Ca^{+2} \text{ or } Th^{+2} \xrightarrow{\text{heat}} (CH_2)_n \boxed{C}\!\!=\!\!O \; + \; \begin{matrix} Ca^{+2}CO_3^{-2} \\ \text{or} \\ Th^{+2}CO_3^{-2} \end{matrix}$$

$$n = 11 \text{ to } 18$$

Max Stoll *(Swiss, 1899–   ). An outstanding example of the industrial research chemist, Stoll has been Director of Research at Firmenich and Co. in Geneva since 1927. The interest of that firm in perfume chemicals provided part of the impetus for the development of cyclization reactions useful in the preparation of large ring ketones and lactones. His work on the acyloin condensation, along with other methods, has led to the synthesis of several natural products of scientific and industrial importance, e.g., muscone, Exaltone, and the civetones (both cis and trans). In addition to these very well known contributions, Stoll has made important advances in the synthesis of dibasic acids and hydroaromatic epoxides.*

Courtesy of Dr. Stoll

Although this reaction did show the existence of large rings and provided a method of preparing them, it still had serious limitations. The most important of these was that the yield reached a maximum of about 5% at the 16-carbon system and was at most a trace in the medium rings. Inasmuch as this reaction is carried out by heating an ionic salt in the solid state, it was suggested that the high probability of intermolecular reactions and polymer formation accounted for the low yields.

On this assumption, it was thought that a cyclization reaction that occurred in homogeneous solution would be desirable. The reason deals with the fundamental requirement for a successful cyclization reaction—that the two ends of one molecule have a greater probability of colliding and thus reacting than do the ends of two different molecules. In other words, intramolecular reaction predominates over intermolecular reaction. It seems reasonable that as the reaction mixture becomes more dilute, the chance that two different molecules will meet decreases, whereas the chance that two ends of the same molecule will collide

Vladimir Prelog (Yugoslavian, 1906–   ). *After taking his doctorate in Prague in 1929, Prelog worked and taught in Czechoslovakia and Yugoslavia until 1942 when he joined the faculty of the Technische Hochschule in Zürich. His laboratory has accomplished a great deal in the synthesis of natural products and macrocyclic ring systems. In addition, a large amount of fundamental work has been done on problems of stereochemistry, asymmetric syntheses, steric control, and transannular interactions. Well over 300 scientific papers describe the results of these studies. His work in the area of microbiological and enzymatic reactions has both contributed to our understanding of these processes and resulted in the isolation and identification of important new substances. For his outstanding efforts in organic chemistry, Prelog received the 1969 Roger Adams Medal of the American Chemical Society.*

Courtesy of Professor Prelog

remains constant. The required reaction was found, and, to some extent, the high dilution principle worked as predicted.

$$(CH_2)_n \begin{array}{c} CN \\ \\ CN \end{array} \xrightarrow[\text{of certain anilines}]{\text{lithium salts}} \quad Li^+\, CH^-\!\!-\!CN \\ \qquad\qquad (CH_2)_{n-1}\!\!-\!C\!\equiv\!N \longrightarrow$$

$$(CH_2)_{n-1}\begin{array}{c} CH\!-\!CN \\ \\ C\!=\!\ddot{N}^- \end{array} \xrightarrow{H_2O} \quad (CH_2)_{n-1}\begin{array}{c} CH\!-\!CO_2H \\ \\ C\!=\!O \end{array} \xrightarrow{\text{heat}}$$

$$(CH_2)_n \boxed{} C\!=\!O + CO_2$$

$$n = 11 \text{ to } 19$$

In fact, the increase in yield for the large rings was spectacular, with values between 50 and 80%. The old problem of the medium rings ($n = 7$ to 10) was still present, for this new pathway failed to produce any of these elusive carbocycles. Although it overcame the problem of polymer formation, it did not help the unfavorable situation caused by hydrogens interacting across the medium-sized rings (see Figure 12.1).

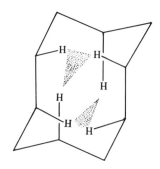

FIGURE 12.1.   Transannular Interactions.

This work had shown the type of method most likely to bring successful cyclization. It was then a matter of trying various long-chain compounds with functional groups at both ends. A number of such systems were tried, but it was not until V. Prelog and M. Stoll modified a certain ester condensation that the real advance was made.

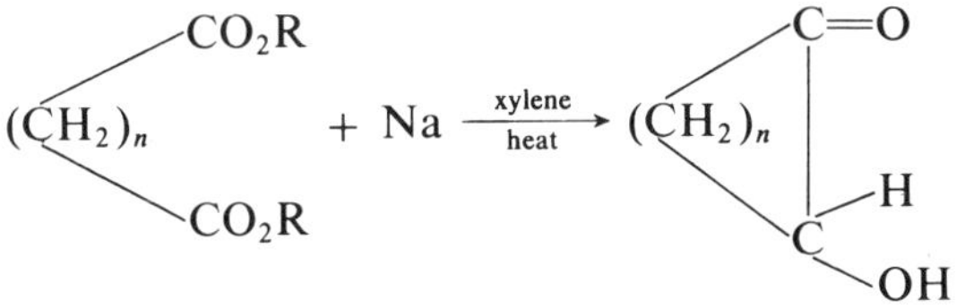

$$(CH_2)_n \begin{array}{c} CO_2R \\ \\ CO_2R \end{array} + Na \xrightarrow[\text{heat}]{\text{xylene}} (CH_2)_n \begin{array}{c} C{=}O \\ \\ C \begin{array}{c} H \\ OH \end{array} \end{array}$$

an acyloin

$$n = 3 \text{ to } 32$$

For example,

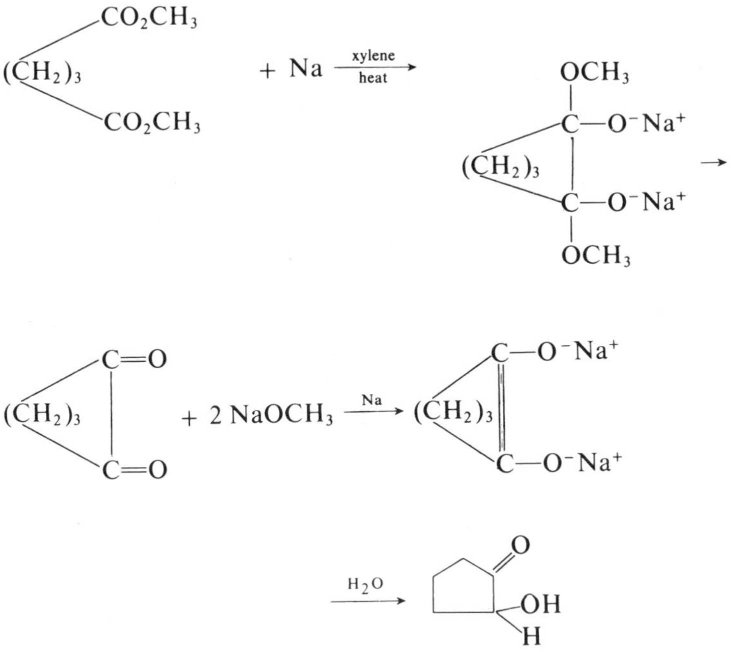

$$(CH_2)_3 \begin{array}{c} CO_2CH_3 \\ \\ CO_2CH_3 \end{array} + Na \xrightarrow[\text{heat}]{\text{xylene}} \qquad (CH_2)_3 \begin{array}{c} OCH_3 \\ \\ C-O^-Na^+ \\ \\ C-O^-Na^+ \\ \\ OCH_3 \end{array} \longrightarrow$$

$$(CH_2)_3 \begin{array}{c} C{=}O \\ \\ C{=}O \end{array} + 2\,NaOCH_3 \xrightarrow{\text{Na}} (CH_2)_3 \begin{array}{c} C-O^-Na^+ \\ \\ C-O^-Na^+ \end{array}$$

$$\xrightarrow{H_2O} \qquad$$

2-hydroxycyclopentanone

In refluxing xylene, the sodium metal melts, and, with high-speed stirring, the particles can be finely dispersed. Under high dilution conditions, the reaction at the sodium surface results in the intramolecular or cyclization product. The mechanism is far from well understood, but the intermediates shown are probably important. The acyloin reaction not only further increases the yield of large carbon rings but also allows the preparation of medium rings in quite respectable yields of at least 50%. This reason alone is sufficient for considering the development of this reaction to be one of the most important recent advances in synthetic organic chemistry. Actually, the application of this reaction has made great contributions to theoretical, mechanistic, and industrial chemistry, as well as to the synthesis of important natural products (for some examples, see the Suggested Additional Readings).

12.4
THE DEATH OF SOCRATES AS VIEWED
BY AN ORGANIC CHEMIST

The deadly poison of the hemlock was well known to ancient cultures, and one of the best-known and most tragic executions of all history, that of Socrates in 399 B.C., was carried out through its use. This topic may seem to be unusual for the conclusion of a text in organic chemistry, but the relationship is very real and of particular importance to us.

Many hundreds of years after the Greeks had doomed their great philosopher, it was found (in 1831) that the major poisonous compound in hemlock is a colorless, strongly basic oil named coniine. Science in the nineteenth century moved at a very leisurely pace, and it was more than 50 years before the famous German chemist Hofmann determined the correct molecular formula, $C_8H_{17}N$.

In these results we see the first two steps required in the study of a naturally occurring organic compound—isolation and elemental analysis. It does not sound too unlike the very things done in a student laboratory, and, allowing for the differences between a student taking a first course and an experienced organic chemist, they are identical. It will be of interest for us to examine some of these differences to appreciate the task of the complete assignment of the structure of a new organic molecule. Generally, this problem requires two basic areas of effort: first, the analysis or degradation of the molecule, which is really a series of chemical reactions producing simpler molecular fragments that can be identified; and second, the synthesis of the compound from other molecules of known structure. The synthesis of coniine is of special interest because it represents the first successful preparation of an alkaloid.

12.4A   Analysis or Degradation of Coniine

The basic nature of coniine is shown by its easy formation of salts with acids; for example,

$$C_8H_{17}N + HCl \rightarrow C_8H_{17}N^+HCl^-$$

When this hydrochloride is distilled with zinc dust, a new base is formed that has lost six hydrogens:

$$C_8H_{17}N^+HCl^- \xrightarrow[\text{heat}]{\text{Zn}} C_8H_{11}N^+HCl^- + 3\,H_2$$

Reduction of this compound with concentrated HI regenerates coniine, but now in an optically inactive racemic mixture, as opposed to the dextrorotatory natural material that rotates plane polarized light $+15.7°$.

$$C_8H_{11}N + HI \rightarrow \underset{\substack{\text{racemic mixture} \\ \text{(a d,l, or } \pm \text{ pair)}}}{C_8H_{17}N}$$

The unsaturated base can also be oxidized to the known compound 2-carboxypyridine or α-picolinic acid.

$$C_8H_{11}N \xrightarrow{[O]}$$

This piece of information is very important because it shows that two carbon atoms are lost, and, therefore, the original compound must have been a 2-propylpyridine.

$$C_8H_{11}N =$$

It was then easy to determine that this compound was the *n*-propyl isomer and not 2-isopropylpyridine. This task was accomplished by comparison of physical properties, for the isopropyl isomer was known from previous research.

The reaction of coniine with acylating agents indicated that it is a secondary amine.

$$C_8H_{16}NH + \overset{O}{\overset{\|}{R}C}Cl \rightarrow C_8H_{16}N\overset{O}{\overset{\|}{C}}R + HCl$$

Mild oxidation produced an optically active aminoaldehyde.

$$C_8H_{17}N + H_2O_2 \rightarrow \overset{*}{N}H_2\overset{*}{C}HCH_2CH_2CH_2\overset{O}{\overset{\|}{C}}H$$

$$\underset{C_3H_7}{|}$$

R-5-aminooctanal

All this information, plus much not recorded here, points to the conclusion that coniine is R-2-propylpiperidine.

coniine

12.4B   Synthesis of Coniine

Once the structure of an organic molecule has been strongly indicated by the isolation and identification of reaction products, it is necessary to confirm it by means of a preparation from simpler compounds of known structure.

An attempted synthesis in the 1880's, made by the application of a known reaction, failed for a reason that should be familiar to you from your earlier study of the Friedel-Crafts reaction.

The rearrangement of the *n*-propyl to an isopropyl group under such drastic conditions is not very surprising.

In 1886, Ladenburg reported the first synthesis of an alkaloid.

$$CH_3-C \underset{O}{\overset{CH_3}{\underset{\underset{C-CH_3}{|}}{\overset{|}{C}}}} \xrightarrow{250°} 3\ CH_3\overset{O}{\overset{\|}{C}}H$$

paraldehyde

$$CH_3\overset{O}{\overset{\|}{C}}H\ +\ \underset{N}{\bigcirc}CH_2^- \ +\ H^+ \rightleftharpoons \underset{N}{\bigcirc}CH_3 \longrightarrow$$

activated by $\diagdown C{=}N\diagup$

$$\underset{N}{\bigcirc}CH_2\overset{OH}{\underset{|}{C}}HCH_3 \xrightarrow{250°} \underset{N}{\bigcirc}CH{=}CHCH_3\ +\ H_2O$$

The paraldehyde decomposes with heat to acetaldehyde, which condenses with 2-methylpyridine to give 2-propenylpyridine. Reduction of this compound with sodium in alcohol produced an

Albert Ladenburg (German, 1842–1911). *Ladenburg made impressive contributions in several areas of organic chemistry. In addition to studying the alkaloids, he was active in the early development of aromatic chemistry and devised several useful synthetic reactions. He also helped to start the study of* organic compounds containing silicon. His teaching was said to be very fine, and as a result, many able students were attracted to his laboratory at Kiel and later at Breslau. He took his doctorate at Heidelburg where Bunsen first interested him in chemistry. As often happens he is unfortunately best remembered for his prism structure of benzene, which was shown not to be correct by Baeyer in the late 1880's. In addition to research and teaching in organic chemistry, Ladenburg taught a course in the history of chemistry and wrote an important textbook on that subject.

Courtesy of the Edgar Fahs Smith Memorial Collection

optically inactive compound that showed properties very similar to those of coniine.

The final step in this total synthesis was the resolution of the racemic mixture to establish firmly the identity of natural coniine. This process was accomplished by fractional crystallization of the diastereoisomeric acid salts of coniine and (+)-tartaric acid.

Once these salts, which differ in physical properties, are separated, it is possible to recover the starting base.

(+)-coniine − (+)-hydrogen tartrate $\xrightarrow[\text{H}_2\text{O}]{\text{Na}^+\text{OH}^-}$
(acid)

(+)-coniine + (+)-tartaric acid (Na⁺ salt)

This process produced the dextrorotatory isomer that proved to be identical in every way to natural coniine.

SUGGESTED ADDITIONAL READINGS

Peroxide Effect

M. S. Kharasch, and F. R. Mayo, "The Addition of Hydrogen Bromide to Allyl Bromide," *J. Amer. Chem. Soc.*, **55**, 2468 (1933).

M. S. Kharasch, H. Engelmann, and F. R. Mayo, "The Addition of

Hydrogen Bromide to 1- and 2-Bromo- and Chloropropenes,"
J. Org. Chem., **2,** 288 (1937).

R. D. Billinger, and K. T. Finley, "Morris Selig Kharasch—A Great
American Chemist," *Chemistry*, **38** (6), 19 (1965).

Acyloin Cyclization

S. M. McElvain, "The Acyloins," *Org. Reactions*, **4,** 256 (1948).

K. T. Finley, "The Acyloin Condensation as a Cyclization Method,"
Chem. Rev., **64,** 573 (1964).

K. T. Finley, "The Synthesis of Carbocyclic Compounds—A Historical Survey," *J. Chem. Educ.*, **42,** 536 (1965).

Structure and Synthesis of Coniine

L. Small, "Alkaloids," in *Organic Chemistry—An Advanced Treatise*
(2nd ed.), ed. H. Gilman (New York: John Wiley & Sons, Inc.,
1943), pp. 1178–79.

L. Marion, "The Pyridine Alkaloids," in *The Alkaloids*, eds. R. H. F.
Manske, and H. L. Holmes (New York: Academic Press, Inc.,
1950), pp. 211–17.

K. T. Finley, "Ladenburg and the Cup of Hemlock," *Chemistry*, **41**
(1), 18 (1968).

PROBLEMS

1. In addition to the "peroxide effect," there are a number of other anti-Markownikoff additions to alkenes; for example,

$$(CH_3)_3N^+—CH=CH_2 + HI \rightarrow (CH_3)_3N^+—CH_2CH_2—I$$

   Draw possible intermediates for this reaction and suggest why anti-Markownikoff addition should be observed.

2. Predict the chief product in each of the following reactions of 2-methylpropene (isobutylene):

   a. Br_2 f . $C_6H_5CO_3H$
   b. HBr **g.** $Br_2 + Cl^-$
   c. HBr (peroxides)   h. $KMnO_4$, cold and dilute
   d. HI (peroxides)   **i .** H_2O and H^+
   e. H_2SO_4 j . Br_2 and H_2O

   Justify your answers on the basis of a reasonable mechanism for each reaction.

3. In the presence of peroxides, carbon tetrachloride will add to alkenes. Predict the products of the addition of CCl_4 to 1-butene and support your answers with a detailed mechanism.

4. Civetone is a natural product very highly valued in preparing perfumes. It reacts with 2,4-dinitrophenylhydrazine but is not easily oxidized. Elemental analysis and molecular weight determination show its molecular formula to be $C_{17}H_{30}O$. Reduction with hydrogen and platinum gives a new compound, $C_{17}H_{34}O$. The oxidation of civetone under mild conditions gives a mixture of acids of the type $HO_2C(CH_2)_nCO_2H$, where $n = 5$, 6, and 7. Oxidation under other conditions gives $C_{17}H_{30}O_5$. Draw a structure for civetone and show how it is consistent with these facts.

5. The actual synthesis of civetone involves some difficulties you are not completely ready for. However, it will be sufficient to point out that a carbonyl group must be protected during a reduction reaction in another part of the molecule. Now you should be able to write a synthesis of dihydrocivetone ($C_{17}H_{32}O$), which is a reduction product of civetone.

6. Hydrolysis of the alkaloid atropine yields tropic acid the molecular formula of which is $C_9H_{10}O_3$. Tropic acid dehydrates readily to atropic acid, which can then be hydrogenated to hydratropic acid. Each of these three acids can be oxidized to benzoic acid. Tropic acid can be oxidized (under carefully controlled conditions) to a dicarboxylic acid. Draw the structure of each of the preceding compounds. Propose a synthesis of tropic acid starting with benzene, ethanol, and inorganic reagents. Is your product optically active? If tropic acid should exist in enantiomeric forms, describe a method for its resolution.

Solving Analytical Problems

It might be well for us to look at the methods one might apply in solving the "roadmap" or qualitative organic analytical problem. You should keep in mind that there is no ideal way to attack these problems; everyone must work out his own. Skill at solving these puzzles (like any other kind) comes only from practice. As you read these examples, pay careful attention to the methods employed and do not be concerned about any reactions or names with which you are unfamiliar. Later in your study of organic chemistry, a rereading of these notes may be useful.

Problem A. An organic compound of molecular formula $C_5H_{12}O$ reacted with sodium to release hydrogen and gave a Lucas test after about 5 min. When the material was passed over hot alumina, it was converted to an alkene, which could be oxidized to a neutral substance and an acid with a neutralization equivalent of 60 ± 1.

The first problem is always one of finding a place to start, and this point is where the individuality of each person's approach shows up most clearly. Perhaps the best generalization possible is simply to look around for something familiar to you. In this case, it might be the molecular formula, the Lucas reaction, or the oxidation product. For practice, let us try all three of these approaches as a start. To one person, $C_5H_{12}O$ looks just like C_nH_{2n+2} which tells him that this compound is saturated. To someone else, the moderately slow Lucas reaction immediately suggests a secondary alcohol $RR'CHOH$. Finally, someone may seize upon the oxidation products and say that acetic acid must have been one of them, inasmuch as it will have the correct neutralization equivalent value.

Now it is quite true that none of our hypothetical students have a solution, but they have all made a start. These initial thoughts may be right or wrong and the solution will be faster and easier if they are right; still, even an incorrect first idea will get you started and in time will point the way to a better idea. How does this process work? The next step is to follow through the consequences of our first thought. For example, if we had started by deciding that this compound was saturated, our next thought would be that you can make quite a few different ones from $C_5H_{12}O$. Possible are not only different structural isomers, but functional group isomers as well:

$$CH_3CH_2CH_2CH_2CH_2OH \qquad CH_3CH_2CH_2OCH_2CH_3$$

and many others. Clearly, we shall require additional information if we are to find a solution. Reaction with sodium eliminates ethers, and, as we have said, the Lucas test indicates a secondary alcohol.

$$\overset{\displaystyle OH}{\underset{\displaystyle |}{CH_3CHCH_2CH_2CH_3}} \qquad \overset{\displaystyle OH}{\underset{\displaystyle |}{CH_3CH_2CHCH_2CH_3}} \qquad \overset{\displaystyle OH}{\underset{\displaystyle |}{CH_3CHCHCH_3}} \\ \underset{\displaystyle \quad\quad\quad\quad |}{\underset{\displaystyle \quad\quad\quad\quad CH_3}{}}$$

The number of possibilities has been greatly reduced. A little thought will reveal that any of these isomers can (and probably would) dehydrate over alumina to give an olefin capable of being oxidized to acetic acid (if this process is not clear, write out all possibilities). In other words, the neutral oxidation product is the key to the structure. Because we only have three carbons left with which to work, acetone is the sole possible netural product. Acetone, in turn, can only result from the dehydration product of one of the preceding alcohols.

$$
\underset{\substack{|\\ CH_3}}{\overset{\substack{OH\\|}}{CH_3CHCHCH_3}} \xrightarrow{-H_2O} CH_3CH=C\overset{CH_3}{\underset{CH_3}{\Big\langle}} \xrightarrow{[O]}
$$

$$
CH_3CO_2H + CH_3\overset{\overset{\textstyle O}{\|}}{C}CH_3
$$

This same solution would have been arrived at from our other starting points and by much the same reasoning. Let us emphasize once again there is no "right" way.

Problem B. Compound (A), $C_{10}H_{10}O_2$, gives positive Tollens', Fehling's, and iodoform tests. If (A) is reduced under the proper conditions, a hydrocarbon, $C_{10}H_{14}$, is formed that gives only a single monobromo substitution product when treated with Br_2 and Fe.

The low carbon-to-hydrogen ratio and the substitution reaction with bromine indicate that we are dealing with an aromatic compound. The various carbonyl reagents suggest both an aldehyde and a methyl ketone (or secondary alcohol adjacent to a methyl group). Ten carbons allow us to have only one ring—that is, it must be a substituted benzene. If the hydrocarbon is to produce only a single monobromo product, it and the compound from which it is derived must be symmetrical. The only way the four carbons left can be so arranged is as two chains of two carbons each located *para* to one another.

One technique that often pays off is simply to subtract molecular formulas of compounds. The difference can be of great help in deciding what the unknown must be. For example, our unknown and its reduction product differ by $+ H_4 - O_2$, or viewed differently, each oxygen was replaced by two hydrogens. Thus, we are dealing with two carbonyl oxygens, giving us the detailed structure of the unknown:

$$CH_2CHO$$

$$\xrightarrow{Ag(NH_3)_2^+}$$

$$\xrightarrow{Na^+OI^-}$$

$$CCH_3$$
$$\|$$
$$O$$

$$Ag + CH_3\overset{O}{\underset{\|}{C}}\!-\!\!\bigcirc\!\!-\!CH_2CO_2^-NH_4^+$$

$$Na^{+\,-}O_2CCH_2\!-\!\!\bigcirc\!\!-\!CO_2^-Na^+ + CHI_3$$

Problem C. An organic compound (A) with molecular formula $C_7H_{12}O$ is reduced by H_2/Pt to a new compound (B), $C_7H_{14}O$. Compound (B) does not react with sodium or permanganate solution, but evolves methyl iodide when refluxed with HI. If one oxidizes (A), reduces the product with $LiAlH_4$, and then refluxes with HI, *n*-hexane is obtained.

There is a wealth of information here about this unknown; once again, let us emphasize that the best place to start is wherever you "see" something meaningful to you. The two molecular formulas are a good possibility. Subtraction shows that H_2 has been added, which, of course, suggests an alkene. However, you must always be on guard, not against making a judgment about the meaning of data but about being too quick to decide that a conclusion is the only one possible. In the present case, the addition of H_2 by catalytic methods could mean a carbonyl, a small ring, or an alkene. Closer inspection reveals that the formula of (B) is still not saturated, but $C_nH_{2n}O$. Our discussion so far makes this analysis fairly easy, and we conclude that a five-, six-, or seven-membered ring must be involved (anything else would have been reduced).

Now that the basic carbon skeleton has been limited, we should examine the oxygen functional group. Failure to react with sodium suggests that it is not a hydroxyl group, which, in turn, eliminates the possibility of a carbonyl group in (A). The reactions with HI to give CH_3I or a hydrocarbon are characteristic of ethers and, of course, require a methyl ether. The number of possible compounds has now been sharply limited, inasmuch as we must have the following structural features:

or , $\overset{\diagup}{\diagdown}C\!=\!C\overset{\diagdown}{\diagup}$, $-OCH_3$ and CH_3-

and *n*-hexane must be a reduction product after an initial oxidation.

This last sequence of reactions may be the key to the question of how we should put these parts together. If we simply try a random combination, we might choose 3-methoxycyclohexene:

$$HOCH_2CHCH_2CH_2CH_2CH_2OH \xrightarrow{\text{HI}} \textit{n-hexane}$$
$$\overset{|}{OCH_3}$$

We might be tempted to stop at this point, because we have an answer that clearly satisfies all the requirements. This fact brings us face-to-face with one of the similarities between textbook roadmap problems and research in organic structure determination: the experiments you have done may not give a unique solution. Take a look at our solution. There is nothing in the data that fixes the position of the methoxy group. It could be 1- or 4-methoxycyclohexene just as well as the isomer we have chosen. Inasmuch as we are looking for other possibilities, how about the 5-membered ring compounds? There are several possibilities, but some can be eliminated by the requirement that *n*-hexane be obtained, which has the effect of putting the methyl group on the double bond:

We are still left with several additional possible structures for compound (A):

You must be on the lookout for the possibility of other structures that fit the given data. Often the way a question is worded will give you a hint — for example, "Suggest *a* possible structure..." and "Are there any other compounds that are consistent with the data?" An excellent chapter (12) devoted to this matter of solving roadmap problems can be found in Shriner, Fuson, and Curtin. It contains a good number of problems worked out in some detail.

Modern Methods of Analysis

The discussion of qualitative organic analysis up to this point has presented a method that is only infrequently used in detail in today's research laboratories. That is not to say that it is without value; in fact, nearly all of our research chemists have been trained in these techniques (many of them using the five editions of the book by Professors Shriner, Fuson, and Curtin). The ability to manipulate observe, and reason, which such a course can strengthen, is fundamental to good research.

In recent years, new and powerful analysis techniques have been developed that greatly reduce both the time and the sample size required for an analysis of either a known or an unknown compound. The matter of sample size is a very important one, because the chromatographic techniques for the isolation and purification of compounds are usually best suited to very small amounts of material. It should be mentioned that this situation is also rapidly changing as new instruments are being constructed which allow the preparation of larger quantities of pure substances. This fact raises one more point: not only have new techniques been developed recently, but our engineers and factories have been able to produce large numbers of rugged, relatively inexpensive, precision instruments capable of putting these techniques within the reach of the individual organic chemist.

339

Inasmuch as these methods are the mainstream of today's organic analysis, what is it they do and how do they do it? It is only fair to warn you that these ideas, although not untrue, will be greatly simplified and therefore subject to many exceptions. Our series of brief sketches will include (1) mass spectra (ms), (2) infrared spectra (ir), (3) ultraviolet spectra (uv), and (4) nuclear magnetic resonance spectra (nmr).

II.1
MASS SPECTRA

This area represents an exception to the reasons given for the rapid growth of instrumental methods, in that the mass spectrometer is a rather expensive instrument which must be operated and maintained by specialists. Despite these factors, the technique is so powerful that a great deal of work is being done with it.

The basic operation in obtaining a mass spectrum is to vaporize a sample of the compound and allow it to be struck by a beam of electrons. The pressure of the instrument is kept low, and the inlet can be heated so that a wide variety of organic compounds (even many with low vapor pressure) can be studied. The electrons have the effect of ionizing the molecule, and it, in turn, breaks up into many fragments including positive ions. These ions are electrostatically accelerated, separated (often magnetically) and electronically counted. The abundance of ions at each mass is measured in terms of the mass to charge ratio (m/e); inasmuch as the charge is 1 for most ions, a plot of the relative abundance of ions of various masses is obtained.

The **fragmentation pattern**, as this plot is called, is very characteristic of an organic compound, and with the buildup of large libraries of spectra of known compounds, it is possible to compare spectra to identify a known compound. For an unknown compound, this method is also extremely useful. First, it is often possible to locate the **molecular ion** or **parent peak** resulting from the removal of one electron from the molecule. The m/e value for this peak (which is often the largest or **base peak**) is a very accurate molecular weight of the compound.

A further use of the mass spectrum lies in the fact that experience allows us to predict to some extent the fragmentation pattern that would be observed with certain structural features.

For example, we should expect that stable carbonium ions (*t*-butyl or allyl cations) will be formed and small stable molecules (H_2O, NH_3, CO) will be eliminated. Thus, a mass spectrum can often be said to be consistent with that expected for a given structure, but only comparison with an authentic sample of known structure can be considered very strong evidence for the structural assignment. As an example of the mass spectrum, let us look at the simple, symmetrical hydrocarbon 2,2-dimethylpropane (see Figure II.1).

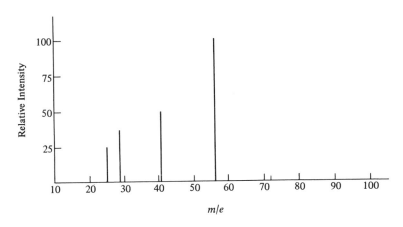

FIGURE II.1.   Fragmentation Pattern of 2,2-Dimethylpropane.

	m/e	Relative intensity	Probable structure
$(C_4H_9)^+$	57	100	$(CH_3)_3C^+$
$(C_3H_5)^+$	41	41.5	$CH_2{=}CHCH_2^+$
$(C_2H_5)^+$	29	38.5	$CH_3CH_2^+$
$(C_2H_3)^+$	27	15.7	$CH_2{=}CH^+$

$$CH_3CCH_3 \xrightarrow{\ e^-\ } (C_5H_{12})^+$$

CH₃CCH₃ structure with two CH₃ groups, parent peak (molecular ion) $m/e = 72$, relative intensity = 0.01   (and others)

This example illustrates the great stability of the *t*-butyl cation, which is very much more intense than the parent peak or neopentane cation.

The most serious limitations on the use of mass spectra for the study of the structure of organic compounds are the need for some vapor pressure on the part of the compound and the difficulty of interpretation of the spectrum because of secondary reactions and rearrangements. The former is not very serious because nearly all organic compounds have the small volatility required. Even in those few cases where the vapor pressure is too low — for example, the sulfonic acids — derivatives (sulfonyl fluorides) can be prepared. Progress is being made in understanding the reactions of compounds under electron bombardment. This problem does not affect the most common uses of mass spectra for showing the identity of two compounds and getting a very accurate molecular weight.

II.2
INFRARED SPECTRA

The bonds holding organic compounds together are not rigid but can bend and stretch with respect to one another. When energy of the proper frequency is put into a molecule, these movements can be increased and the absorption of the energy measured and recorded. The portion of the electromagnetic spectrum having the proper frequencies for most organic bonds lies at longer wavelengths (lower frequency and less energy) than the red part of the visible spectrum—hence, the name infrared. The portion of the infrared that is of most interest for organic structure work is generally taken to be approximately 2.5 to 15 μ (microns or 10^{-4} cm), in terms of wavelength, or 4000 to 667 cm^{-1} in frequency. If the "near" and "far" infrared is included, it extends from 12,500 to 100 cm^{-1}.

The spectrophotometers most commonly used produce the infrared radiation by an electrically heated filament or "glow bar." The beam of radiation is often split in two, with one-half passing through air and the other through the sample. The optics of the spectrophotometer must transmit infrared radiation; NaCl is often used. A measurement of the difference in intensity of the two beams is then made and recorded as absorption versus frequency on a chart designed for the purpose. The sample can be prepared in several different forms; among those commonly used are (1) a neat liquid or gas, (2) a solution, (3) a paste or mull in a hydrocarbon oil, and (4) a pellet of finely divided solid pressed together with potassium bromide powder. An obvious advantage of this spectrophotometric method (uv and nmr as well) is that when it is necessary, the sample can be recovered after the spectrum is obtained.

An infrared spectrum typically shows a great number of absorptions, only a limited number of which can be assigned with certainty to a particular vibration. Despite this limitation, the infrared spectrum is of very great use. For example, like the mass spectrum, it is very characteristic of a compound, and if an authentic sample is available or can be prepared, the identity of its infrared spectrum with that of the unknown is very strong evidence that they are the same. For this reason, the 7- to 16-μ region is often referred to as the "fingerprint" area.

Even if the compound is completely new, the ir can be of great help in proposing a structure. Through the study of large numbers of organic compounds, absorptions characteristic of certain functional groups have been assigned.† The appearance of one of these absorptions gives a very strong hint as to the group present, especially when, as is usually the case, the compound is not a true "unknown," but has been prepared and/or isolated so that something of its chemistry is already known.

TABLE II.1 INFRARED FREQUENCIES CHARACTERISTIC OF CERTAIN FUNCTIONAL GROUPS*

Bond	Type of compound	Frequency range, cm^{-1}
C—H	alkanes	2850–2960 and 1350–1470
	alkenes	3020–3080 (m) and 675–1000
	aromatic	3000–3100 (m) and 675–870
	alkynes	3300
O—H	alcohols, acids	3100–3600 and 2500–3000
C=C	alkenes	1640–1680 (v)
C≡C	alkynes	2100–2260 (v)
C⋯C	aromatic	1500–1600 (v)
C—O	alcohols, ethers, acids, esters	1080–1300
C=O	aldehydes, ketones, acids, esters	1690–1760
N—H	amines	3300–3500 (m)
C—N	amines	1180–1360
C≡N	nitriles	2210–2260 (v)
NO_2	nitro compounds	1515–1560 and 1345–1385

*The absorptions are strong unless indicated: m is moderate and v is variable.

†Many of these have been tabulated for quick reference. Now it is becoming possible to match spectra by computer.

Table II.1 gives a very brief list of some frequencies characteristic of certain functional groups.

The interpretation of the ir spectrum of an unknown compound is not at all a simple matter, but certain absorptions often stand out, as the spectra in Figure II.2 indicate.

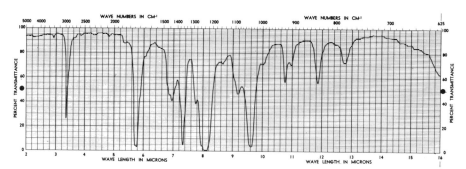

FIGURE II.2a.*   Ethyl acetate (CH$_3$ 2980, CH$_2$ 2900, C═O 1740, OC─O 1240, O─CH$_2$ 1040, the pattern at 1470 to 1440 is characteristic of acetates).

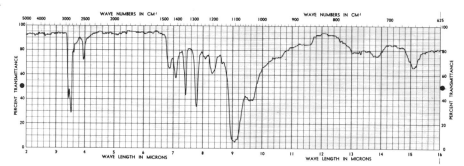

FIGURE II.2b.* β,β'-Dimercaptodiethyl ether (CH$_2$ 2920 and 2895, SH 2520, CH$_2$ 1450 to 1300, O─CH$_2$ 1100, C─S 650).

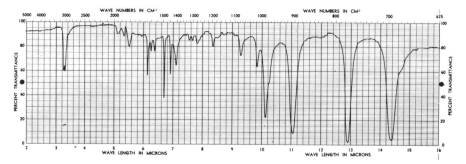

FIGURE II.2c.*   Styrene (═CH 3010 and 3030, Ar 2000 to 1700, C═C 1630, Ar 1600 to 1400, the pattern at 990 and 905 is characteristic of a vinyl group).

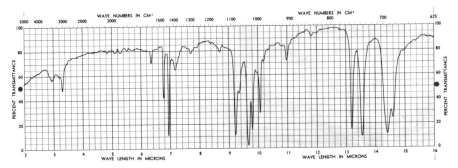

FIGURE II.2d.*   Diphenyl sulfoxide (H$_2$O in KBr 3400, CH 3030, Ar 1960 to 1750, C—C 1570 to 1440, S—O 1037, CH 758 and 738, Ar 695, C—S 685).

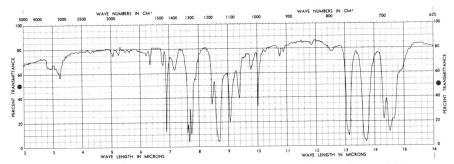

FIGURE II.2e.*   Diphenyl sulfone (H$_2$O in KBr 3400, CH 3030, Ar 1600 to 1450, SO$_2$ 1300 and 1150, CH 1100 to 1000, 762, and 690, C—S usually weak and probably in the group at 695 to 680).

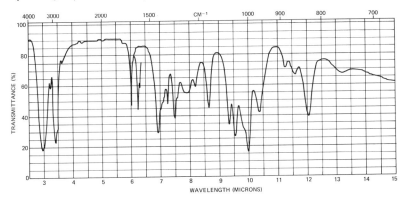

FIGURE II.2f.†   3-Methyl-2-cyclopenten-1-ol (OH 3400, CH$_3$ and CH$_2$ 2950 and 2900, C=C 1670, CH$_3$ and CH$_2$ 1450 and 1330, C—O 1000, C=CH probably 830).

*We are indebted to Miss Thelma Davis of the Eastman Kodak Research Laboratories for these spectra and their interpretation.

†Dr. Henry M. Hess (Eastman Kodak Company) kindly supplied this spectrum.

In the spectral region of 220 to 400 nm, which is just beyond the violet end of the visible spectrum (hence ultraviolet), we find another useful source of information about the structure of organic molecules. Like the ir, a uv spectrophotometer takes a beam of radiation (usually from a hydrogen- or deuterium-discharge lamp), splits it into two paths, and measures the difference in energy after one has passed through the sample and the other through the reference. Most often, the sample is dissolved in some suitable solvent (H_2O, 95% ethanol, etc.), and the reference is the neat solvent. Quartz cells must be used because glass absorbs uv radiation.

Unlike the ir spectrum, the uv spectrum is usually made up of a few bands of absorption; because of the higher energy of the radiation, these are the result of electronic excitation. In other words, the electrons of a particular energy are promoted to a higher energy level. The large number of subenergy levels in a given electronic energy level leads to a broad band made up of many individual transitions. It is usual simply to refer to the wavelength of maximum absorbance (λ_{max}) and to the intensity of that absorbance (ϵ_{max}, the molar absorptivity).

Another difference between the application of ir and uv spectroscopy is that the latter is used to examine electronic patterns in the molecule and less often to identify a specific functional group. In fact, the isolated functional group in most cases absorbs outside of the wavelength region, which can be obtained without special equipment (O_2 absorbs very strongly at 200 nm and below). The uv spectrum is a powerful tool for determining the relationship between functional groups, particularly conjugation. Table II.2 will illustrate the effect of conjugation on the values of λ_{max} and ϵ_{max}.

A comparison of the recorded figures for the isolated functional groups and the conjugated systems reveals a marked change in the position and/or the intensity of absorption. Four additional points concerning ultraviolet spectroscopy should be mentioned. First, the position of λ_{max} is very strongly influenced by structure—for example, number of alkyl groups, presence of rings, geometric isomerism, and so on—which can, in some cases, be used to get more structural detail (see Woodward's

TABLE II.2　THE ULTRAVIOLET ABSORPTION OF SELECTED ORGANIC MOLECULES

Compound	λ_{max}, nm	ϵ_{max}	Solvent
$CH_2{=}CH_2$	171	15,530	vapor
$\underset{\displaystyle CH_3CH}{\overset{\displaystyle O \atop \|}{}}$	160	20,000	vapor
CH_3CO_2H	208	32	ethanol
CH_3NO_2	201	5000	methanol
CH_3CN	167	weak	vapor
$CH_2{=}CHCH{=}CH_2$	217	20,900	hexane
$\underset{\displaystyle CH_3CH{=}CHCH}{\overset{\displaystyle O \atop \|}{}}$	218	18,000	ethanol
$CH_3CH{=}CHCO_2H$	206	13,500	ethanol
$CH_3CH{=}CHNO_2$	229	9400	ethanol
$CH_2{=}CHCN$	215	680	ethanol
C_6H_6	198; 255	8000; 230	cyclohexane

rules). Second, in many molecules the position of λ_{max} will shift in an understandable manner with changes in solvent; thus, it is necessary to specify the solvent used, and it is sometimes possible to make use of the observed shifts in deciding upon a structure. Third, there are relationships between the observed absorbance (A; also called optical density) of a sample and the concentration of material in solution (Lambert's and Beer's laws). In dilute solution, the following expression often obtains:

$$\epsilon = \frac{A}{cl}$$

ϵ = molar absorptivity

c = molar concentration

l = cell length (cm)

Thus, the concentration of a material can be obtained, which is of great importance in many research programs; for example, determining purity or following the rate of a reaction. Fourth, what has been said here about the ultraviolet spectrum is also true of the visible region (400 to 800 nm). The usual source is a tungsten-filament lamp, and glass cells may be used.

Figure II.3 provides some typical illustrations of ultraviolet and visible spectra.

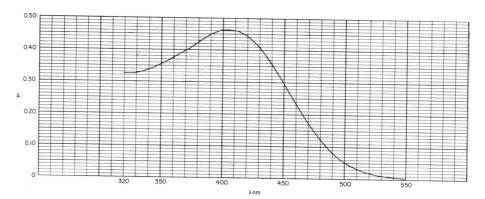

FIGURE II.3a.   *N*-2-nitrophenylpiperidine.   4 × 10⁻⁴ *M*, solvent methanol, 1 cm cell (visible).

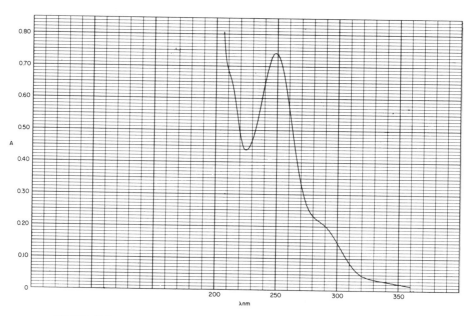

FIGURE II.3b.   2-Nitrofluorobenzene.   11.4 × 10⁻⁵ *M*, solvent methanol, 1 cm cell (ultraviolet).

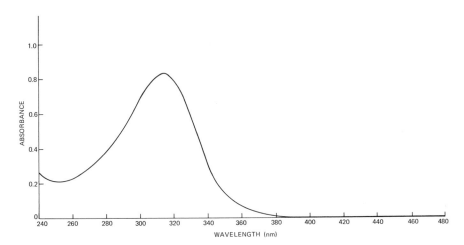

FIGURE II.3c.*   2,2'-Dithiobis-(5-nitropyridine). 3.36×10^{-5} M, solvent absolute ethanol, 1 cm cell (ultraviolet).

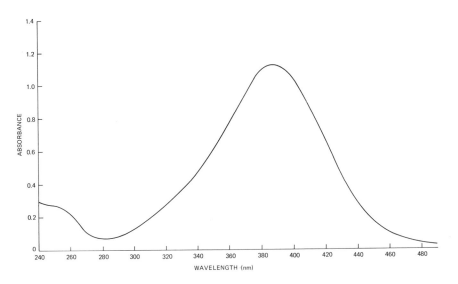

FIGURE II.3d.*   2-Mercapto-5-nitropyridine thione. 6.72×10^{-5} M, solvent absolute ethanol, 1 cm cell (ultraviolet-visible).

*We are grateful to Dr. D. R. Grassetti and the Arequipa Foundation for these spectra.

The ability to interpret mass, infrared, ultraviolet, and visible spectra (at least as practiced by the typical organic chemist) is in large measure empirical. From a large number of spectra, certain characteristic patterns have evolved enabling us to state with some confidence that a given molecule does or does not have a given structural feature. The final spectroscopic tool we are going to examine is perhaps the most powerful from the point of view of gaining detailed knowledge of the structure of a compound. This power, however, is gained from a deeper study of the theoretical background of the technique. Inasmuch as our interest is simply a broad view of the method and its uses, we shall not go into the necessary physics of the magnetic properties of nuclei and the effects of external magnetic fields. This factor will result in limiting our discussion to the observations and their meaning in terms of the structure of the molecule with very little explanation of the reasons why they should be true.

Although nuclear magnetic resonance spectroscopy is not limited to protons, they are so common in organic molecules that a great deal of nmr work has been devoted to them; we shall confine our discussion to such spectra. In one popular interpretation, the proton is imagined as a tiny, spinning bar magnet. If such a magnet is placed in a beam of radiation in the radio-frequency (rf) range and a superimposed magnetic field is varied in strength, there will be a field strength at which the radiation will have sufficient energy to cause the nuclei (tiny magnets) to "flip" from the more stable orientation (with the field) to the less stable orientation (opposite to the field). At this point, absorption of energy occurs and a signal (resonance) can be recorded. Other theories to explain the absorption of energy are less naïve but beyond the scope of this text.

If this greatly simplified picture were the whole story, all protons in an organic molecule would be expected to absorb at the same field strength and we should learn very little. Fortunately, this resonance frequency depends on the magnetic field that the proton actually experiences rather than the applied field. The so-called effective field is influenced by the environment of the proton. It is then true that all equivalent protons will absorb at the same effective field strength, but at different applied fields.

In practice, the applied field is varied at a constant rf value and the absorption of radiation plotted against applied field strength.

There are four basic kinds of information we can obtain from an nmr spectrum:

1. the number of different "kinds" of protons;
2. the electronic environment of each kind of proton;
3. how many of each kind of protons there are;
4. the environment of a proton with respect to other nearby protons.

To a first approximation, the number of different kinds of protons will be the same as the number of different isomers that can be made by substituting a new group for one proton at a time.

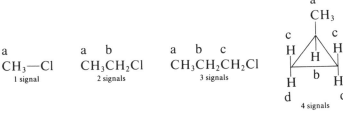

It should be pointed out that the preceding examples indicate the number of signals that should be observed. Fewer absorptions will be found if the environments are not different enough to separate the signals. Very frequently, more signals will be found, as discussed later.

The magnetic field used to obtain an nmr spectrum will cause the electrons of the molecule to circulate, causing secondary magnetic fields. These secondary fields are characteristic of the type of molecule being studied, and a given proton can have its effective field enhanced or diminished by those of nearby nuclei. By using a standard [$(CH_3)_4Si$, tetramethylsilane or TMS is very common] and by measuring the difference between its resonance and that of the proton in question, a value of the **chemical shift** can be obtained. If we look at a spectrum of toluene (see Figure II.4), these first two points become clear:

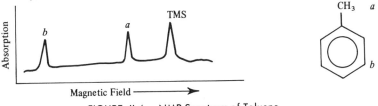

FIGURE II.4.   NMR Spectrum of Toluene.

The first thing to notice is that although we should expect four different kinds of protons, only two are observed. This fact is not usually true of monosubstituted aromatic compounds, but in this case the difference among *o*, *m*, and *p* protons is too small for them to be separated. The π electrons of the ring strongly augment the applied field; therefore, the resonance shows up at a low field strength relative to TMS. The alkyl side-chain protons feel some of the effect of the ring electrons, and are therefore shifted somewhat downfield from the TMS.

A very useful aspect of the intensity of the absorption signal is that its area is proportional to the number of that kind of proton. In practice, an electronic integrator is a part of the spectrometer, and the spectrum has a stepped trace that can be converted to the relative numbers of protons. For example, in the case of toluene we should find that the peak area for side-chain versus aromatic protons is about 3:5. If we looked at *p*-xylene, we should find the ratio, for peaks that incidentally show chemical shifts similar to those for toluene, would be 3:2 (or 6:4). It is usually possible to assign some peak or collection of peaks with enough certainty to fix the actual molecular ratio.

A few nmr spectra show one absorption for each kind of proton (or fewer), but most compounds have spectra that appear to be much more complicated—for example, the spectrum of ethyl chloride (see Figure II.5), which we earlier said should show two signals:

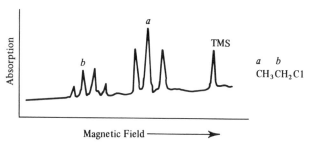

FIGURE II.5.   NMR Spectrum of Ethyl Chloride.

The reason for there being seven signals deals with the presence of a different kind of proton nearby. In general, a set of *n* equivalent protons will split a signal for nearby protons into $n + 1$ signals. Thus, the methyl protons should be split into a triplet by the methylene protons ($n = 2$), and the methylene protons should be split into a quartet by the methyl protons ($n = 3$). The ratio of the total area under the triplet to that under the quartet will be 3:2. The areas under the individual peaks are related to the number of possible orientations of the spins of the neighboring protons relative to the magnetic field.

It can be seen that each of the spectra discussed in these notes can contribute a good deal of information to the elucidation of the structure of an organic compound. When one considers that the data can be obtained quickly and with a very small sample (recoverable, except from mass spectrometry), it is entirely reasonable that these methods have all but replaced the older "wet" qualitative analysis for the actual work of the research chemist.

SUGGESTED ADDITIONAL READINGS

General

> Bordwell, excellent integration of ir throughout.
> Morrison and Boyd, Chapter 13.
> Pasto and Johnson, Part II.
> Roberts and Caserio, Chapter 2.
> Shriner, Fuson, and Curtin, Chapter 9.

J. R. Dyer, *Applications of Absorption Spectroscopy of Organic Compounds* (Englewood Cliffs, N.J.: Prentice-Hall, Inc., 1965).

R. M. Silverstein and G. C. Bassler, *Spectrometric Identification of Organic Compounds* (New York: John Wiley & Sons, Inc., 1964).

Mass Spectra

F. W. McLafferty and R. S. Gohlke, "Expanded Analytical Horizons Through Mass Spectrometry," *Chem. Eng. News*, May 18, 1964, pp. 96–108.

E. L. Eliel, T. J. Prosser, and G. W. Young, "The Use of Mass Spectrometry in Organic Analysis," *J. Chem. Educ.*, **34,** 72 (1957).

Infrared Spectra

L. J. Bellamy, *The Infra-red Spectra of Complex Molecules* (2nd ed.; London: Methuen & Co., Ltd., 1959).

R. T. Conley, "The Integration of Infrared Spectroscopy into Organic Qualitative Analysis," *J. Chem. Educ.*, **35,** 453 (1958).

P. R. Jones, "Infrared Spectroscopy and Molecular Architecture," *Chemistry*, **38** (2), 5 (1965).

Ultraviolet and Visible Spectra

J. R. Edisbury, *Practical Hints on Absorption Spectrometry* (New York: Plenum Press, 1967).

C.N.R. Rao, *Ultra-violet and Visible Spectroscopy* (New York: Plenum Press, 1967).

Nuclear Magnetic Resonance Spectra

L. M. Jackman, *Applications of Nuclear Magnetic Resonance Spectroscopy in Organic Chemistry* (London: Pergamon Press, 1959).

J. D. Roberts, *Nuclear Magnetic Resonance: Applications to Organic Chemistry* (New York: McGraw-Hill Book Company, 1959).

F. A. Bovey, "Nuclear Magnetic Resonance," *Chem. Eng. News*, August 30, 1965, pp. 98–121.

R. K. Kullnig, C. M. Martini, and F. C. Nachod, "Nuclear Magnetic Resonance Spectroscopy. Part I," *Chemistry*, **38** (5), 6 (1965); "Part II," *Chemistry*, **38** (7), 17 (1965).

The Synthesis

of Organic Compounds

III.1
INTRODUCTION

One of the fundamental concerns of the organic chemist is the conversion of one molecule of known characteristics to a new one of different structure. In its simplest form, this process is a definition of every organic reaction; however, the term synthesis usually implies a series of reactions carefully chosen to bring about the desired transformation in the highest yield and the shortest time. A course in basic organic chemistry frequently makes use of problems of the synthetic type to assist the student in learning, remembering, and understanding the reactions presented. It is our purpose in this section to examine the general methods that are useful in solving synthetic problems, both on paper and in the laboratory.

If you read this section near the beginning of your study of organic chemistry, you should concern yourself only with the general methods. The specific compounds and reactions will probably be unfamiliar and it will not be worthwhile to study the details. Later in your exposure to the problems of organic chemistry, you should reread these notes. Perhaps then you will

355

both sharpen your appreciation of the general methods and also see in the examples new and interesting reactions and sequences.

III.2
IN GENERAL

In every synthetic problem, there is the statement, "given _____, prepare _____." The text, test, or lecture fills in both blanks for you, thereby removing two of the greatest problems of real life. In fact, relatively little can be taught about these problems in the formal sense. Only experience, a good memory, and extensive reading can help one to predict what compounds should be made and to know what starting material represents the best point of departure. However, do not infer that "made-up" synthetic problems are uninteresting or unproductive; a very great deal of stimulating thought is required to work out routes that can be defended as reasonable. Also remember that the best way to learn something is to make use of it.

Given an objective and a starting point, it is often useful simply to reflect for a time (the length of time depends on the circumstances) with both of these in mind. The relationship between the two compounds may suggest at least the general direction to be taken.

1. Is the desired compound generally a larger or smaller molecule than the starting material?

(a) larger—a sequence of reactions that add groups will be required

(b) $\rightarrow HO_2CCH_2CH_2CO_2H$ smaller—reactions involving breaking bonds are indicated

2. Is the product in a higher or lower oxidation state than the starting material?

(c) $CH\equiv CH \rightarrow HO_2CCH_2CH_3$ higher—the use of an oxidizing reaction of some kind must be involved

(d) $CH_3O_2C(CH_2)_4CO_2CH_3 \rightarrow$ [cyclohexane ring structure]   lower—at least one important step will be a reduction

3. What mechanistic types of reactions can be listed that seem to be proceeding in the desired direction?

(e) [benzene ring] $\rightarrow$ [benzene ring with $CO_2CH_2CH_3$ and H_3C substituents]   aromatic substitution, Grignard, and esterification

(f) $CH{\equiv}CH \rightarrow CH_3CH{=}CHCHCH_2CH_3$ with OH on the labeled carbon   addition, condensation, elimination, and Grignard

4. Is there some critical or key step that you can see in the problem? Are there any potential difficulties to be avoided? Let us consider the previous examples.

  (a) Requires an acylation, and the deactivating effect of the nitro group must be considered.
  (b) Ring opening is the key step and the chain must be shortened.
  (c) The chain is lengthened and oxidation takes place.
  (d) Cyclization and reduction occur.
  (e) Selective oxidation (or avoiding it) is the critical step.
  (f) The chain is lengthened with the additional complication of getting two functional groups in the right place.

III.3
THE ACTUAL SYNTHESIS

With a little practice, the preceding procedure takes much less time to do than to write or read about. If it is done with care, the problem of writing a good synthesis can be made much easier. It also provides an answer to the most often heard complaint of students: "I don't know where to start." Now we shall consider each of the above examples in detail. Keep in mind that there are many possible answers to most synthetic problems and after you have listed them you must try to decide on the one most likely to be successful.

Problem A. This case is one of those (quite usual) where working in reverse is an attractive possibility. This method is put into practice by thinking to yourself, "How would I prepare the desired compound in one reaction, if I could start with any compounds I want?"

In this example, it is clear that in one step we have gotten half the desired molecule back to the starting material; now we can focus our attention on the other half. The acid chloride is a sensitive part of the molecule and should be introduced last. Hence,

The synthesis of an aromatic ring with two functional groups, such as *m*-nitrobenzoic acid, presents a number of possible reaction sequences. Frequently some of these can be eliminated rapidly; for example,

Grignard reagents in general cannot be prepared with oxygen-containing functions present. An important exception is the ether group.

The second route appears to be a good one, but the problem arises in the preparation of *m*-nitrotoluene. Nitrobenzene is very unreactive in Friedel-Crafts alkylations, and the nitration of toluene gives mostly the *ortho* and *para* isomers. On the other hand, the nitration of benzoic acid, prepared by the oxidation of toluene, should be a useful preparative method.

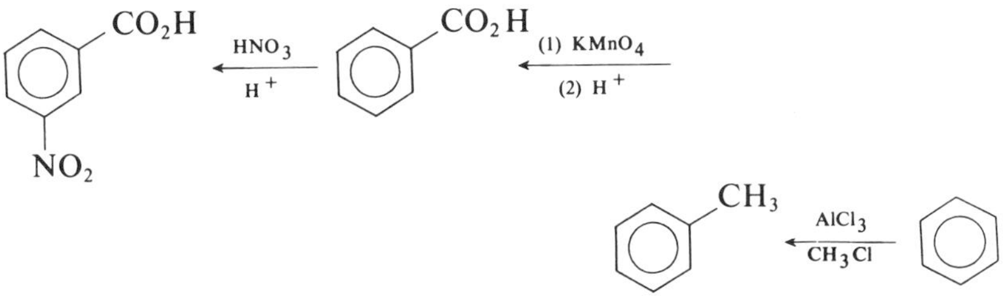

The only remaining problem is the preparation of methyl chloride. Often, low molecular weight alcohols and halides are included as starting materials, just as in actual practice they are readily available. If they are not, students can and do acquire a small list of basic compounds from inorganic starting materials. The following are typical:

$$CO + 2 H_2 \rightarrow CH_3OH \quad \text{(special catalysts, high temperature and pressure)}$$

$$CaC_2 + 2 H_2O \rightarrow CH\equiv CH + Ca(OH)_2$$

Problem B. The opening of a ring to give a dicarboxylic acid is a well-known process, but the present example requires a four-membered ring and we have a six-membered ring readily available. The easiest procedure in this case may be to start in the middle of the problem:

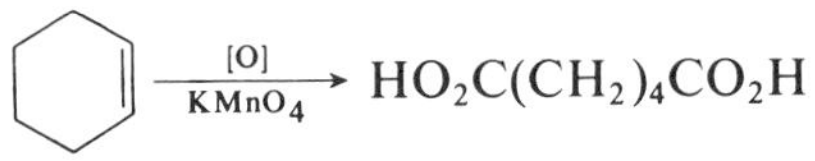

To obtain cyclohexene from our starting material, we must reduce the ring and leave a group that can be eliminated. Cyclohexanol appears to be a logical choice in terms of these requirements, and it fits nicely into the alkyl aryl ether's chemistry:

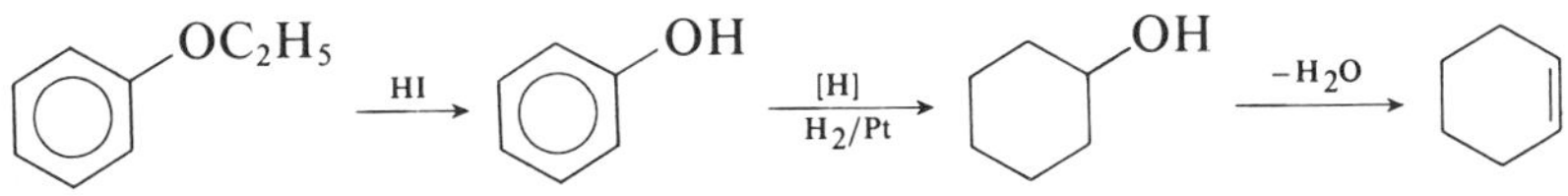

Getting a shorter carbon chain might be accomplished by further oxidation—for example, if the following diene were available:

$$CH_2=CH(CH_2)_2CH=CH_2 \xrightarrow[KMnO_4]{[O]} HO_2C(CH_2)_2CO_2H$$

This compound could be made from a diol, which would, in turn, be obtained by reduction of the acid acquired earlier from cyclohexene:

$$HO_2C(CH_2)_4CO_2H \xrightarrow[\text{(2) } H_2O]{\text{(1) LAH}} HO(CH_2)_6OH \xrightarrow{-2 H_2O}$$

$$CH_2{=}CH(CH_2)_2CH{=}CH_2$$

Problem C. The required 1-butyne for a one-step preparation of propanoic acid by oxidation is available in a straightforward manner:

$$HO_2CCH_2CH_3 \xleftarrow{[O]} CH{\equiv}CCH_2CH_3 \leftarrow$$

$$CH_3CH_2Br + CH{\equiv}C^-Na^+$$

The ethyl bromide and sodium acetylide also result from standard reactions:

$$CaC_2 + 2 H_2O \rightarrow CH{\equiv}CH \xrightarrow[Na^+NH_2^-]{NH_3} CH{\equiv}C^-Na^+ + NH_3$$

$$CH{\equiv}CH + H_2 \xrightarrow[\text{catalyst}]{\text{Lindlar's}} CH_2{=}CH_2 \xrightarrow{HBr} CH_3CH_2Br$$

Problem D. Cyclization and the diester starting material suggest the acyloin condensation:

$$CH_3O_2C(CH_2)_4CO_2CH_3 \xrightarrow[\text{xylene}]{Na}$$

The desired hydrocarbon obviously requires the reduction of the two oxygen functions, and, although in actual practice there are several methods available, we are restricted by limited experience to displacement and elimination reactions. The latter seems most useful:

Problem E. The aromatic acid is the most demanding part of this problem, because we must have the correct isomer and avoid oxidation of the methyl group. A good possibility would be the Grignard reaction:

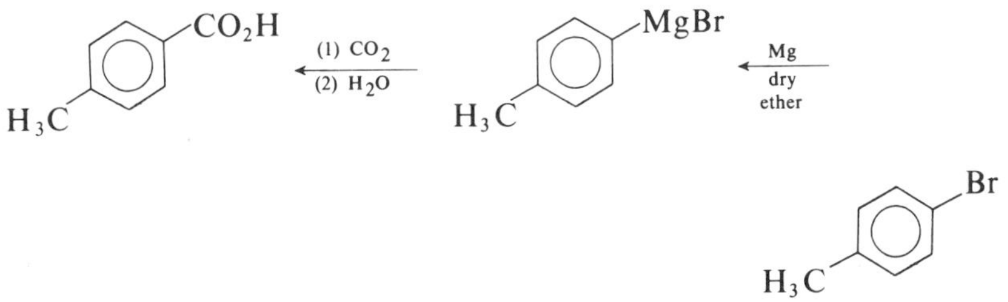

The preparation of *p*-bromotoluene can be accomplished in two different ways:

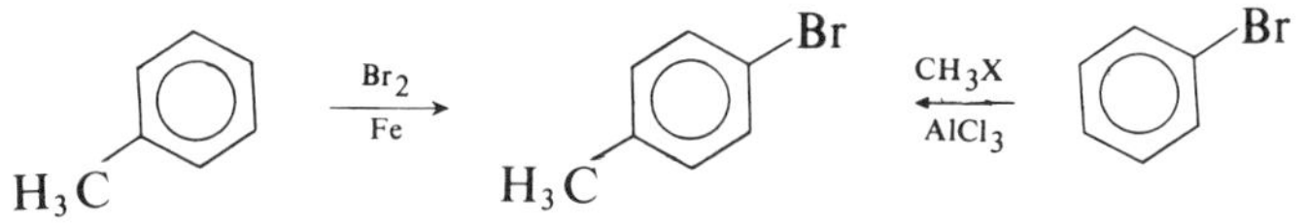

In both of these reactions, the *ortho* isomer would also be produced, but we are generally allowed to assume that these are separable. The bromination of toluene requires the proper conditions (catalyst and the absence of ultraviolet radiation) to avoid side-chain reaction. The alkyl compounds can be prepared simply:

$$CH_3OH \text{ (see Problem A)} + HX \rightarrow CH_3X + H_2O$$

$$CH{\equiv}CH + H_2O \xrightarrow[H^+]{Hg^{+2}} CH_3CHO \xrightarrow[LAH]{[H]} CH_3CH_2OH$$

or

$$CH_3CH_2I \text{ (see Problem C)} + OH^- \rightarrow CH_3CH_2OH + I^-$$

The final step can be a direct esterification:

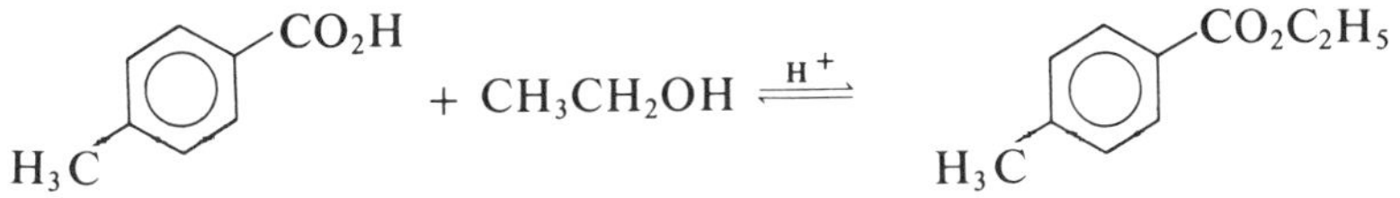

Problem F. The synthesis of alcohols often suggests the use of a Grignard reagent:

$$CH_3CH{=}CH\underset{}{\overset{OH}{\overset{|}{C}}}HCH_2CH_3 \xleftarrow[(2)\ H_2O]{(1)\ \text{dry ether}} CH_3CH{=}CH\overset{O}{\overset{\|}{C}}H + CH_3CH_2MgI$$

The required unsaturated aldehyde should make you think of an aldol condensation:

$$CH_3CH{=}CHC\overset{O}{\overset{\|}{H}} \xleftarrow{-H_2O} CH_3\overset{OH}{\overset{|}{C}}HCH_2\overset{O}{\overset{\|}{C}}H \xleftarrow{-OH} 2\ CH_3\overset{O}{\overset{\|}{C}}H$$

The acetaldehyde and ethyl iodide have already been discussed.

III.4
CONCLUSION

It is our hope that these suggestions and examples will help you to begin solving synthetic organic problems in a systematic and enjoyable manner. Keep in mind that there is no one way to approach these problems. Each of you will have to develop a method that suits you; the important thing is to try something. The more logical and reasonable the better, but something is better than nothing in the job of solving a problem. We have all been faced by synthetic problems for which we could not see a reasonable route or perhaps even the best place to start. Usually, just picking a compound and/or reaction "out of the air" will at least suggest the direction in which one should proceed for a better start.

SUGGESTED ADDITIONAL READINGS

The best source of information for the synthesis of a known compound is, of course, the original literature. Thanks to *Chemical Abstracts*, it is possible to find the literature for most of this century if you have the name, formula, or even the name of the man who prepared the compound desired. For the older literature, Beilstein's *Handbook of Organic Chemistry* is the source. For a new compound, or for information about a particular reaction, the best procedure is to examine one of the many fine recent books devoted to the synthesis of organic compounds:

H. O. House, *Modern Synthetic Reactions* (New York: W. A. Benjamin, Inc., 1965).

G. Sosnovsky, *Free Radical Reactions in Preparative Organic Chemistry* (New York: The Macmillan Company, 1964).

K. B. Wiberg, *Oxidation in Organic Chemistry* (New York: Academic Press Inc., 1965).

H. Krauch and W. Kunz, *Organic Name Reactions* (2nd rev. ed.; New York: John Wiley & Sons, Inc., 1964).

L. F. Fieser and M. Fieser, *Reagents for Organic Synthesis* (New York: John Wiley & Sons, Inc., 1967). Volume II, 1969.

H. C. Brown, *Hydroboration* (New York: W. A. Benjamin, Inc., 1962).

R. E. Ireland, *Organic Synthesis* (Englewood Cliffs, N. J.: Prentice-Hall, Inc., 1969).

The following are continuing series devoted to preparative organic chemistry:

Organic Reactions. New York: John Wiley & Sons, Inc., 17 vols., 1942 to date.

Organic Synthesis. New York: John Wiley & Sons, Inc., 46 vols., 4 collected vols., 1941 to date.

W. Theilheimer, *Synthetic Methods of Organic Chemistry.* Basel, Switzerland: S. Karger, AG., 20 vols., 1946 to date.

Bibliography

The following brief list of the current textbooks from which the Suggested Additional Readings lists have been drawn are, in our opinion, of very high quality. They are designed as texts for a full year course in organic chemistry or to supplement such a course. We believe that these sources are the next logical step in the study of organic chemistry after the material in this text has been mastered. One point that is especially important for the beginning student is the fact that many of the books listed here have numerous problems. The greater number of these are not only good solid problems, but interesting and thought provoking as well. The two workbooks devoted solely to problems are strongly recommended.

In addition to the books cited in the reading lists, three journals have published papers on topics of interest in elementary organic chemistry: *Journal of Chemical Education, J. Chem. Educ.; Scientific American, Sci. Am.*; and *Chemistry, Chemistry. The Journal of Chemical Education* and *Chemistry* have each published a series containing many pertinent papers: "Textbook Errors" [an index is contained in *J. Chem. Educ.*, **44**, 356 (1967)]; and "Chance Favors the Prepared Mind" [e.g., *Chemistry*, **41**, (3), 18 (1968)].

Separate bibliographies have been prepared for organic synthesis and spectroscopy (pp. 362–363 and 353–354, respectively).

General Organic Texts

Bordwell, Frederick G., *Organic Chemistry*. New York: The Macmillan Company, 1963.

Cason, James, *Principles of Modern Organic Chemistry*. Englewood Cliffs, N. J.: Prentice-Hall, Inc., 1966.

Cram, Donald J., and George S. Hammond, *Organic Chemistry* (2nd ed.). New York: McGraw-Hill Book Company, 1964.

Morrison, Robert Thornton, and Robert Neilson Boyd, *Organic Chemistry* (2nd ed.). Boston: Allyn and Bacon, Inc., 1966.

Nussenbaum, Siegfried, *Organic Chemistry: Principles and Applications*. Boston: Allyn and Bacon, Inc., 1963.

Roberts, John D., and Marjorie C. Caserio, *Basic Principles of Organic Chemistry*. New York: W. A. Benjamin, Inc., 1965.

Royals, E. Earl, *Advanced Organic Chemistry*. Englewood Cliffs, N. J.: Prentice-Hall, Inc., 1953.

Mechanisms

Breslow, Ronald, *Organic Reaction Mechanisms*. New York: W. A. Benjamin, Inc., 1965.

Gould, Edwin S., *Mechanism and Structure in Organic Chemistry*. New York: Holt, Rinehart & Winston, Inc., 1959.

Pryor, William A., *Introduction to Free Radical Chemistry*. Englewood Cliffs, N. J.: Prentice-Hall, Inc., 1966.

Saunders, William H., Jr., *Ionic Aliphatic Reactions*. Englewood Cliffs, N. J.: Prentice-Hall, Inc., 1965.

Stewart, Ross, *The Investigation of Organic Reactions*. Englewood Cliffs, N. J.: Prentice-Hall, Inc., 1966.

Wilson, E. Bright, Jr., *An Introduction to Scientific Research*. New York: McGraw-Hill Book Company, 1952.

Structure

Allinger, Norman J., and Janet Allinger, *Structure of Organic Molecules*. Englewood Cliffs, N. J.: Prentice-Hall, Inc., 1965.

Herz, Werner, *The Shape of Carbon Compounds*. New York: W. A. Benjamin, Inc., 1963.

Analysis

Pasto, Daniel J., and Carl R. Johnson, *Organic Structure Determination*. Englewood Cliffs, N. J.: Prentice-Hall, Inc., 1969.

Shriner, Ralph L., Reynold C. Fuson, and David Y. Curtin, *The Systematic Identification of Organic Compounds* (5th ed.). New York: John Wiley & Sons, Inc., 1964.

Biochemistry

Karlson, P., *Introduction to Modern Biochemistry* (2nd ed., trans. by Charles H. Doering). New York: Academic Press Inc., 1965.

Mahler, Henry R., and Eugene H. Cordes, *Biological Chemistry*. New York: Harper & Row, Publishers, 1966.

Steiner, Robert F., *The Chemical Foundations of Molecular Biology*. Princeton, N. J.: D. Van Nostrand Co., Inc., 1965.

History

Benfey, O. Theodor, *From Vital Force to Structural Formulas*. Boston: Houghton Mifflin Company, 1964.

Ihde, Arron J., *The Development of Modern Chemistry*. New York: Harper & Row, Publishers, 1964.

Nomenclature

Benfey, Otto Theodor, *The Names and Structures of Organic Compounds*. New York: John Wiley & Sons, Inc., 1966.

Traynham, James G., *Organic Nomenclature: A Programmed Introduction*. Englewood Cliffs, N. J.: Prentice-Hall, Inc., 1966.

Special Topics

Gutsche, C. David, *The Chemistry of Carbonyl Compounds*. Englewood Cliffs, N. J.: Prentice-Hall, Inc., 1967.

Stille, John K., *Industrial Organic Chemistry*. Englewood Cliffs, N. J.: Prentice-Hall, Inc., 1968.

Stock, Leon M., *Aromatic Substitution Reactions*. Englewood Cliffs, N. J.: Prentice-Hall, Inc., 1968.

Problem Workbooks

Hansch, Corwin, and George Helmkamp, *Organic Chemistry* (2nd ed.). McGraw-Hill Book Company, 1963.

Henderson, R. B., D. M. Goldish, E. R. Harris, K. L. Marsi, D. L. Mayfield, and C. E. Osborne, *Problems in Organic Chemistry*. Englewood Cliffs, N. J.: Prentice-Hall, Inc., 1968.

Answers to Selected Problems

1. a. 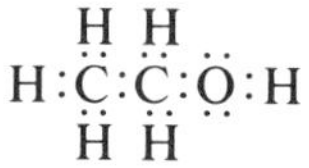 H:C̈:C̈:Ö:H   CH₃—CH₂—ÖH
         H H
         H H

   c. Li⁺ :F̈:⁻   none

   f. 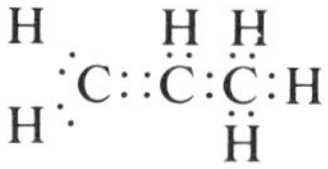   H   H H
          :C::C̈:C̈:H   H₂C=CH—CH₃
       H   H

          H   .C. H
       H :C: :C: H   H₂C—CH₂
       H   H   CH₂

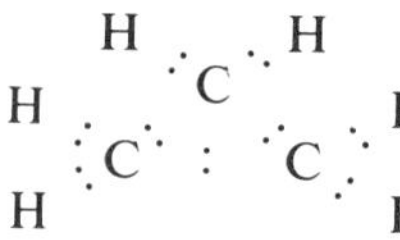

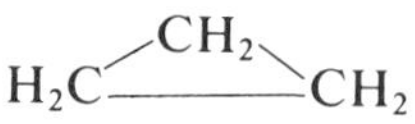

   g. Na⁺:C:::N⁻   Na⁺ C≡N⁻

   k. 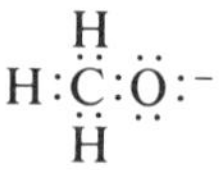 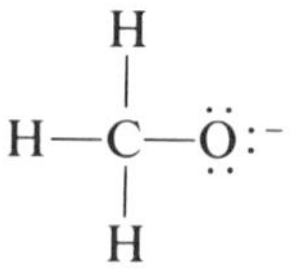   H   H
       H:C̈:Ö:⁻   H—C—Ö:⁻
          H   H

2. a. Covalent and polar covalent (O—H).
   c. Ionic.
   f. Covalent.
   g. Ionic, covalent (C=N), and coordinate covalent (C → N).
   k. Covalent.

3. a. CH_3CH_2—OH

   f. H_2C=$CHCH_3$

CHAPTER 2

1. a.

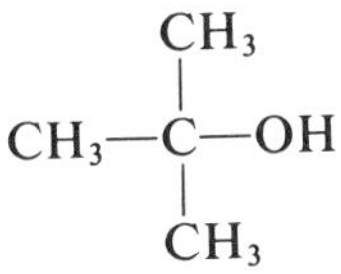

   CH_3—$\overset{\overset{\displaystyle CH_3}{|}}{\underset{\underset{\displaystyle CH_3}{|}}{C}}$—OH   and $CH_3CH_2CH_2CH_2$—OH

   b. CH_3—OH   and CH_3CH_2—OH   and others
   c. —OH
   d. $C_nH_{2n+2}O$
   e. $CH_3CH_2CH_2CH_2CH_2$—OH   and others

3. b.

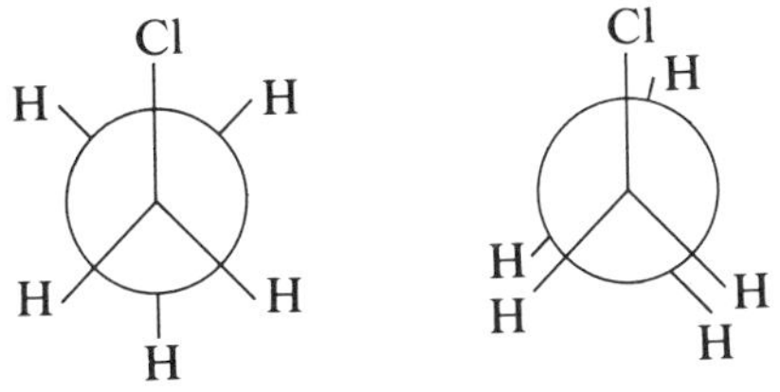

4. a. 2   h. 8
   c. 2   j. None.

   a 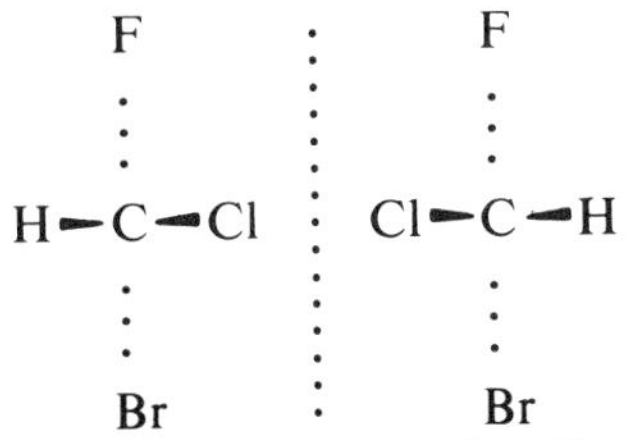 pair of enantiomers

   (R)-fluorochlorobro-
   momethane

   (S)-fluorochloro-
   bromomethane

c.

CO$_2$H	CO$_2$H	
⋮	⋮	
H—C—NH$_2$	H$_2$N—C—H	a pair of enantiomers
⋮	⋮	
C$_2$H$_5$	C$_2$H$_5$	
2(R)-aminobutanoic acid	2(S)-aminobutanoic acid	

h.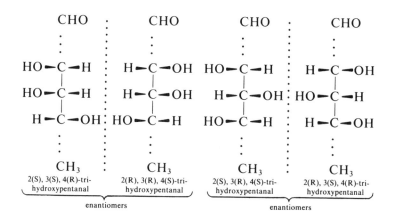

Either member of any enantiomeric pair is a diastereomer of either member of any other enantiomeric pair.

CHAPTER 3

2. b.

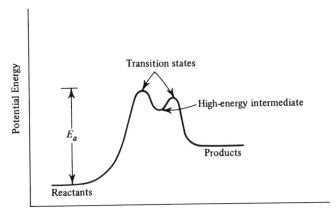

A second activation energy is required for the conversion of the intermediate to product, but it is so small that it does not play any significant role.

4. a.

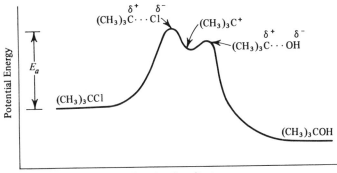

b. rate $= k[(CH_3)_3CCl]$

c.

$$CH_3 \underset{+}{\overset{\displaystyle CH_3}{\underset{\displaystyle CH_3}{\diagdown C \diagup}}}$$

d. Ionic nucleophilic substitution (at saturated carbon) $S_N 1$.

e. Substrate $(CH_3)_3CCl$, nucleophile OH^-.

f. Yes. It should form a more stable carbonium ion ($3° > 1°$).

g. Those solvents which promote ionization and have high dielectric constants (e.g., H_2O, CH_3OH, etc.). No. The charge is being shifted, but inasmuch as the substrate is not dissociating to free ions, the solvent requirements should not be so great.

CHAPTER 4

1. a.

$$CH_2\text{==}CCH_3 + HBr \rightarrow CH_3\overset{Br}{\underset{CH_3}{\overset{|}{C}}}CH_3$$

2-methylpropene   2-bromo-2-methylpropane

c. $CH_3C\text{≡}CCH_3 + 2\ HCl \rightarrow CH_3CH_2\overset{Cl}{\underset{Cl}{\overset{|}{C}}}CH_3$

     2-butyne   2,2-dichlorobutane

e. $CH_3CH\text{==}CH_2 + Na \xrightarrow{\ NH_3\ } NR$
      propene

g. $CH\text{≡}C^-Na^+ + CH_3CH_2I \rightarrow CH\text{≡}CCH_2CH_3$
    sodium acetylide   iodoethane   1-butyne

i. 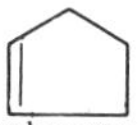 $\xrightarrow[\text{alcohol}]{\text{KOH}}$ NR
   cyclopentene

k. $CH_3CH\text{==}\underset{CH_3}{\overset{|}{C}}CH_2CH_3 + HCl \rightarrow CH_3CH_2\underset{CH_3}{\overset{Cl}{\overset{|}{C}}}CH_2CH_3$

                                       3-methyl-3-chloropentane

m. 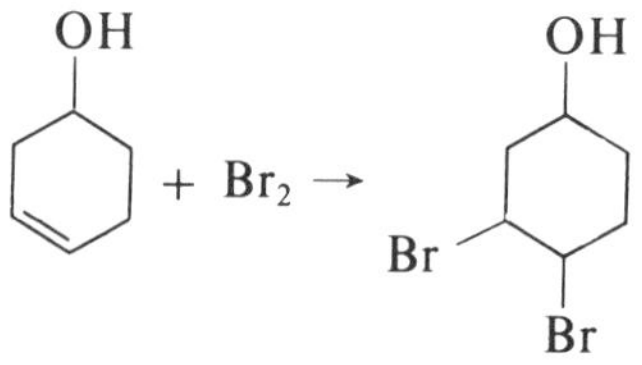 $+\ Br_2 \rightarrow$

   cyclohexen-4-ol   3,4-dibromocyclohexanol

3. b. $CH_2\text{==}CHCH\text{==}CH_2$ cyclobutene
    1,3-butadiene

      $CH_2\text{==}C\text{==}CHCH_3$    1-methylcyclopropene
       1,2-butadiene

$CH\equiv CCH_2CH_3$
1-butyne

3-methylcyclopropene

$CH_3C\equiv CCH_3$
2-butyne

bicyclo [1.1.0] butane

4. a. $CH_3:CH_3\ sp^3$

f. $CH \odot C \odot CH_3$

$\quad sp \qquad sp^3$

c.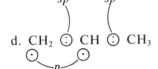

d. CH$_2$ ⊙ CH ⊙ CH$_3$

h. $CH_3:CH_2:\ddot{O}:^-\ Na^+$

$\quad sp^3 \qquad$ ionic

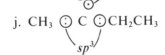

j. $CH_3 \odot C \odot CH_2CH_3$

$\qquad\qquad sp^3$

5. b. No geometric isomerism.

　　　　　cis　　　　　　　　　　*trans*

g.

h.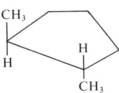

j.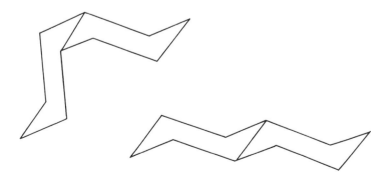

6.

b.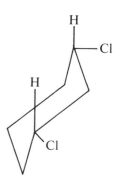

| *cis*-diaxial | *trans*-equatorial- | *cis*-diequatorial |
| least stable | axial | most stable |

7. a. $CH_3CH_3 + Br_2 \xrightarrow{h\nu} CH_3CH_2Br$ radical substitution
    ethane   bromoethane   (chain reaction)

b. $CH_3CH_2CHCH_2OH + H_3PO_4 \rightarrow CH_3CH_2C{=}CH_2$ elimination
             $|$ $|$
           CH_3 CH_3
   2-methyl-1-butanol   2-methyl-1-butene

e.

    + HCl →   addition

   cyclohexene   chlorocyclohexane

8. a. $Br{:}Br \xrightarrow{h\nu} 2\ Br\cdot$

    $Br\cdot + CH_3CH_3 \rightarrow CH_3CH_2^{\cdot} + HBr$

    $CH_3CH_2^{\cdot} + Br_2 \rightarrow CH_3CH_2Br + Br^{\cdot}$

b. $CH_3CH_2CHCH_2OH + H^+ \rightarrow CH_3CH_2CHCH_2\overset{+}{O}H_2 \rightarrow$
            $|$ $|$
          CH_3 CH_3

                   $CH_3CH_2CHCH_2^+ \xrightarrow{-H^+} CH_3CH_2C{=}CH_2$
                          $|$ $|$
                         CH_3 CH_3

e.

    + H⁺ →   + Cl⁻ →

9. a. CH_3CHBr, CH_2CH_2, etc., to Br_3CCBr_3
        $|$ $|$ $|$
       Br Br Br

b. $CH_3CH{=}CCH_3$
           $|$
          CH_3

11. (A)

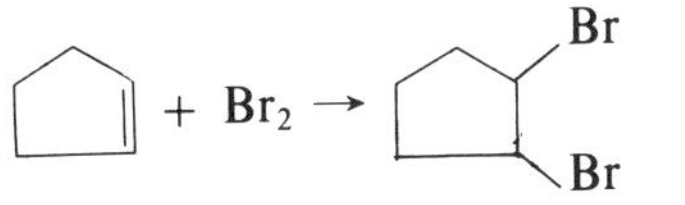

cyclopentene   1,2-dibromocyclopentane

(B) CH_2=CHCH=CHCH$_3$ + 2 Br$_2$ → CH$_2$CHCHCHCH$_3$

Br Br Br Br

1,3-pentadiene   1,2,3,4-tetrabromopentane

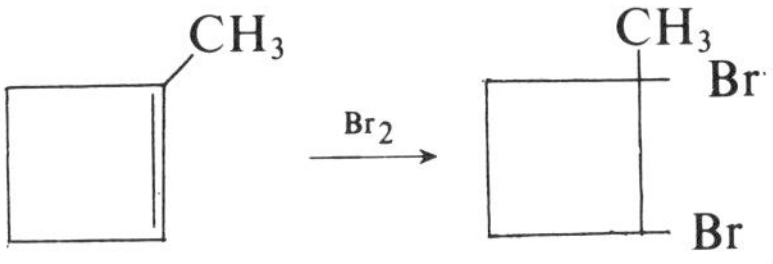

1-methylcyclobutene   1,2-dibromo-1-methylcyclo-
(among others)   butane

13.

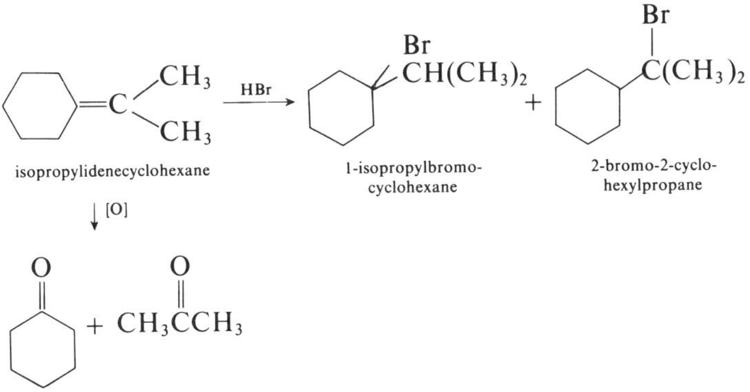

isopropylidenecyclohexane   1-isopropylbromo-   2-bromo-2-cyclo-
                                 cyclohexane   hexylpropane

cyclohexanone   acetone

This compound is not the only one that fits the data. For example,

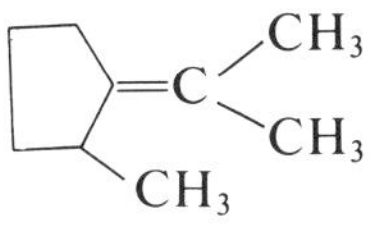

2-isopropylidenemethylcyclopentane

15. a. HC≡CH $\xrightarrow[\text{Lindlar}]{\text{H}_2}$ H$_2$C=CH$_2$ $\xrightarrow{\text{HBr}}$ CH$_3$CH$_2$Br

acetylene   ethylene   ethyl bromide

c.

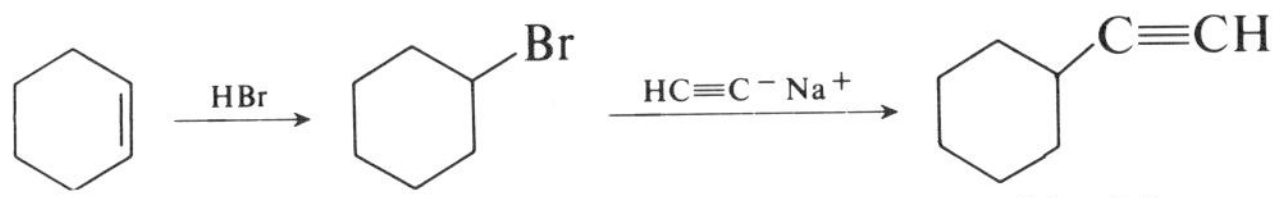

cyclohexene   bromocyclohexane   cyclohexylethyne

e. HC≡CCH$_2$CH$_3$ $\xrightarrow[\text{Lindlar}]{\text{H}_2}$ H$_2$C=CHCH$_2$CH$_3$ $\xrightarrow[\text{peroxide}]{\text{HBr}}$

1-butyne   1-butene

BrCH$_2$CH$_2$CH$_2$CH$_3$

butyl bromide

g. $HC\equiv CCH_2CH_3 \xrightarrow[NH_3]{Na} Na^{+-}C\equiv CCH_2CH_3 \xrightarrow{CH_3CH_2Br}$

sodium ethylacetylide

$CH_3CH_2C\equiv CCH_2CH_3 \xrightarrow{HCl} CH_3CH_2CH_2\overset{\overset{\displaystyle Cl}{|}}{\underset{\underset{\displaystyle Cl}{|}}{C}}CH_2CH_3$

3-hexyne

3,3-dichlorohexane

16. (A) $CH_3CH=C\overset{\nearrow CH_3}{\searrow CH_3} \xrightarrow{KMnO_4}$ (B) $CH_3\overset{\overset{\displaystyle CH_3}{|}}{CH}\overset{|}{C}CH_3 \xrightarrow{KMnO_4}$

2-methyl-2-butene   2-methyl-2,3-butanediol

(C) CH_3CO_2H + (D) $CH_3\overset{\overset{\displaystyle O}{\|}}{C}CH_3$

acetic acid   acetone

(A) $\xrightarrow{Cl_2}$ (E) $CH_3\overset{\overset{\displaystyle CH_3}{|}}{CH}\overset{|}{C}CH_3 \xrightarrow[\text{alcohol}]{KOH}$ (F) $CH_2=CH\overset{\overset{\displaystyle CH_3}{|}}{C}=CH_2$

                           Cl Cl

2-methyl-2,3-dichlorobutane   2-methyl-1,3-butadiene

CHAPTER 5

2. a.

c.

e.

g.

i.

k.

m. SO$_3$H

I

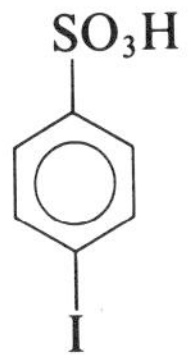

o.

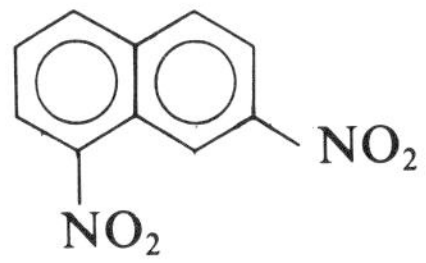

NO$_2$

NO$_2$

q.   Br   Br
       | |
   CH$_3$CCH$_2$CH$_2$CCH$_3$
       | |
      CH$_3$ CH$_3$

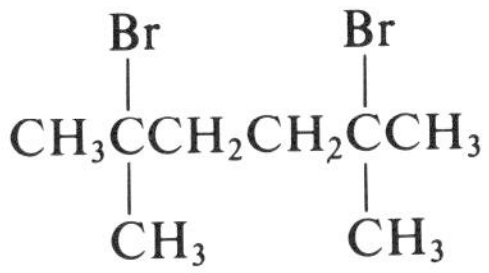

s.   CH$_3$

CH(CH$_3$)$_2$

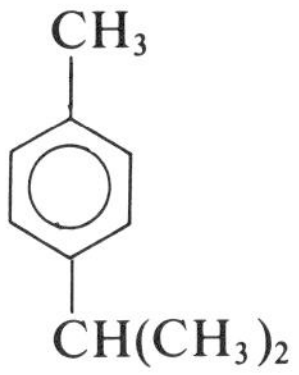

3. a. *m*-chloronitrobenzene
   c. 4-methylbenzoic acid
      (*p*-toluic acid)
   e. toluene
   g. 2(or *β*)-fluoronaphthalene

   i. 2(or *β*)-nitronaphthalene
   k. 4(or *p*)-nitrobenzoic acid
   m. 3(or *m*)-methylbenzene-
      sulfonic acid (*m*-toluene-
      sulfonic acid)
   o. 1,3,5-tribromobenzene

4. a.   Br

    + CH$_3$CH$_2$Cl $\xrightarrow{\text{AlCl}_3}$

           Br   CH$_2$CH$_3$

           +

           Br

           CH$_2$CH$_3$

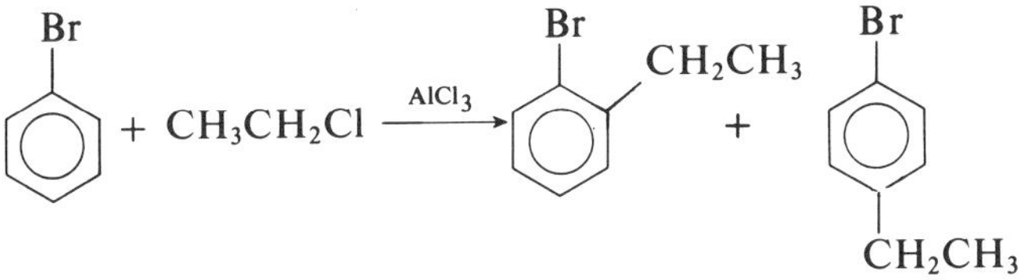

   bromobenzene   chloroethane   *o*-bromoethylbenzene   *p*-bromoethyl-
                                                                   benzene

c.   OH

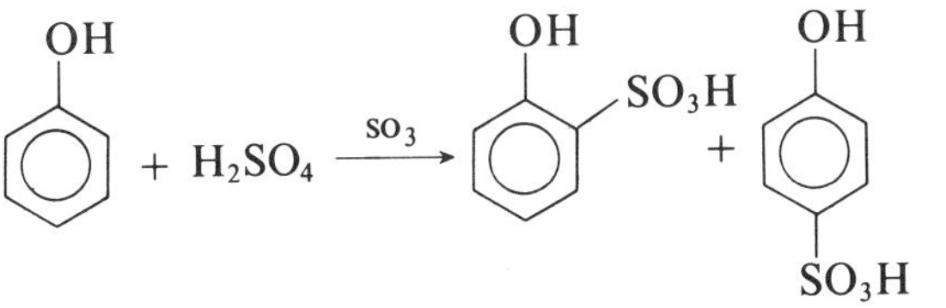

   + H$_2$SO$_4$ $\xrightarrow{\text{SO}_3}$

       OH   SO$_3$H

       +

       OH

       SO$_3$H

   phenol   *o*-hydroxybenzene-   *p*-hydroxybenzene-
                     sulfonic acid   sulfonic acid

e. CH$_3$CHCH$_3$

   + Cl$_2$ $\xrightarrow{h\nu}$

           CH$_3$
           |
           CCl
           |
           CH$_3$

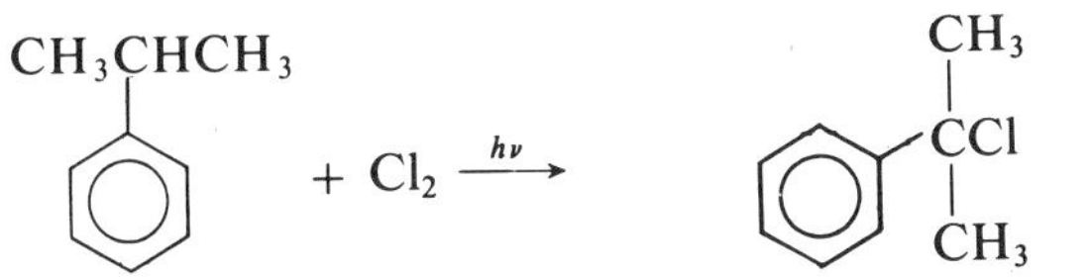

   isopropylbenzene   *α*-chloroisopropylbenzene

g.   CO$_2$H

   + Br$_2$ $\xrightarrow{\text{Fe}}$

            CO$_2$H

            Br

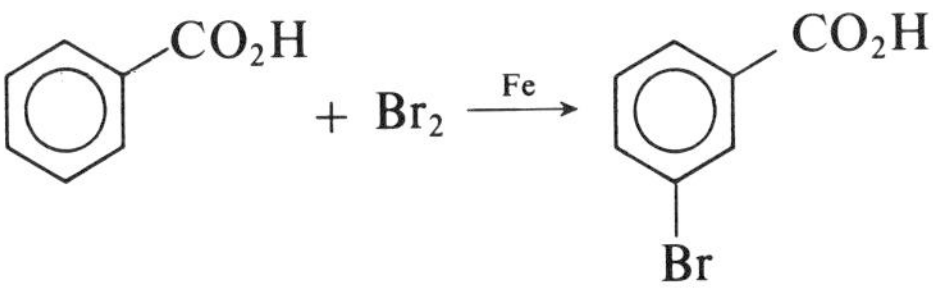

   benzoic acid   *m*-bromobenzoic acid

i.

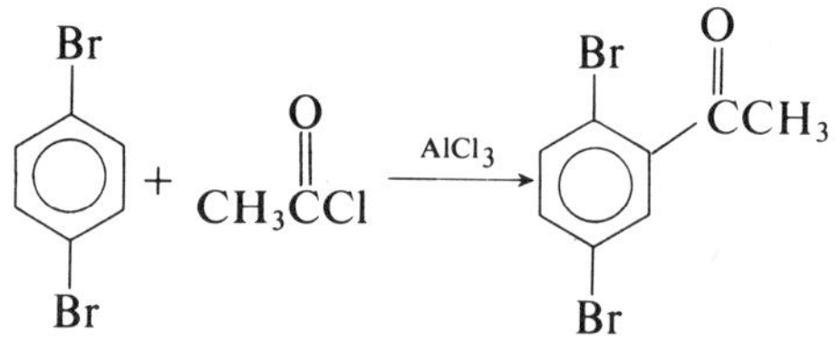

p-dibromobenzene | acetyl chloride → 2', 5'-dibromoacetophenone (methyl 2,5-dibromophenyl ketone)

5. a.

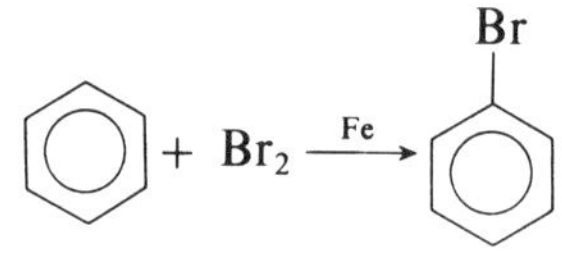

benzene + Br₂ → bromobenzene

c.

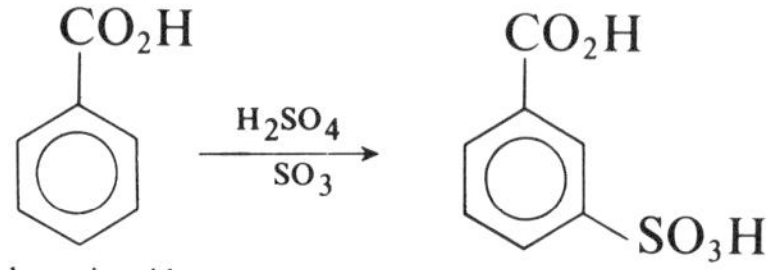

benzoic acid → m-carboxybenzenesulfonic acid

e.

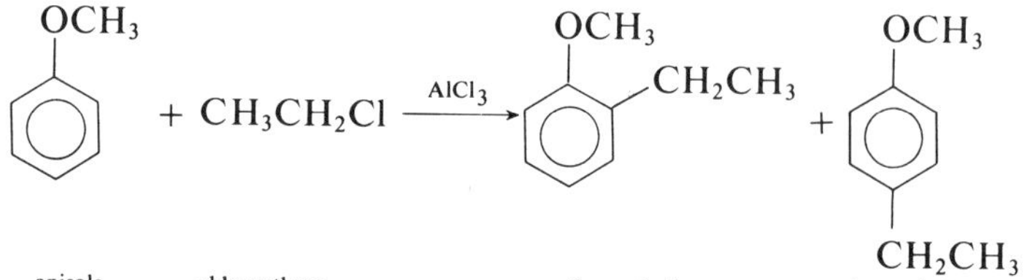

anisole (methyl phenyl ether) + chloroethane → o-methoxyethylbenzene (methyl o-ethylphenyl ether) + p-methoxyethylbenzene (methyl p-ethylphenyl ether)

7. (A)

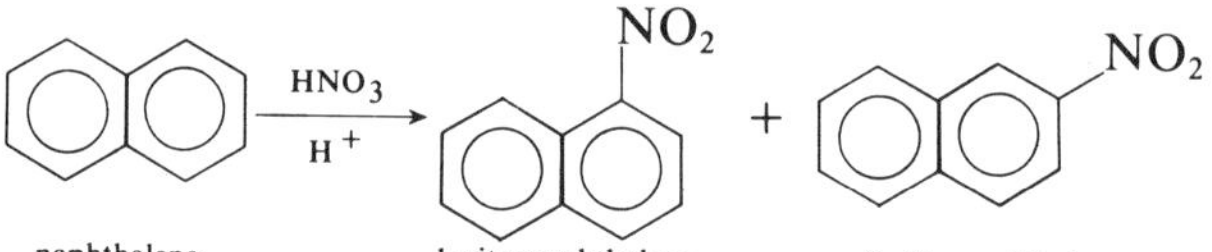

naphthalene → 1-nitronaphthalene + 2-nitronaphthalene

(B)

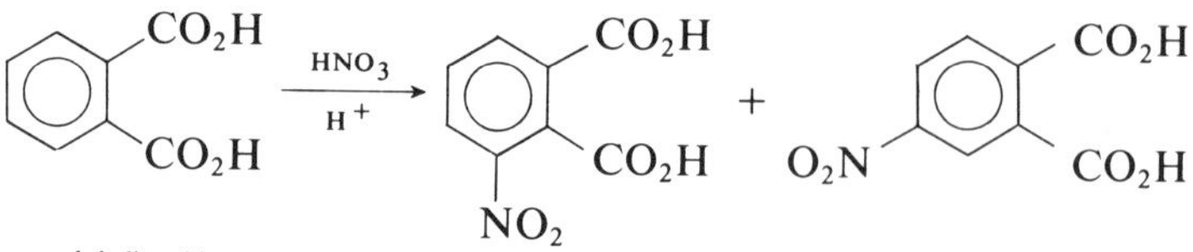

phthalic acid → 3-nitrophthalic acid + 4-nitrophthalic acid

9. b.

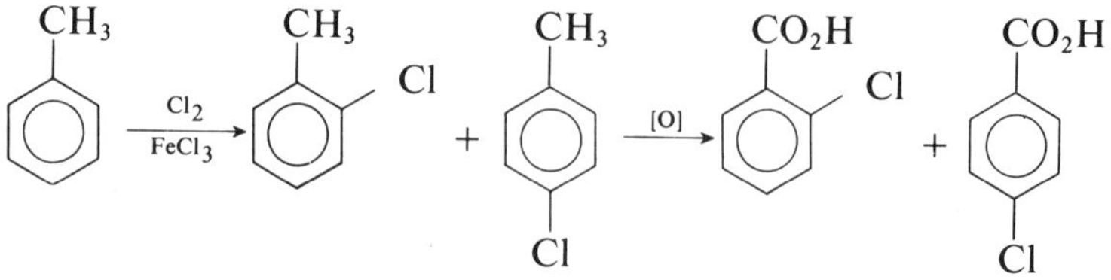

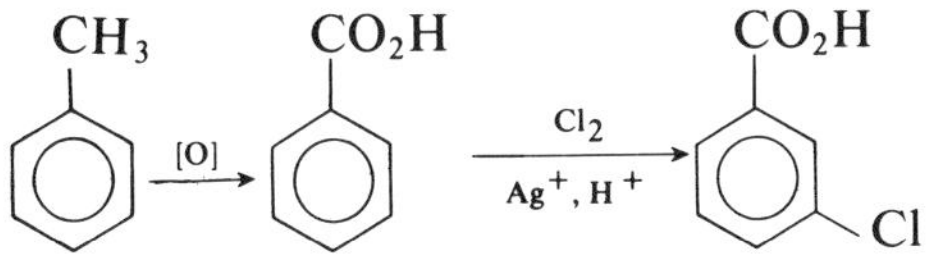

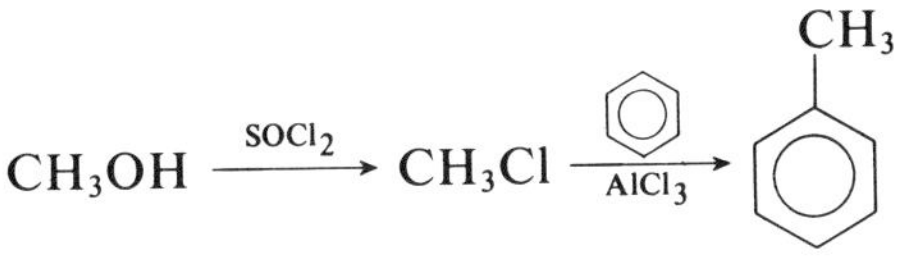

CH_3 / CO_2H → $\xrightarrow{[O]}$ → CO_2H $\xrightarrow[Ag^+, H^+]{Cl_2}$ → CO_2H, Cl

$CH_3OH \xrightarrow{SOCl_2} CH_3Cl \xrightarrow{AlCl_3}$ CH_3 (toluene)

11. (A)

CH_2CH_2OH $\xrightarrow{H_2SO_4}$

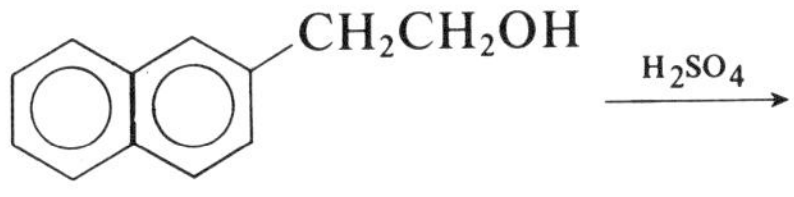

2-(2-naphthyl)ethanol (and others)

(B)

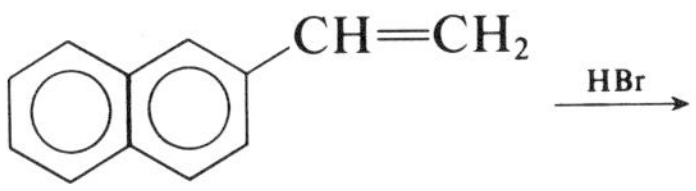

$CH=CH_2$ $\xrightarrow{HBr}$

2-vinylnaphthalene

(C)

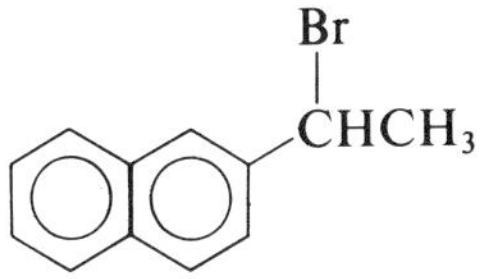

$\overset{Br}{\underset{}{CHCH_3}}$

α-bromo-2-ethylnaphthalene (β isomer also possible)

13.

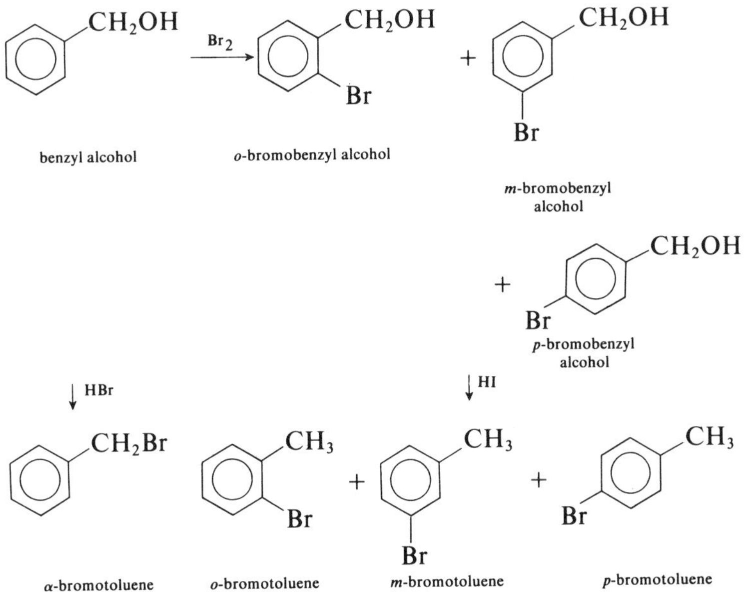

CH_2OH $\xrightarrow{Br_2}$ CH_2OH, Br + CH_2OH, Br

benzyl alcohol   o-bromobenzyl alcohol   m-bromobenzyl alcohol

+ CH_2OH, Br

p-bromobenzyl alcohol

↓ HBr   ↓ HI

CH_2Br CH_3, Br + CH_3, Br + CH_3, Br

α-bromotoluene   o-bromotoluene   m-bromotoluene   p-bromotoluene

15. The electron-withdrawing substituents (Br and NO$_2$) should stabilize the anion and therefore increase the acidity relative to hydrogen. The following resonance contributors are instructive:

increasing acidity:

K_a = CH$_3$ < H < Br < NO$_2$
0.67   1.1   5.6   690   (all × 10^{-10})

CHAPTER 6

1. a. 2-methyl-1-butanol β-methylbutyl alcohol
 c. 2-cyclopentylethanol β-cyclopentylethyl alcohol
 e. α-isobutoxytoluene   benzyl isobutyl ether
 g. p(or 4)-bromoanisole   methyl p-bromophenyl ether
 i. 1-nitro-4-(1-chloropropyl)-   4-nitro-1-(α-chloro-n-
     cyclohexane   propyl)-cyclohexane
 k. p(or 4)-chlorophenoxyethane or   ethyl p-chlorophenyl ether
     p(or 4)-ethoxychlorobenzene

2. a.   e.   i.

 c.   g.

3. a. CH$_3$CH$_2$CHCH$_2$CH$_2$OH $\xrightarrow{\text{H}_2\text{SO}_4}$
               |
               CH$_3$

$$CH_3CH_2CHCH=CH_2 \quad CH_3CH_2C=CHCH_3$$

$$\overset{|}{CH_3} \qquad\qquad\qquad \overset{|}{CH_3}$$

3-methyl-1-pentene   3-methyl-2-pentene

c.

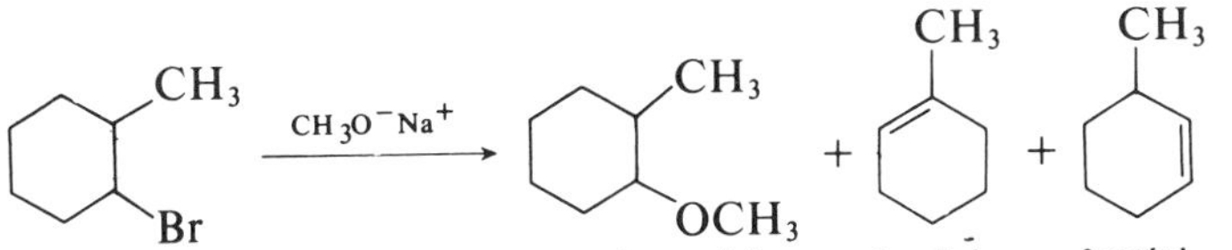

2-methoxymethyl-cyclohexane   1-methyl-cyclohexene   3-methyl-cyclohexene

e.

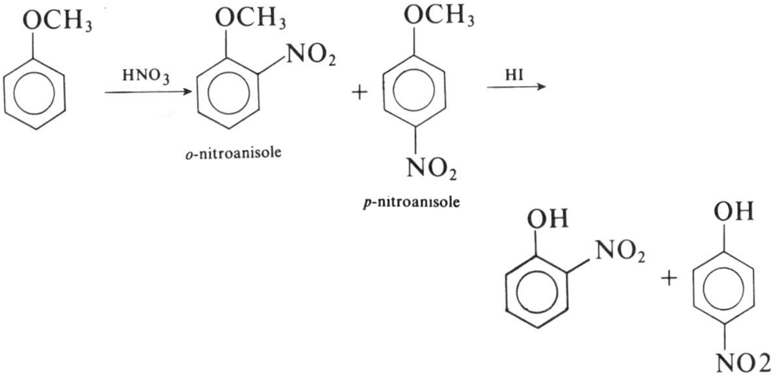

o-nitroanisole

p-nitroanisole

o-nitrophenol   p-nitrophenol

g.

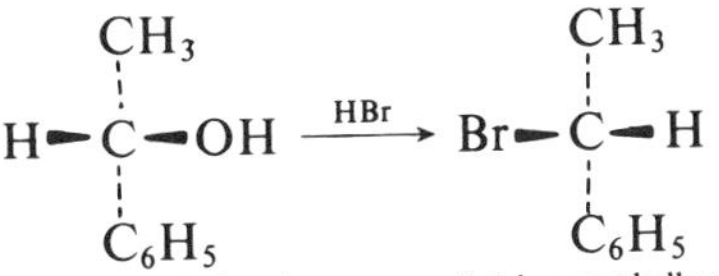

$$\underset{\underset{C_6H_5}{|}}{\overset{\overset{CH_3}{|}}{H-C-OH}} \xrightarrow{HBr} \underset{\underset{C_6H_5}{|}}{\overset{\overset{CH_3}{|}}{Br-C-H}}$$

S-1-phenylethanol   R-1-bromoethylbenzene

4. a. $CaC_2 + H_2O \rightarrow HC{\equiv}CH \xrightarrow[NH_3]{Na} HC{\equiv}C^-Na^+$

$$CH_3OH + HBr \rightarrow CH_3Br \Bigg\} \rightarrow CH_3C{\equiv}CH$$

$$\xrightarrow[\text{Lindlar}]{H_2} CH_3CH=CH_2 \xrightarrow{HBr}$$

$$\underset{\overset{|}{Br}}{CH_3CHCH_3} \xrightarrow{HC{\equiv}C^-Na^+} \underset{\overset{|}{CH_3}}{CH_3CHC{\equiv}CH}$$

$$\xrightarrow[\text{Lindlar}]{H_2} \underset{\overset{|}{CH_3}}{CH_3CHCH=CH_2} \xrightarrow{B_2H_6} (\underset{\overset{|}{CH_3}}{CH_3CHCH_2CH_2})_3B$$

$$\xrightarrow[H_2O_2]{OH^-} \underset{\overset{|}{CH_3}}{CH_3CHCH_2CH_2OH}$$

c.

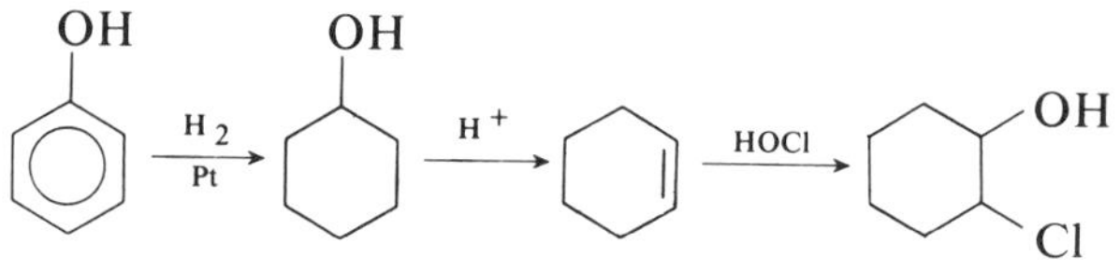

e.

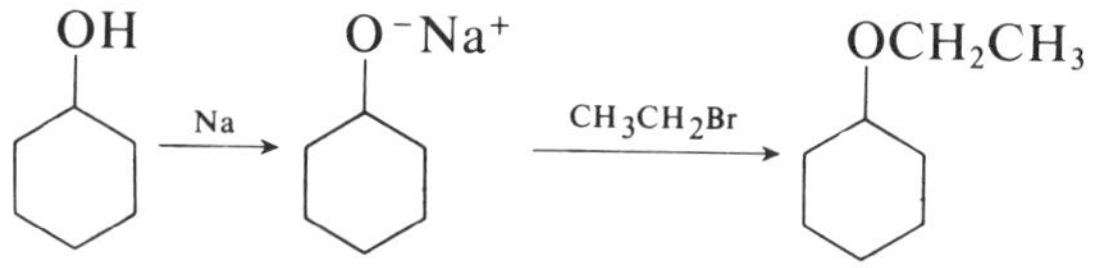

g. $CH_3CH_2CHCH_3$ $\xrightarrow[\text{alcohol}]{\text{KOH}}$

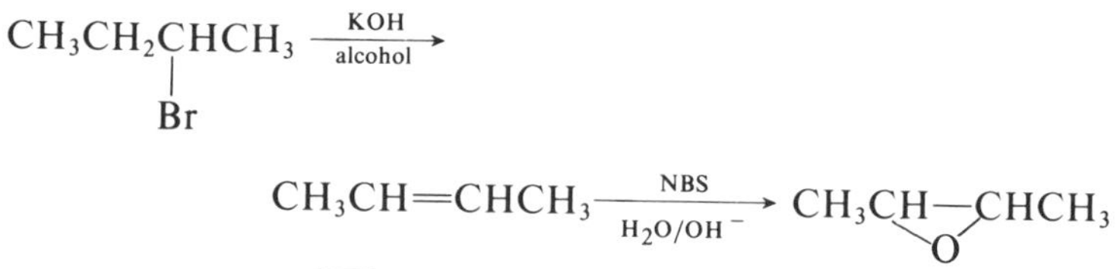

 $\underset{Br}{|}$

$CH_3CH=CHCH_3 \xrightarrow[H_2O/OH^-]{NBS} CH_3CH-CHCH_3$

 $\underset{O}{\diagdown}$

5.(A) $CH_3CH_2CHO-\bigcirc \xrightarrow{HI}$ (B) I (C) $CH_3CHCH_2CH_3$

 $\underset{CH_3}{|}$ $\underset{I}{|}$

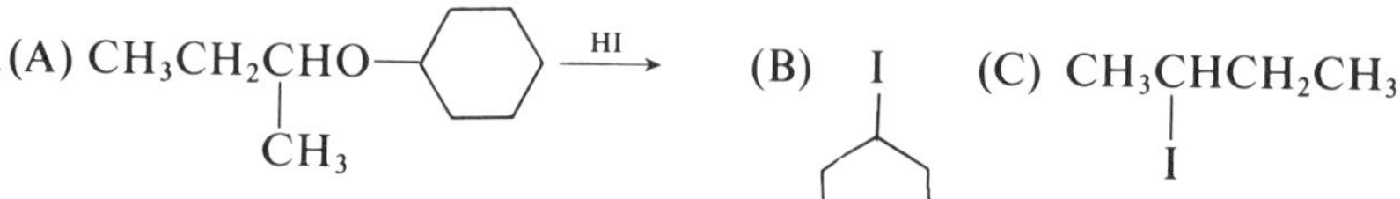

sec-butyl cyclohexyl ether   iodocyclohexane   2-iodobutane

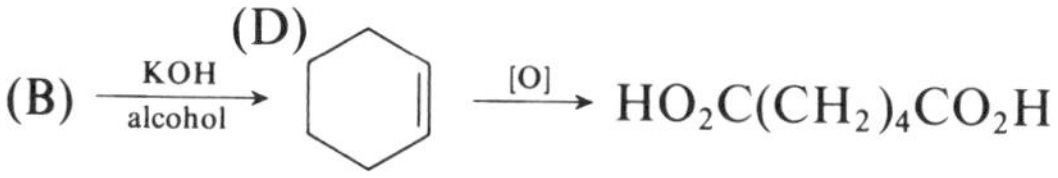

(B) $\xrightarrow[\text{alcohol}]{\text{KOH}}$ (D) $\bigcirc \xrightarrow{[O]} HO_2C(CH_2)_4CO_2H$

         cyclohexene   adipic acid

(C) $\xrightarrow[\text{alcohol}]{\text{KOH}}$ (E) $CH_3CH_2CH=CH_2$ + (F) $CH_3CH=CHCH_3$

                 1-butene   2-butene

                 $\downarrow$ [O] $\downarrow$ [O]

         $CH_3CH_2CO_2H + CO_2$ CH_3CO_2H

                 propanoic acid   acetic acid

(A) could also be

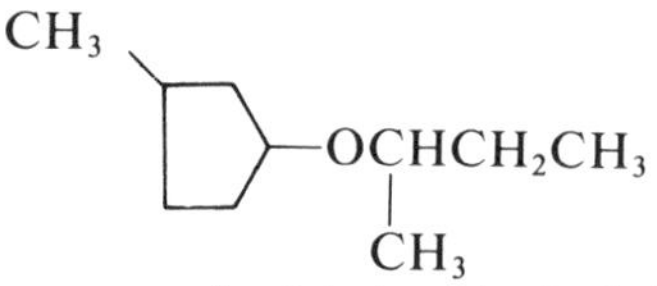

3-methylcyclopentyl *sec*-butyl ether

7. (A)

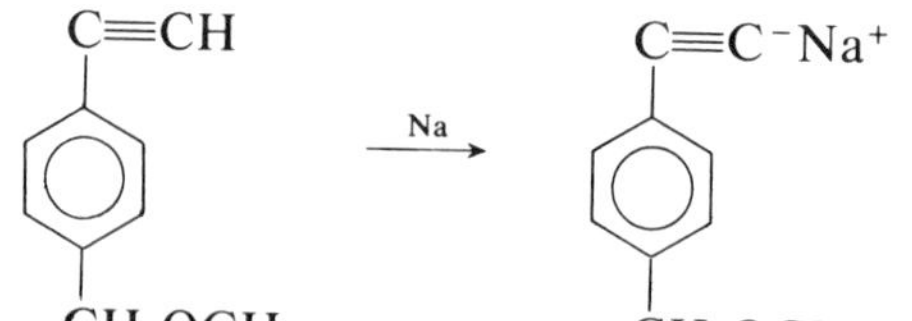

α-methoxy-*p*-tolylacetylene   sodium α-methoxy-*p*-tolylacetylide

$H^+ \downarrow \overset{H_2O}{HgSO_4}$

(B)

CH₃OCH₂——⟨benzene ring⟩——CCH₃ (with =O)
$\overset{HI}{\longrightarrow}$

(C)

CCH₃ (with =O above ring)
⟨benzene ring⟩
CH₂I
$\overset{[O]}{\longrightarrow}$ (D)

CCH₃ (with =O above ring)
⟨benzene ring⟩
CO₂H

p-acetylphenyl methyl ether

p-iodomethylaceto-phenone

p-acetylbenzoic acid

$\downarrow$ [O]

CO₂H
⟨benzene ring⟩ Br
CO₂H
$\overset{Br_2}{\underset{Fe}{\longleftarrow}}$ (E)

CO₂H
⟨benzene ring⟩
CO₂H

2-bromoterephthalic acid

terephthalic acid

9. A.b. The intermediate carbonium ion normally has a planar spatial arrangement of the three groups or atoms attached to it. In a complex ring system of this kind, it requires a great deal of strain and bond distortion to form the planar carbonium ion and thus reactivity is lowered.

B. b. If the reaction takes place by only an S_N2 route, only one product would be obtained. It is often difficult to prevent some S_N1 reaction from taking place, especially with a reactive potential carbonium ion such as this one (see Part A. a.). If it happens, two products would be found (see part A. d.):

$$
\left.
\begin{array}{c}
CH_3CH{=}CHCH_2{+} \\
\updownarrow \\
CH_3\underset{+}{C}HCH{=}CH_2
\end{array}
\right\}
\overset{-CN}{\longrightarrow}
\begin{array}{c}
CH_3CH{=}CHCH_2CN \\
+ \\
CH_3\underset{|}{C}HCH{=}CH_2 \\
CN
\end{array}
$$

CHAPTER 7

1. a. $CH_3\underset{|}{C}{=}CH_2 \overset{[O]}{\longrightarrow} CH_3\overset{O}{\overset{\|}{C}}CH_3 + CO_2$
           CH_3

   2-methylpropene   acetone

d. $CH\equiv CCH_2CH=CH_2 \xrightarrow{[O]} HO_2CCH_2CO_2H + 2 CO_2$

1-penten-4-yne   malonic acid

2. a. $CH_3CO_2H + NaOH \rightarrow CH_3CO_2^-Na^+ + H_2O$

acetic acid   sodium acetate

c. $(CH_2)_4 \overset{CO_2^-}{\underset{CO_2^-}{\diagdown}} Ca^{+2} \xrightarrow{heat}$ [cyclopentanone] $=O + CaCO_3$

calcium adipate   cyclopentanone

e. $CH_3CH=CHCO_2H \xrightarrow{Br_2} CH_3CHCHCO_2H$

                                   Br Br

2-butenoic acid   2,3-dibromobutanoic acid

g.

[benzene ring with CO_2H] $+ Br_2 \xrightarrow{Fe}$ [benzene ring with CO_2H and Br]

benzoic acid   *m*-bromobenzoic acid

i.

$CH_3CO_2^-Na^+ + Br$—[benzene ring]—$\overset{O}{\overset{\|}{C}}CH_2Br \rightarrow$

sodium acetate   *p*-bromophenacyl bromide
                      (2,4'-dibromoacetophenone)

$CH_3CO_2CH_2\overset{O}{\overset{\|}{C}}$—[benzene ring]—$Br$

p-bromophenacyl acetate

3. a. $CH_3CH_2CO_2H + SOCl_2 \rightarrow CH_3CH_2COCl + HCl + SO_2$

propanoic acid   propanoyl chloride

c. $C_6H_5CO_2CH_2CH_3 + NaOH \xrightarrow{H_2O}$

ethyl benzoate

$C_6H_5CO_2^-Na^+ + CH_3CH_2OH$

sodium benzoate   ethanol

e. $CH_3CH_2COCl + CH_3CH_2O^-Na^+ \rightarrow$

propanoyl chloride   sodium ethoxide

$CH_3CH_2CO_2CH_2CH_3 + NaCl$

ethyl propanoate

g.

[benzene ring with CH_3 top and CH_2CH_3 bottom] $\xrightarrow{[O]}$ [benzene ring with CO_2H top and CO_2H bottom]

p-methylethylbenzene   terephthalic acid

i. $CH_3CH_2CH_2MgBr + CO_2 \xrightarrow[\text{ether}]{\text{dry}}$

    propyl magnesium bromide

$$CH_3CH_2CH_2CO_2^- \, Mg^{+2} Br^-$$

                     magnesium bromide butanoate

5.

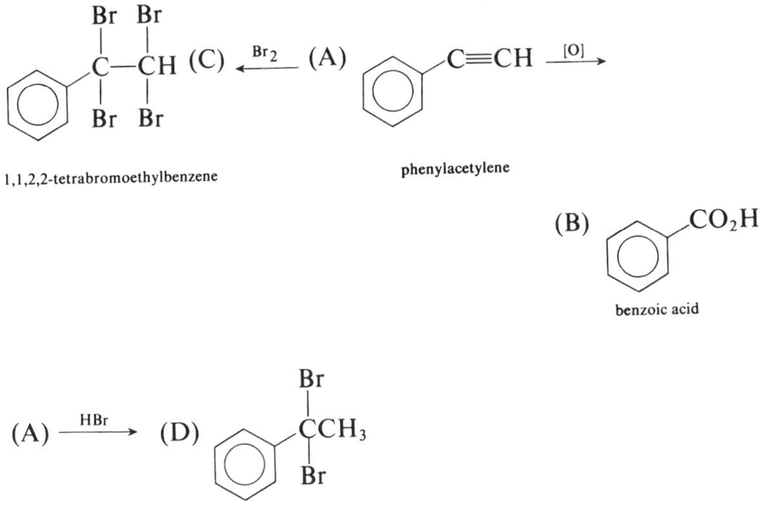

1,1,2,2-tetrabromoethylbenzene   phenylacetylene

(B)

benzoic acid

(A) $\xrightarrow{\text{HBr}}$ (D)

1,1-dibromoethylbenzene

7. (A) $\xrightarrow{[O]}$ (B) $\rightarrow$ (C)

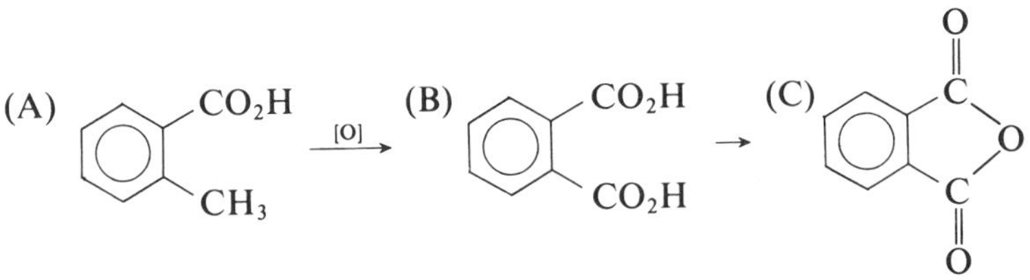

    o-toluic acid   phthalic acid   phthalic anhydride

9. (A) $\xrightarrow[\text{Fe}]{\text{Br}_2}$ (B) $+ CH_3CH_2CH_2Br \xrightarrow{\text{Mg}}$

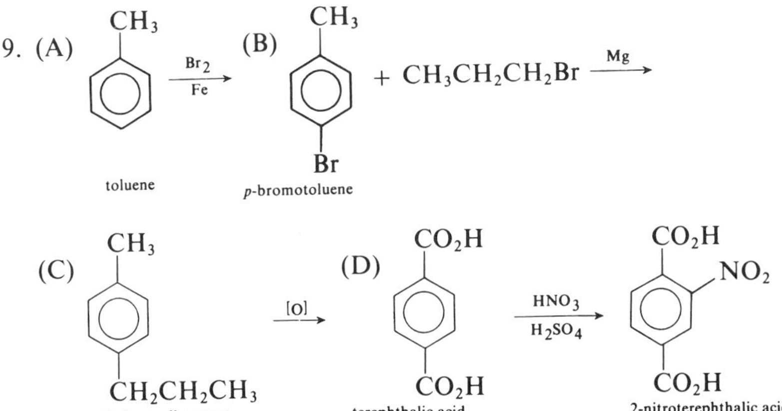

    toluene   p-bromotoluene

(C) $\xrightarrow{[O]}$ (D) $\xrightarrow[\text{H}_2\text{SO}_4]{\text{HNO}_3}$

    p-methylpropylbenzene   terephthalic acid   2-nitroterephthalic acid

11. 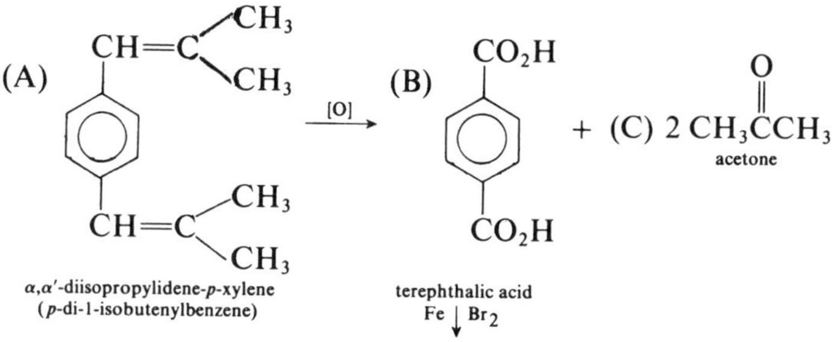 (A)

α,α'-diisopropylidene-p-xylene
(p-di-1-isobutenylbenzene)

(B)

terephthalic acid
Fe $\downarrow$ Br$_2$

+ (C) 2 CH$_3$CCH$_3$
acetone

[(A) might have only a
p-methyl or vinyl group,
among others.]

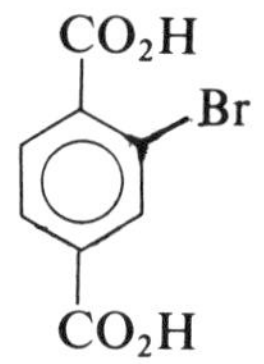

13. 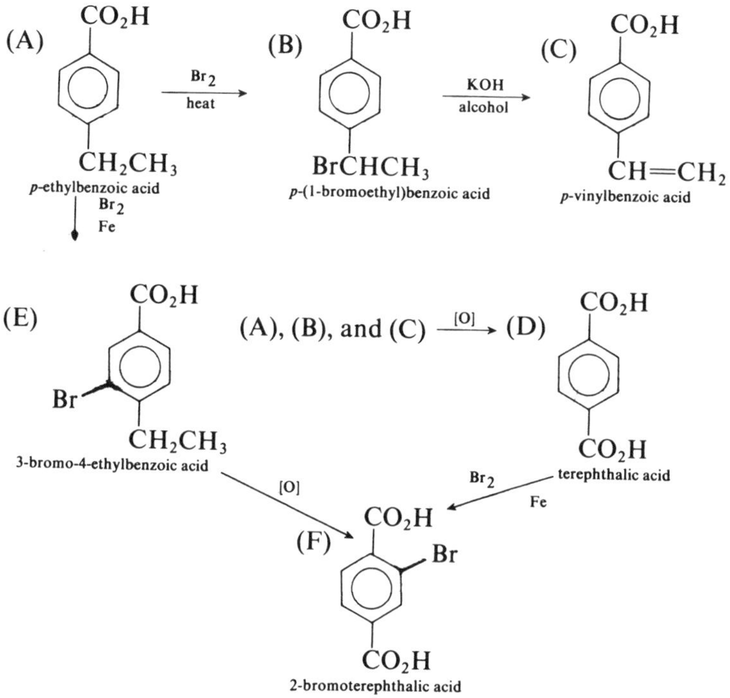 (A)

p-ethylbenzoic acid

$\xrightarrow[\text{heat}]{\text{Br}_2}$

(B)

p-(1-bromoethyl)benzoic acid

$\xrightarrow[\text{alcohol}]{\text{KOH}}$

(C)

p-vinylbenzoic acid

Br$_2$ $\downarrow$ Fe

(E)

3-bromo-4-ethylbenzoic acid

(A), (B), and (C) $\xrightarrow{[O]}$ (D)

terephthalic acid

Br$_2$ Fe

[O]

(F)

2-bromoterephthalic acid

15. a.

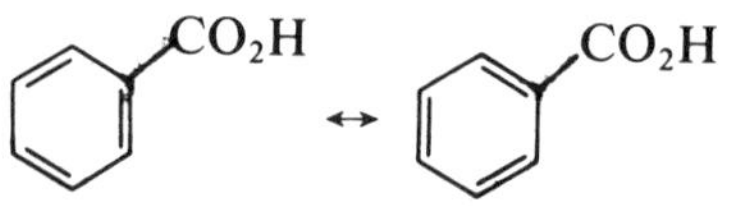

$\leftrightarrow$

b.

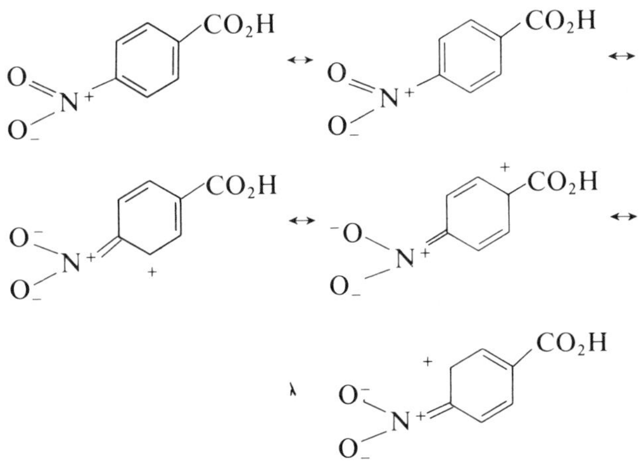

CO_2H　　↔　　CO_2H　　↔

CO_2H　　↔　　CO_2H　　↔

λ　　CO_2H

c.

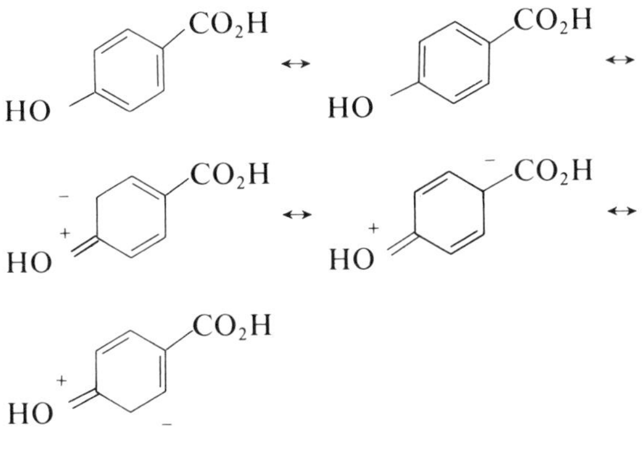

CO_2H　　↔　　CO_2H　　↔

CO_2H　　↔　　CO_2H　　↔

CO_2H

d.

CO_2H　　↔　　CO_2H　　↔　　CO_2H　　↔

CO_2H　　↔　　CO_2H

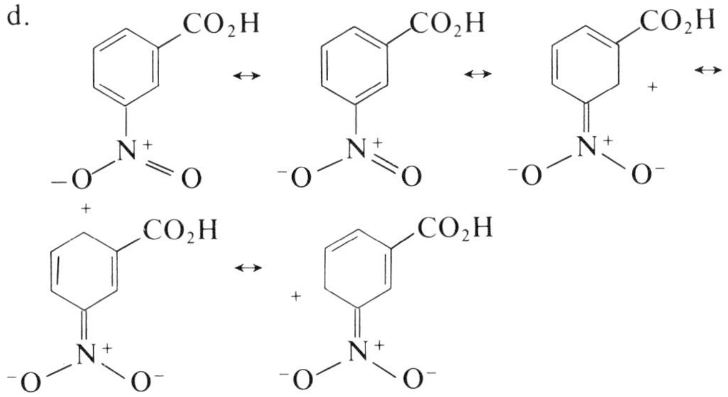

e.

16.   *Acids* p-NO_2 > m-NO_2 > benzoic > m-CH_3 > p-OH
       actual K_a($\times$ 10^5)   36   32   6.3   5.4   2.6

Both nitrobenzoic acids show their electron-withdrawing character in the resonance contributors, the effect of which will be to aid in spreading out the negative charge created in ionization, thus greater acidity. The p-nitro group exerts a stronger effect (see resonance structure with the positive charge at the carbon bearing the carboxyl group) than the m-nitro group. The p-hydroxyl group, in a similar fashion, repels electrons (into the ring) and thus retards ionization and weakens the acid. The m-methyl group does not act by resonance, but exhibits a small acid-weakening effect by inductively releasing electrons to the ring.

17. $Br_2 \xrightarrow{h\nu} 2\ Br\cdot$

Termination reactions.
No. The latter is an electrophilic, ionic reaction.

The mechanisms of the reactions require either a hydrogen atom that can be extracted or a site for electrophilic attack. When all possible sites for substitution (either radical or ionic) are considered, those shown as products are far more important than any others. This fact can be related both to the ease of attack by the reagent and to the stability of the intermediate formed in the reaction.

19. a.

c. O_2N—⟨benzene⟩—CO_2H > Cl—⟨benzene⟩—CO_2H > ⟨benzene⟩—CO_2H

20. a.

c. CH_3CHBr $\xrightarrow[\text{(3) H}_2\text{O}]{\text{(1) Mg} \atop \text{(2) CO}_2}$ CH_3CHCO_2H
    | |
    CH_3 CH_3

e.

CHAPTER 8

1 and 3. a. isopropylamine (primary)
          c. *m*-nitroaniline (primary)
          e. methyl *t*-butylamine (secondary)
          g. ethylenediamine or 1,2-diaminoethane (both primary)
          i. tetra-*n*-butylammonium chloride

2 and 3. a. $CH_3\overset{O}{\overset{\|}{C}}N(CH_2CH_2CH_2CH_3)_2$

c. ⟨◯⟩—NH—⟨◯⟩   (secondary)

e. $CH_3(CH_2)_9NH_2$ (primary)

g. (structure: benzamide with 2-Br, 4-Br substituents; $\overset{O}{\overset{\|}{C}}NH_2$)   i. (cyclobutane ring)—$N^+(CH_3)_3I^-$

4. a.

(structure: benzene with NO_2 top, Cl at 3 and 5 positions)
$\xrightarrow[\text{HCl}]{\text{Zn}}$
(structure: benzene with $NH_3^+Cl^-$ top, Cl at 3 and 5 positions)

3,5-dichloronitrobenzene   3,5-dichloroanilinium chloride

c. $(CH_3)_2CHNH_2 + CH_3I \rightarrow (CH_3)_2CHN^+(CH_3)_3I^-$
       isopropylamine   iodomethane   trimethylisopropylammonium iodide

e. NH_2 $NH_3^+Cl^-$

(benzene with NH_2) + HCl → (benzene with $NH_3^+Cl^-$)

aniline   anilinium chloride
                                   (aniline hydrochloride)

g. $CH_3CH_2NH_2 + HCl \xrightarrow{H_2O} CH_3CH_2NH_3^+Cl^-$
     ethylamine   ethylammonium chloride

5.

(cyclohexane with NO_2) $\xrightarrow{[H]}$ (cyclohexane with NH_2)

nitrocyclohexane   cyclohexylamine

A variety of isomers are also possible as well as other nitrogen-containing starting materials not covered in this text.

7. (A) (benzene)—CH_2Cl $\xrightarrow{NH_3}$ (B) (benzene)—CH_2NH_2 $\xrightarrow{[O]}$

α-chlorotoluene   benzylamine

(C) (benzene)—CO_2H

benzoic acid

9. (A) $CH_3CH_2\overset{\overset{\displaystyle O}{\|}}{C}N\overset{\displaystyle CH_3}{\underset{\displaystyle CH_3}{\big<}}$ $\xrightarrow{\text{NaOH}}$ (B) $CH_3\underset{\underset{\displaystyle CH_3}{|}}{N}H + CH_3CH_2CO_2^-Na^+$

     N,N-dimethylpropanoamide   dimethylamine   sodium propanoate

11. a. $CH_3CH{=}CH_2$ $\xrightarrow{\text{HBr}}$ $CH_3\underset{\underset{\displaystyle Br}{|}}{C}HCH_3$ $\xrightarrow{Na^+CN^-}$ $CH_3\underset{\underset{\displaystyle CH_3}{|}}{C}HCN$

$\xrightarrow[\text{(2) } H_2O]{\text{(1) LAH}}$ $CH_3\underset{\underset{\displaystyle CH_3}{|}}{C}HCH_2NH_2$

c. CH_3CH_2OH $\xrightarrow{\text{HBr}}$ CH_3CH_2Br $\xrightarrow{NH_3}$ $(CH_3CH_2)_2NH$ $\xrightarrow{CH_3CO_2H}$

$CH_3CO_2^{-+}NH_2(CH_2CH_3)_2$ $\xrightarrow{P_2O_5}$ $CH_3\overset{\overset{\displaystyle O}{\|}}{C}N(CH_2CH_3)_2$

e.

Br-C_6H_5 $\xrightarrow[\text{Pt}]{H_2}$ Br-cyclohexane $\xrightarrow[\text{alcohol}]{\text{KOH}}$ cyclohexene $\xrightarrow{[O]}$ $(CH_2)_4\overset{\overset{\displaystyle CO_2H}{|}}{\underset{\underset{\displaystyle CO_2H}{|}}{}}$ $\xrightarrow{NH_3}$

$(CH_2)_4\overset{\overset{\displaystyle CO_2^-NH_4^+}{|}}{\underset{\underset{\displaystyle CO_2^-NH_4^+}{|}}{}}$ $\xrightarrow{P_2O_5}$ $(CH_2)_4\overset{\overset{\displaystyle CONH_2}{|}}{\underset{\underset{\displaystyle CONH_2}{|}}{}}$ $\xrightarrow{\text{LAH}}$ $H_2N(CH_2)_6NH_2$

12. b.

13. The question with which we are concerned is that of the availability of the electron pair on nitrogen.

$$PhNH_2 + H^+ \rightleftharpoons PhNH_3{}^+$$

In the case of anilines, we can discuss this problem in terms of the following resonance contributors:

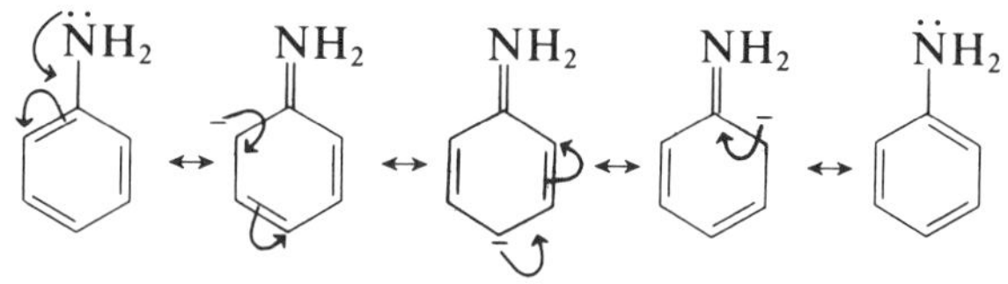

The more the electron pair of nitrogen is delocalized into the ring the weaker will be the base. Electron-withdrawing groups should be base weakening and electron-releasing groups base strengthening. Thus,

$$\begin{matrix} p\text{-}CH_3 \\ p\text{-}CH_3O \end{matrix} > H > \begin{matrix} p\text{-}NO_2 \\ p\text{-}Cl \end{matrix}$$

The p-methoxy group, unlike the p-methyl group, can release electrons by resonance as well as by induction. Therefore, p-methoxyaniline should be a stronger base than p-methylaniline.

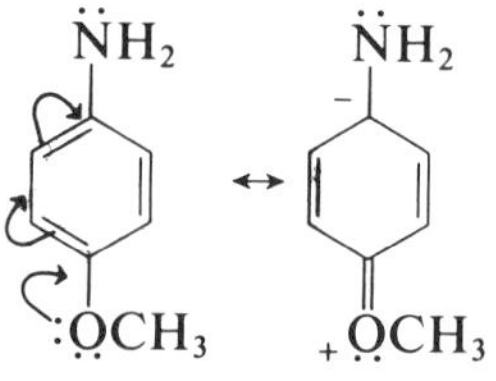

The p-nitro group has greater delocalizing abilities than the p-chloro group; thus, p-nitroaniline should be a weaker base than p-chloroaniline.

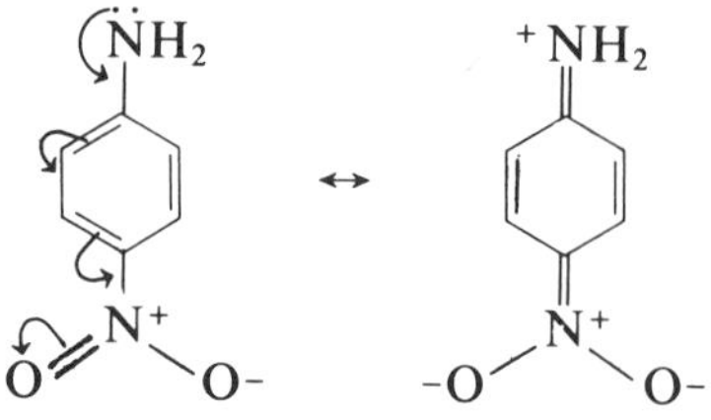

An alternative point of view is that the groups tend to stabilize or destabilize the positive charge of the anilinium ion. This argument leads to the same relative order of base strengths.

$$p\text{-}OCH_3 > p\text{-}CH_3 > H > p\text{-}Cl > p\text{-}NO_2$$

15	4.9	4.2	1.5	0.001 actual $K_b(\times 10^{10})$

CHAPTER 9

1. a. acetaldehyde   methanal
   c. *p*-nitrobenzaldehyde   same
   e. isovaleraldehyde   3-methylbutanal
   g. di-*n*-propyl ketone 2,4-   very uncommon
      dinitrophenylhydrazone
   i. isopropyl cyclohexyl ketone   isobutyrocyclohexane

2. a.

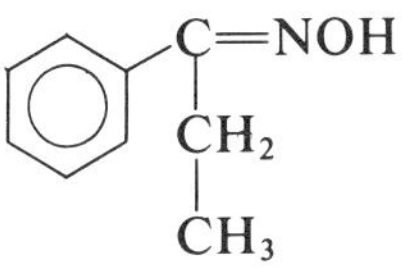

   c. CHO structure with I

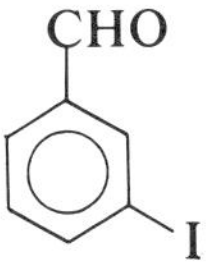

   e. $CH_3CH_2C=CHCHO$ (with phenyl substituent)

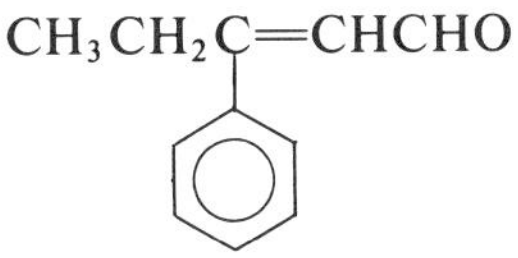

   g.

   $$CH_3\overset{O}{\underset{\|}{C}}CH_2\overset{O}{\underset{\|}{C}}CH_2CH_3$$

   i. $CH_3CH_2CH_2$—⟨ ⟩—$\overset{O}{\underset{\|}{C}}$—⟨ ⟩—$CH_2CH_2CH_3$

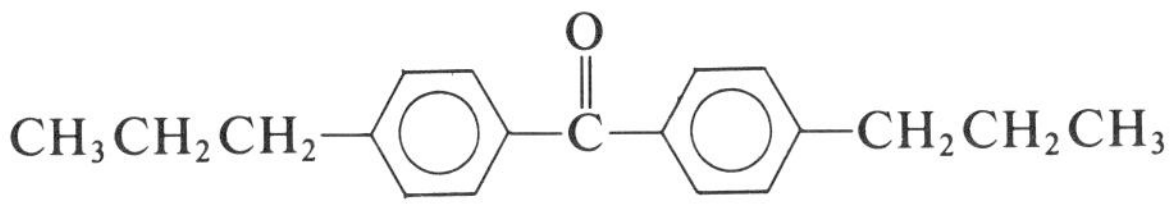

3. a. $CH_3\overset{O}{\underset{\|}{C}}H$ + CH_3MgBr → $CH_3\overset{O^-Mg^{+2}Br^-}{\underset{|}{C}}HCH_3$

       acetaldehyde   methyl magnesium   isopropoxy magnesium
                  bromide   bromide

   c. $2\ CH_3CH_2CHO$ + $Na^{+-}OCH_2CH_3$ $CH_3CH_2\overset{OH}{\underset{|}{C}}HCHCHO$

                                                       $\overset{}{\underset{|}{C}H_3}$
       propanal   sodium ethoxide   2-methyl-3-hydroxypentanal

   e. $CH_3CH_2CHCH_2OH$ CH_3CH_2CHCHO

          2-phenyl-1-butanol   2-phenylbutanal

   $\xrightarrow{[O]}$ $\xrightarrow{[O]}$

   $CH_3CH_2CHCO_2H$

   2-phenylbutanoic acid

   $\downarrow [O]$

   CO_2H

   benzoic acid

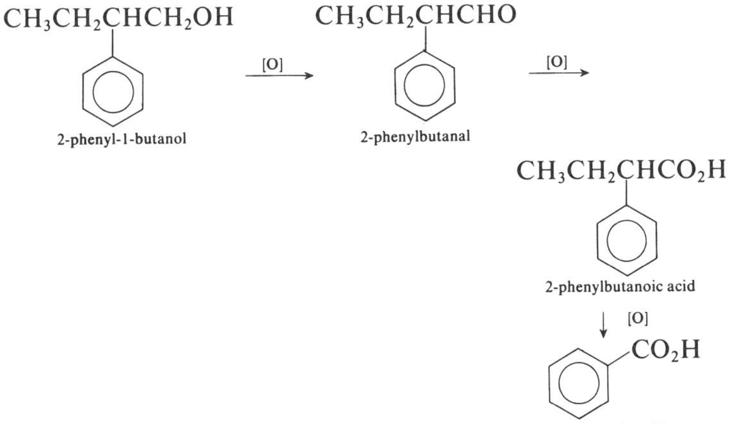

g. $CH\equiv CH + H_2O \xrightarrow[H^+]{HgSO_4}$ $CH_3\overset{O}{\overset{\|}{C}}H$

acetylene   acetaldehyde

i.

chlorobenzene   acetyl chloride   2'-chloroacetophenone (*o*)   +

4'-chloroacetophenone (*p*)

4. a. $CH_3CH_2CO_2CH_2CH_3 + NaOH \xrightarrow{H_2O} CH_3CH_2CO_2^-Na^+$
ethyl propanoate   sodium propanoate

$+ CH_3CH_2OH$
ethanol

c. $CH_3CH_2\overset{O}{\overset{\|}{C}}CH_3 + CH_3CH_2CH_2MgBr \rightarrow$
     2-butanone   *n*-propyl magnesium bromide

$$CH_3CH_2CH_2\overset{\overset{\displaystyle CH_3}{|}}{\underset{\underset{\displaystyle CH_3CH_2}{|}}{C}}O^-Mg^{+2}Br^-$$
3-methyl-3-hexoxide magnesium bromide

e. $CH_3CH_2O^-Na^+ + (CH_3)_2CHCH_2Cl \rightarrow$
   sodium ethoxide   2-methyl-1-chloropropane

$(CH_3)_2CHCH_2OCH_2CH_3$
ethyl isobutyl ether

g. $(CH_3)_2CH\overset{O}{\overset{\|}{C}}CH_3 + NaOI \rightarrow (CH_3)_2CHCO_2^-Na^+ + CHI_3$
   3-methylbutanone   sodium 2-methylpropanoate   iodoform
   (methyl isopropyl ketone)

i. $C_6H_5\overset{O}{\overset{\|}{C}}CH_3 + C_6H_5MgI \rightarrow C_6H_5\overset{\overset{\displaystyle O^-Mg^{+2}I^-}{|}}{\underset{\underset{\displaystyle CH_3}{|}}{C}}C_6H_5$
     acetophenone   phenyl magnesium iodide   1,1-diphenylethoxy
                                    magnesium iodide

k. $CH_3\overset{O}{\overset{\|}{C}}CH_3 + Na^+{}^-SO_3H \rightarrow$ $\overset{\displaystyle CH_3}{\underset{\displaystyle CH_3}{>}}C\overset{\displaystyle OH}{\underset{\displaystyle SO_3^-Na^+}{<}}$
     acetone   sodium 2-hydroxy-2-propane-
                                 sulfonate

5.

b.

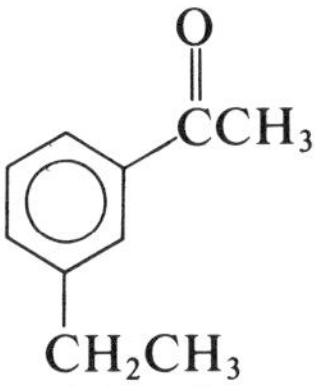

m-ethylacetophenone

$+ Na^{+-}SO_3H \rightarrow$

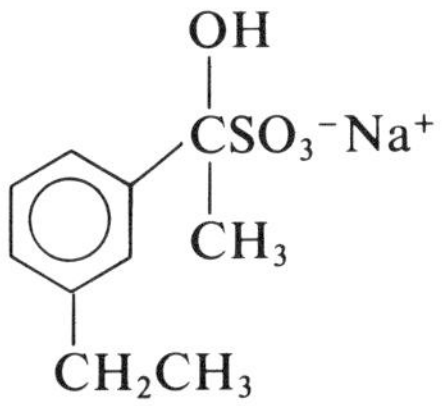

others, no reaction

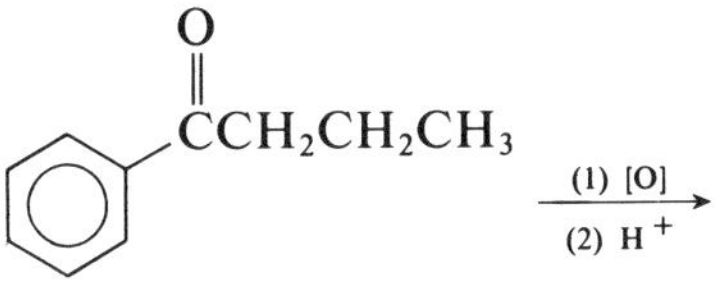

bisulfite addition product

n-propyl phenyl ketone

$\xrightarrow[\text{(2) H}^+]{\text{(1) [O]}}$

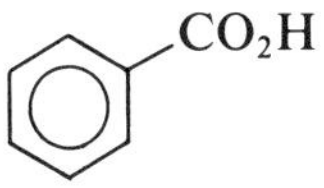

benzoic acid

titration gives
neutralization equivalent = 122;
the others would require a
neutralization equivalent of 83

The iodoform test and the number of mononitrosubstitution products could also be used.

7. (A)

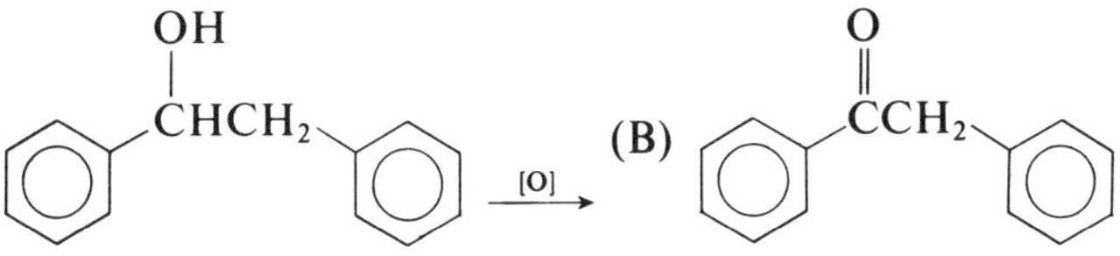

1,2-diphenylethanol

$\xrightarrow{[O]}$

(B)

phenyl benzyl ketone
(2-phenylacetophenone)

H_2SO_4

2,4-dinitrophenyl-
hydrazine

(A) $H_2SO_4 \rightarrow$ (D)

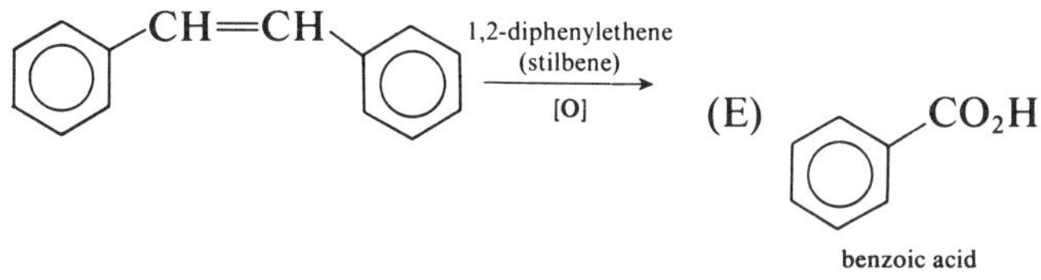

CH=CH   1,2-diphenylethene
(stilbene)
$\xrightarrow{[O]}$

(E) CO_2H

benzoic acid

(B) 2,4-dinitro-
phenylhydrazine $\longrightarrow$ (C)

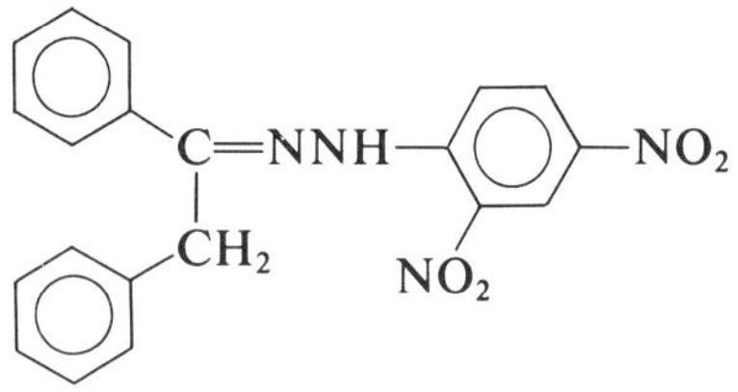

C=NNH—NO₂

CH₂   NO₂

phenyl benzyl ketone 2,4-dinitrophenylhydrazone

9. (A) $HO_2C(CH_2)_4CO_2H$ $\xrightarrow{Ca(OH)_2}$ (CH₂)₄ CO_2^- CO_2^- Ca^{+2} $\xrightarrow{heat}$ (B)

adipic acid   calcium adipate   cyclopentanone

—NHNH₂

=NNH—

cyclopentanone phenylhydrazone

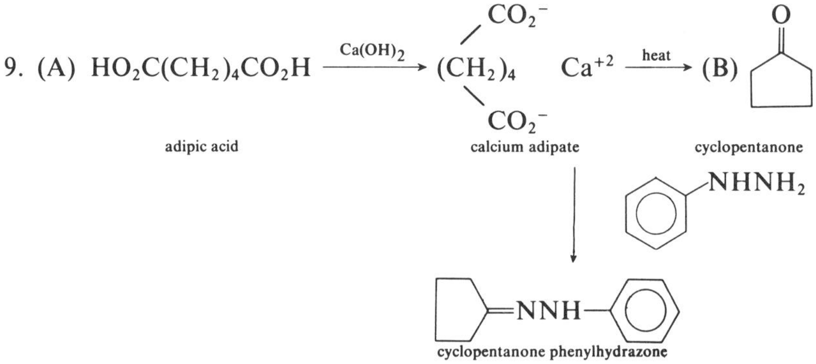

11. $CH_3\overset{O}{\overset{\|}{C}}CH_2CH_2CH_2OH$ + $CH_3\overset{O}{\overset{\|}{C}}Cl$ → $CH_3\overset{O}{\overset{\|}{C}}CH_2CH_2CH_2O_2CCH_3$
   5-hydroxy-2-pentanone   acetyl chloride   4-ketopentyl acetate

$\xrightarrow{[O]}$ $CH_3\overset{O}{\overset{\|}{C}}CH_2CH_2CO_2H$
   4-ketopentanoic acid

CH_3
C=NNH—

+ —NHNH₂ → HOCH₂CH₂CH₂

phenylhydrazine   5-hydroxy-2-pentanone phenylhydrazone

+ NaOI → CHI₃ + $HOCH_2CH_2CH_2CO_2^-Na^+$
        iodoform   sodium 4-hydroxybutanoate

+ $Ag(NH_3)_2^+$ → no reaction

12. $CH_3\overset{O}{\overset{\|}{C}}CH_2CH_2CHO \xrightarrow{[H]} CH_3CH_2CH_2CH_2CH_3$

4-ketopentanal

$+$

(phenyl ring with NHNH$_2$)

$\rightarrow CH_3\overset{NNH-\text{(phenyl)}}{\overset{\|}{C}}CH_2CH_2CH=NNH-\text{(phenyl)}$

4-ketopentanal diphenylhydrazone

$+ \ NaOH/I_2 \rightarrow CHI_3 + Na^{+-}O_2CCH_2CH_2CO_2^-Na^+$

iodoform　　　　　　　sodium succinate

$\xrightarrow{[O]} CH_3\overset{O}{\overset{\|}{C}}CH_2CH_2CO_2H \ +$ (phenyl ring with NHNH$_2$)

4-ketopentanoic acid

$\underset{HO_2CCH_2CH_2}{\overset{CH_3}{\diagdown}}C=NNH-\text{(phenyl)}$

4-ketopentanoic acid phenylhydrazone

$+ \ Cu(OH)_2 \rightarrow CH_3\overset{O}{\overset{\|}{C}}CH_2CH_2CO_2^-Na^+ + Cu_2O$

sodium 4-ketopentanoate

15. $\underset{CH_3}{\overset{CH_3}{\diagdown}}CH\overset{O}{\overset{\|}{C}}CH_2CH_3 + H_2NOH \rightarrow \underset{CH_3}{\overset{CH_3}{\diagdown}}CH\overset{NOH}{\overset{\|}{C}}CH_2CH_3$

2-methyl-3-pentanone　　　　　　　2-methyl-3-pentanone oxime

$\xrightarrow{[H]} (B) \ \underset{CH_3}{\overset{CH_3}{\diagdown}}CH\overset{OH}{\overset{|}{C}}HCH_2CH_3$

2-methyl-3-pentanol

$\downarrow H_2SO_4$

$(C) \ \underset{CH_3}{\overset{CH_3}{\diagdown}}C=CHCH_2CH_3$

2-methyl-2-pentene

$[O]\downarrow$

$(D) \ CH_3\overset{O}{\overset{\|}{C}}CH_3 \qquad (E) \ CH_3CH_2CHO$

acetone　　　　　　　　propionaldehyde

$(D) \begin{cases} + \ Ag(NH_3)_2^+ \rightarrow \text{no reaction} \\ + \ NaOI \rightarrow CHI_3 + CH_3CO_2^-Na^+ \end{cases}$

　　　　　　　　　iodoform　　　sodium acetate

$$(E) \begin{cases} + \text{ Ag(NH}_3)_2{}^+ \rightarrow \text{CH}_3\text{CH}_2\text{CO}_2{}^-\text{NH}_4{}^+ + \text{Ag} \\ \qquad\qquad\qquad\quad \text{ammonium propanoate} \\ + \text{ NaOI} \rightarrow \text{no reaction} \end{cases}$$

17. (A)

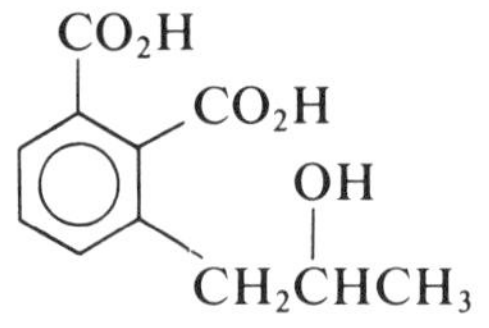

3-(2-hydroxypropyl)phthalic acid

$\xrightarrow{\text{CH}_3\text{COCl}}$ This test is usually for −OH, but the acidic H's will react.

↓ NaOI   ↘ H₂SO₄

(F)

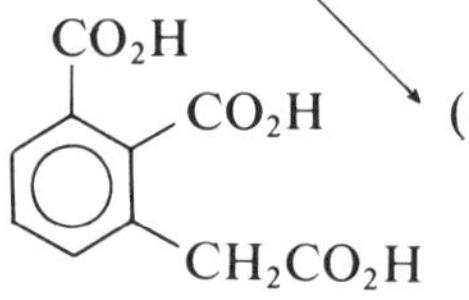

2,3-dicarboxyphenylacetic acid

(B)

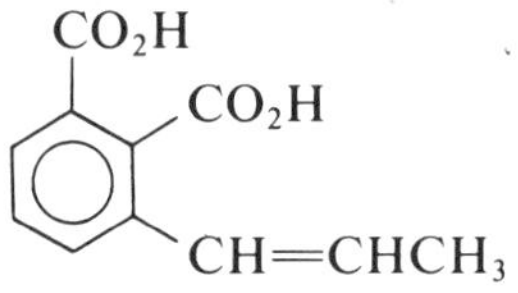

3-propenylphthalic acid

$\xrightarrow{\text{[O]}}$

(C)

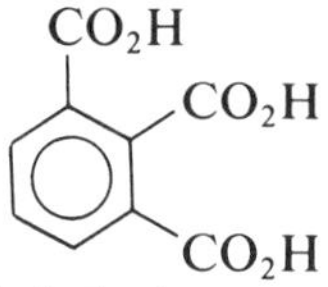

1,2,3-tricarboxybenzene

+ (D) CH₃CO₂H
acetic acid

↓

(E)

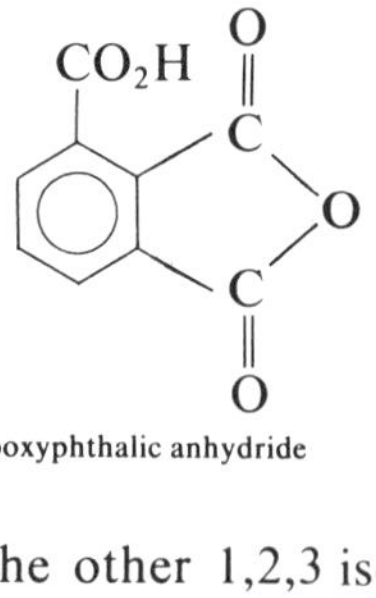

3-carboxyphthalic anhydride

The 1,2,4 isomers, as well as the other 1,2,3 isomers, are not excluded by the data. There is a good chance that in practice (E) would titrate just as (C) did, inasmuch as the anhydride would hydrolyze rapidly.

18. a. $\text{CH}_3\text{CH}_2\text{CHO} \xrightarrow{\text{LAH}} \text{CH}_3\text{CH}_2\text{CH}_2\text{OH} \xrightarrow{\text{H}_2\text{SO}_4}$

$\text{CH}_3\text{CH}=\text{CH}_2 \xrightarrow{\text{Br}_2} \text{CH}_3\text{CHCH}_2\text{Br} \xrightarrow[\text{alcohol}]{\text{KOH}} \text{CH}_3\text{C}\equiv\text{CH}$
$\qquad\qquad\qquad\qquad\qquad\quad |$
$\qquad\qquad\qquad\qquad\quad\text{Br}$

c. $CH_3CO_2H \xrightarrow{\text{LAH}} CH_3CH_2OH \xrightarrow[\text{heat}]{\text{Cu}} CH_3CHO$

$CO + H_2 \rightarrow CH_3OH \xrightarrow{\text{HBr}} CH_3Br \xrightarrow{\text{Mg}} CH_3MgBr$ $\Bigg\} \rightarrow$

$$\underset{\displaystyle CH_3CHCH_3}{\overset{\displaystyle OH}{|}}$$

e. $CH_3\overset{O}{\overset{||}{C}}CH_3 \xrightarrow{\text{OH}^-} CH_3\underset{\displaystyle CH_3}{\overset{\displaystyle OH}{\underset{|}{\overset{|}{C}}}}CH_2\overset{O}{\overset{||}{C}}CH_3 \xrightarrow{\text{LAH}}$

$CH_3\underset{\displaystyle CH_3}{\overset{\displaystyle OH}{\underset{|}{\overset{|}{C}}}}CH_2\overset{OH}{\overset{|}{C}}HCH_3 \xrightarrow{\text{H}_2\text{SO}_4} CH_2{=}\underset{\displaystyle CH_3}{\overset{|}{C}}CH{=}CHCH_3$

g.

19. b. The Grignard reagent would react with another molecule of the starting material as soon as it was formed.

$CH_3\overset{O}{\overset{||}{C}}CH_2CH_2MgCl + CH_3\overset{O}{\overset{||}{C}}CH_2CH_2Cl \rightarrow$

$$CH_3\overset{O}{\overset{||}{C}}CH_2CH_2\underset{\displaystyle CH_3}{\overset{\displaystyle OMgCl}{\underset{|}{\overset{|}{C}}}}CH_2CH_2Cl$$

A better route would involve the reaction with cyanide ion followed by hydrolysis.

$CH_3\overset{O}{\overset{||}{C}}CH_2CH_2Cl \xrightarrow{\text{CN}^-} CH_3\overset{O}{\overset{||}{C}}CH_2CH_2CN \xrightarrow{\text{H}^+ \text{(aq)}}$

$$CH_3\overset{O}{\overset{||}{C}}CH_2CH_2CO_2H$$

20. b. $HC{\equiv}CH \xrightarrow{\text{Na}} HC{\equiv}C^-Na^+ \xrightarrow{CH_3CH_2Br}$

$CH_3CH_2C{\equiv}CH \xrightarrow[\text{Lindlar}]{\text{H}_2} CH_3CH_2CH{=}CH_2 \xrightarrow{B_2H_6}$

$$(CH_3CH_2CH_2CH_2)_3B \xrightarrow[\text{OH}^-]{\text{H}_2\text{O}_2} CH_3CH_2CH_2CH_2OH$$

$$HC{\equiv}CH \xrightarrow[\text{Lindlar}]{\text{H}_2} H_2C{=}CH_2 \xrightarrow{\text{HBr}} CH_3CH_2Br$$

$$\downarrow \text{Mg}$$

$$H_2C{=}CH_2 \xrightarrow[\text{(2) OH}^-]{\text{(1) HOCl}} H_2C{-}CH_2 \xrightarrow{CH_3CH_2MgBr} \atop \diagdown O \diagup$$

$$CH_3CH_2CH_2CH_2OH$$

In addition to the Grignard reaction shown, the following reactants could be used:

$$CH_3CH_2CH_2MgBr + CH_2O \rightarrow CH_3CH_2CH_2CH_2OH$$

CHAPTER 10

2.
$$\underset{CH_2OH}{\overset{CHO}{|}} \xrightarrow[\text{(aq)}]{\text{Na}^+\text{CN}^-} \quad \underset{CH_2OH}{\overset{CN}{\underset{|}{H-C-OH}}} + \underset{CH_2OH}{\overset{CN}{\underset{|}{HO-C-H}}}$$

$$H^+\downarrow \text{(aq)}$$

$$\underset{CH_2OH}{\overset{CO_2H}{\underset{|}{H-C-OH}}} + \underset{CH_2OH}{\overset{CO_2H}{\underset{|}{HO-C-H}}}$$

The lactone does not form in this case because it would require a four-membered ring. An acid will not reduce to an aldehyde under conditions you have learned, but a look at the list of Suggested Additional Readings shows that there is a well-known method called the **Rosenmund reduction**, which can be applied to the acid chloride.

$$\left.\begin{array}{c} CO_2H \\ | \\ H-C-OH \\ | \\ CH_2OH \\ + \\ CO_2H \\ | \\ HO-C-H \\ | \\ CH_2OH \end{array}\right\} \xrightarrow[\text{ClCCCl}]{\overset{OO}{\|}} \left.\begin{array}{c} COCl \\ | \\ H-C-OH \\ | \\ CH_2OH \\ + \\ COCl \\ | \\ HO-C-H \\ | \\ CH_2OH \end{array}\right\} \xrightarrow[\text{Pd(BaSO}_4)]{\text{H}_2} \begin{array}{c} CHO \\ | \\ H-C-OH \\ | \\ CH_2OH \\ + \\ CHO \\ | \\ HO-C-H \\ | \\ CH_2OH \end{array}$$

You should also note the formation of the acid chloride by ex-
change with **oxalyl chloride**. This excellent method prevents the
conversion of the hydroxyl groups to chloro groups, a side reaction
that could occur with the usual reagents—for example, $SOCl_2$.
Now we simply repeat the Kiliani-Fischer synthesis.

$$
\left.
\begin{array}{c}
\begin{array}{c} \text{CHO} \\ | \\ \text{H}-\text{C}-\text{OH} \\ | \\ \text{CH}_2\text{OH} \end{array} \\
+ \\
\begin{array}{c} \text{CHO} \\ | \\ \text{HO}-\text{C}-\text{H} \\ | \\ \text{CH}_2\text{OH} \end{array}
\end{array}
\right\}
\xrightarrow[\text{(aq)}]{\text{Na}^+\text{CN}^-}
\left.
\begin{array}{cc}
\begin{array}{c} \text{CN} \\ | \\ \text{H}-\text{C}-\text{OH} \\ | \\ \text{H}-\text{C}-\text{OH} \\ | \\ \text{CH}_2\text{OH} \end{array} + &
\begin{array}{c} \text{CN} \\ | \\ \text{HO}-\text{C}-\text{H} \\ | \\ \text{H}-\text{C}-\text{OH} \\ | \\ \text{CH}_2\text{OH} \end{array} \\[2em]
\begin{array}{c} \text{CN} \\ | \\ \text{H}-\text{C}-\text{OH} \\ | \\ \text{HO}-\text{C}-\text{H} \\ | \\ \text{CH}_2\text{OH} \end{array} + &
\begin{array}{c} \text{CN} \\ | \\ \text{HO}-\text{C}-\text{H} \\ | \\ \text{HO}-\text{C}-\text{H} \\ | \\ \text{CH}_2\text{OH} \end{array}
\end{array}
\right\}
\xrightarrow[\text{(aq)}]{\text{H}^+}
$$

$$
\begin{array}{cccc}
\begin{array}{c} \text{CO}_2\text{H} \\ | \\ \text{H}-\text{C}-\text{OH} \\ | \\ \text{H}-\text{C}-\text{OH} \\ | \\ \text{CH}_2\text{OH} \end{array} + &
\begin{array}{c} \text{CO}_2\text{H} \\ | \\ \text{HO}-\text{C}-\text{H} \\ | \\ \text{H}-\text{C}-\text{OH} \\ | \\ \text{CH}_2\text{OH} \end{array} &
\begin{array}{c} \text{CO}_2\text{H} \\ | \\ \text{H}-\text{C}-\text{OH} \\ | \\ \text{HO}-\text{C}-\text{H} \\ | \\ \text{CH}_2\text{OH} \end{array} + &
\begin{array}{c} \text{CO}_2\text{H} \\ | \\ \text{HO}-\text{C}-\text{H} \\ | \\ \text{HO}-\text{C}-\text{H} \\ | \\ \text{CH}_2\text{OH} \end{array} \\[1em]
\textbf{1} & \textbf{2} & \textbf{3} & \textbf{4}
\end{array}
$$

At this point, the resolution should be made. The first consideration is that as few separations as possible should be carried out.
The remaining steps do not affect the optically active centers. The
second consideration is that one needs good crystalline materials
for fractional crystallization. In this case, the acids are much better
than the aldehydes. Finally, the presence of carboxyl groups provides a good means for actually effecting the resolution.

Compounds **1** and **2** are diastereomers (as are **3** and **4**); therefore, they can be separated by fractional crystallization directly.
The racemic mixtures **1,4** and **2,3**, which are obtained, can be converted to diastereomeric salts by using one enantiomer of an
optically active alkaloid (p. 310).

$\textbf{1} + \textbf{4} + (-)\text{-brucine} \rightarrow (\textbf{1})^-(-)\text{-brucine H}^+ + (\textbf{4})^-(-)\text{-brucine H}^+$

These salts, which show different physical properties, can be
separated by such physical methods as fractional crystallization.
Hydrolysis of the separated salts with mineral acid gives the
desired compound plus the mineral salt of the alkaloid.

$$\textbf{(1)}^-(-)\text{-brucine H}^+ \xrightarrow{\text{H}^+\text{Cl}^-} \begin{array}{c} \text{CO}_2\text{H} \\ | \\ \text{H}-\overset{|}{\text{C}}-\text{OH} \\ | \\ \text{H}-\overset{|}{\text{C}}-\text{OH} \\ | \\ \text{CH}_2\text{OH} \\ \textbf{1} \end{array} \quad + (-)\text{-brucine H}^+\text{Cl}^-$$

Compound **1** can form a five-membered lactone, which can be reduced with the usual sodium amalgam to produce one of desired tetroses. The other three acids can be isolated from the reaction mixture and converted to sugars by the same sequence.

$$\begin{array}{c} \text{O}=\text{C} \\ | \\ \text{H}-\overset{|}{\text{C}}-\text{OH} \\ | \\ \text{H}-\overset{|}{\text{C}}-\text{OH} \\ | \\ \text{CH}_2 \end{array}\Bigg]\text{O} \xrightarrow{\text{Na(Hg)}} \begin{array}{c} \text{CHO} \\ | \\ \text{H}-\overset{|}{\text{C}}-\text{OH} \\ | \\ \text{H}-\overset{|}{\text{C}}-\text{OH} \\ | \\ \text{CH}_2\text{OH} \\ (-)\text{-erythrose} \end{array}$$

3.

$$\begin{array}{c} \text{CHO} \\ | \\ \text{H}-\overset{|}{\text{C}}-\text{OH} \\ | \\ \text{H}-\overset{|}{\text{C}}-\text{OH} \\ | \\ \text{H}-\overset{|}{\text{C}}-\text{OH} \\ | \\ \text{CH}_2\text{OH} \end{array} + \Bigg\{$$

a. $\xrightarrow{\text{HIO}_4}$ $\begin{array}{c} \text{CHO} \\ | \\ \text{CHO} \end{array}$ $+\ 2\ \text{HCO}_2\text{H}\ +\ \text{HCHO}$

c. $\xrightarrow[\text{Ni}]{\text{H}_2}$ $\begin{array}{c} \text{CH}_2\text{OH} \\ | \\ \text{H}-\overset{|}{\text{C}}-\text{OH} \\ | \\ \text{H}-\overset{|}{\text{C}}-\text{OH} \\ | \\ \text{H}-\overset{|}{\text{C}}-\text{OH} \\ | \\ \text{CH}_2\text{OH} \end{array}$

e. $\xrightarrow{\text{(CH}_3\text{CO)}_2\text{O}}$ $\begin{array}{c} \text{CHO} \\ | \\ \text{H}-\overset{|}{\text{C}}-\text{O}_2\text{CCH}_3 \\ | \\ \text{H}-\overset{|}{\text{C}}-\text{O}_2\text{CCH}_3 \\ | \\ \text{H}-\overset{|}{\text{C}}-\text{O}_2\text{CCH}_3 \\ | \\ \text{CH}_2\text{O}_2\text{CCH}_3 \end{array}$

g. $\xrightarrow{\text{H}^+\text{CN}^-}$ $\begin{array}{c} \text{CN} \\ | \\ \text{H}-\overset{|}{\text{C}}-\text{OH} \\ | \\ \text{H}-\overset{|}{\text{C}}-\text{OH} \\ | \\ \text{H}-\overset{|}{\text{C}}-\text{OH} \\ | \\ \text{H}-\overset{|}{\text{C}}-\text{OH} \\ | \\ \text{CH}_2\text{OH} \end{array}$ + $\begin{array}{c} \text{CN} \\ | \\ \text{HO}-\overset{|}{\text{C}}-\text{H} \\ | \\ \text{H}-\overset{|}{\text{C}}-\text{OH} \\ | \\ \text{H}-\overset{|}{\text{C}}-\text{OH} \\ | \\ \text{H}-\overset{|}{\text{C}}-\text{OH} \\ | \\ \text{CH}_2\text{OH} \end{array}$

5. (A)

$$\begin{array}{c} CHO \\ | \\ HO-C-H \\ | \\ H-C-OH \\ | \\ H-C-OH \\ | \\ HO-C-H \\ | \\ CH_2OH \end{array}$$

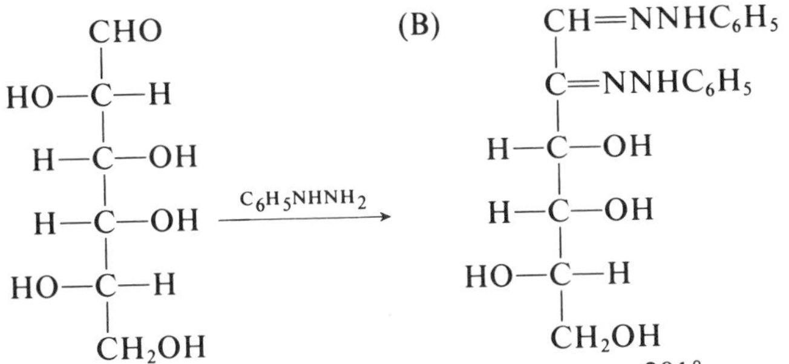

$$mp = 170° \, d$$
$$[\alpha] = +81.7°$$

$\xrightarrow{C_6H_5NHNH_2}$

(B)

$$\begin{array}{c} CH=NNHC_6H_5 \\ | \\ C=NNHC_6H_5 \\ | \\ H-C-OH \\ | \\ H-C-OH \\ | \\ HO-C-H \\ | \\ CH_2OH \end{array}$$

$$mp = 201°$$

(A) $\xrightarrow{HNO_3}$ (C)

$$\begin{array}{c} CO_2H \\ | \\ HO-C-H \\ | \\ H-C-OH \\ | \\ H-C-OH \\ | \\ HO-C-H \\ | \\ CO_2H \end{array}$$

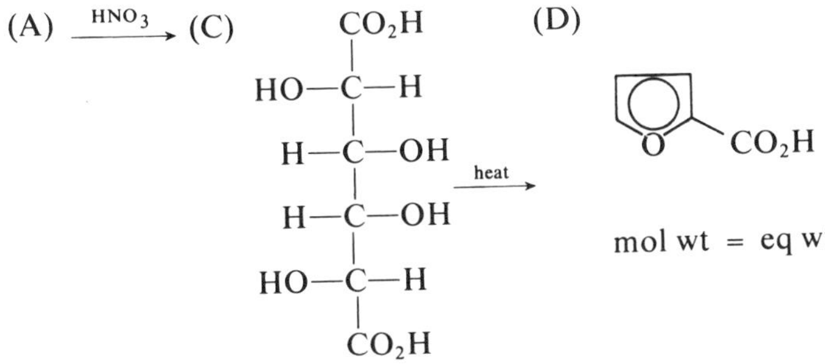

$$mol \; wt = 210$$
$$eq \; wt = 105$$
$$mp = 213°d$$

$\xrightarrow{heat}$

(D)

$$mol \; wt = eq \; wt = 112$$

(D) + BrCH_2C(=O)—⟨C_6H_4⟩—Br →

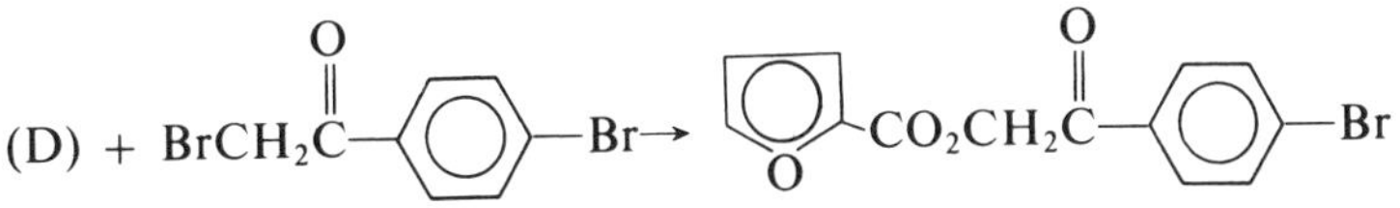

$$mp = 138°$$

7. 25 g of fat = 23.8 g of I_2   iodine number = 95.3

$$\frac{100 \text{ g of fat}}{800 \text{ g/mole of fat}} = 0.125 \text{ mole of fat}$$

$$\frac{95.3 \text{ g of } I_2}{254 \text{ g/mole of } I_2} = 0.375 \text{ mole of } I_2$$

= an average of 3 double bonds per fat molecule

The molecular weight of a fat is an average value, inasmuch as fats are usually complex mixtures of specific glycerides. Thus, it is very possible that some molecules have more than three double bonds and that these are balanced by others containing fewer than the average number.

$$\begin{array}{l} CH_2O_2C(CH_2)_7CH=CH(CH_2)_5CH_3 \\ | \\ CHO_2C(CH_2)_7CH=CH(CH_2)_5CH_3 \\ | \\ CH_2O_2C(CH_2)_7CH=CH(CH_2)_5CH_3 \end{array}$$
palmitolein

9. $C_{47}H_{88}O_6$ mol wt = 748

   iodine number $748:254 = 100:x$

   $$x = 34 \text{ g of } I_2/100 \text{ g of fat}$$

   saponification equivalent $\dfrac{748}{3} = 249.3$ g/eq

   saponification number   KOH = 56,000 mg/mole

   $$\dfrac{56,000}{249.3} = 225 \text{ mg KOH/g of fat}$$

10. b. $CH_3CH_2CH_2OH \xrightarrow{[O]} CH_3CH_2CO_2H \xrightarrow[P]{Br_2} CH_3CHCO_2H$

                                                                      |
                                                                     Br

   propanol   propanoic acid   2-bromopropanoic acid

   $\xrightarrow{-HBr} CH_2{=}CHCO_2H \xrightarrow{peracid} CH_2{-}CHCO_2H \xrightarrow{NH_3} CH_2CHC$

                                                  \ / | |
                                                   O   OH NH

   propenoic acid   epoxypropanoic acid   d,l-serine

   |HOCl

   $CH_2CHCO_2H \xrightarrow{NH_3} CH_2CHCO_2H$

    | | | |
   OH Cl   OH NH$_2$

   2-chloro-3-hydroxy-   d,l-serine
   propanoic acid

   $CH_3CH_2OH \xrightarrow{[O]} CH_3CO_2H \xrightarrow[P]{Cl_2} ClCH_2CO_2H \xrightarrow{CN^-}$

   ethanol   acetic acid   chloroacetic acid

   $NCCH_2CO_2H \xrightarrow{Br_2} NCCHCO_2H \xrightarrow{CH_3OH} NCCHCO_2CH_3$

                              | |
                             Br   Br

   cyanoacetic acid   α-bromocyanoacetic   methyl α-bromocyano-
                              acid   acetate

   $\xrightarrow{[H]} NCCHCH_2OH \xrightarrow{NH_3} HOCH_2CHCN \xrightarrow{H^+(aq)} CH_2CHCO_2H$

                  | | | |
                 Br   NH_2   OH NH_2

   α-bromo-β-hydroxy-   α-amino-β-hydroxy-   d,l-serine
   propanenitrile   propanenitrile

All these routes are fairly long, which illustrates the difficulty of preparing polyfunctional compounds. In actual practice, they would be shorter, because certain intermediates are commercially available—for example, propenoic (acrylic) acid and methylcyanoacetate. The last suggestion probably has the fewest difficulties. The former two could be complicated by isomeric products in the ring opening and addition steps, although the desired products should be the major ones.

   d.

   benzene $\xrightarrow[AlCl_3]{CH_3Cl}$ toluene (CH_3) $\xrightarrow[h\nu]{Br_2}$ α-bromotoluene (CH_2Br) $\xrightarrow{Mg}$ benzyl magnesium bromide (CH_2MgBr)

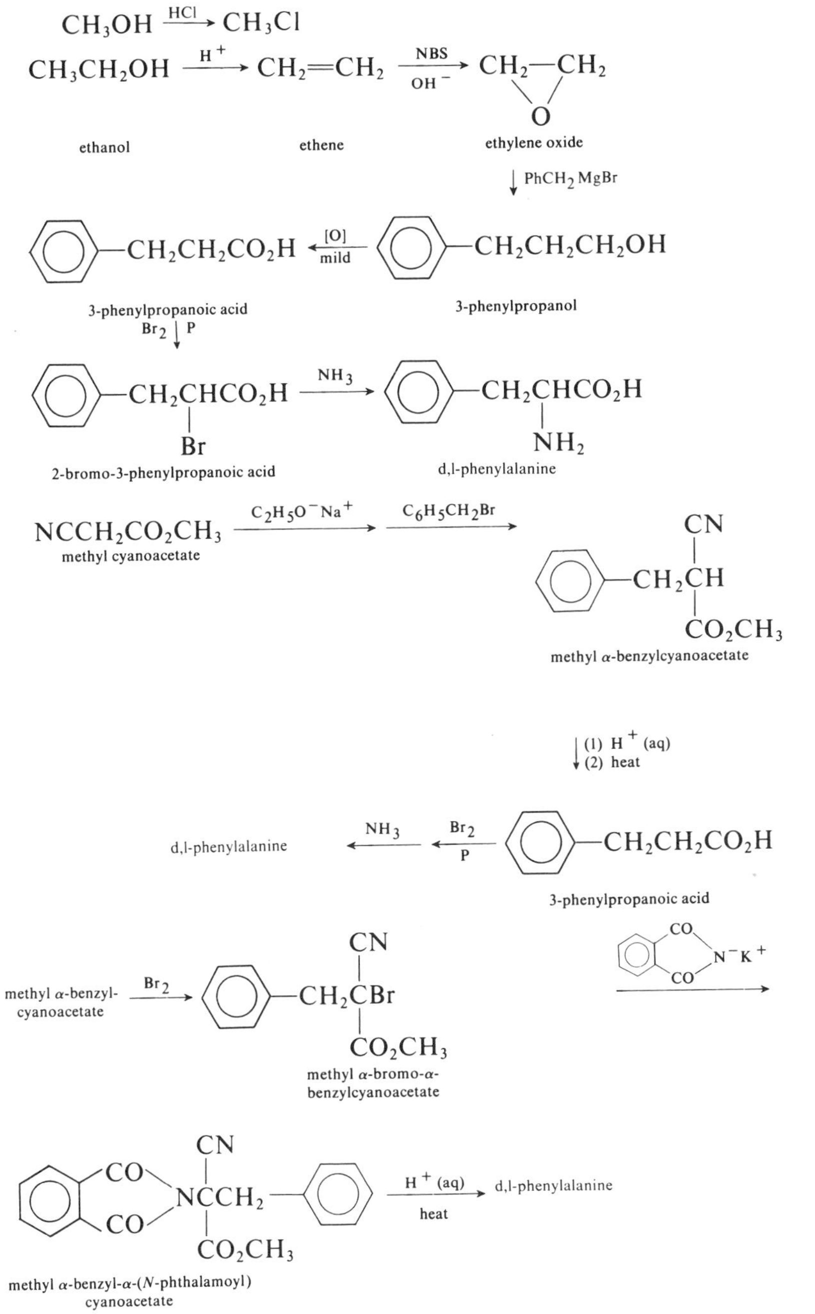

$$CH_3OH \xrightarrow{HCl} CH_3Cl$$

$$CH_3CH_2OH \xrightarrow{H^+} CH_2{=}CH_2 \xrightarrow[OH^-]{NBS} CH_2{-}CH_2$$

ethanol   ethene   ethylene oxide

$\downarrow$ PhCH$_2$MgBr

⬡—CH$_2$CH$_2$CO$_2$H $\xleftarrow[\text{mild}]{[O]}$ ⬡—CH$_2$CH$_2$CH$_2$OH

3-phenylpropanoic acid   3-phenylpropanol

Br$_2$ | P

⬡—CH$_2$CHCO$_2$H $\xrightarrow{NH_3}$ ⬡—CH$_2$CHCO$_2$H
           | |
           Br   NH$_2$

2-bromo-3-phenylpropanoic acid   d,l-phenylalanine

$$NCCH_2CO_2CH_3 \xrightarrow{C_2H_5O^-Na^+} \xrightarrow{C_6H_5CH_2Br}$$
methyl cyanoacetate

CN
|
⬡—CH$_2$CH
|
CO$_2$CH$_3$

methyl α-benzylcyanoacetate

$\downarrow$ (1) H$^+$ (aq)
$\downarrow$ (2) heat

d,l-phenylalanine $\xleftarrow{NH_3}$ $\xleftarrow[P]{Br_2}$ ⬡—CH$_2$CH$_2$CO$_2$H

3-phenylpropanoic acid

methyl α-benzyl-
cyanoacetate $\xrightarrow{Br_2}$

CN
|
⬡—CH$_2$CBr
|
CO$_2$CH$_3$

methyl α-bromo-α-
benzylcyanoacetate

⬡⟨CO—N$^-$K$^+$⟩
    CO

$\longrightarrow$

CN
|
⬡⟨CO⟩NCCH$_2$—⬡ $\xrightarrow[\text{heat}]{H^+ (aq)}$ d,l-phenylalanine
    CO |
                 CO$_2$CH$_3$

methyl α-benzyl-α-(N-phthalamoyl)
cyanoacetate

All these routes appear reasonable, but because of its fewer steps
and high-yield reactions, the direct malonic ester synthesis should
be tried first.

11.

a.
$$\text{C}_6\text{H}_5-\text{CH}_2\text{CHCO}_2\text{H} \xrightarrow[\text{P}_2\text{O}_5]{\text{NH}_3} \text{C}_6\text{H}_5-\text{CH}_2\text{CHCONH}_2$$

(with NH_2 substituent)

2-amino-3-phenylpropanamide

c.
$$\xrightarrow{(\text{CH}_3\text{CO})_2\text{O}} \text{C}_6\text{H}_5-\text{CH}_2\text{CHCO}_2\text{H}$$

(with NHCOCH_3 substituent)

N-acetyphenylalanine

d.
$$\xrightarrow{\text{HNO}_2} \text{C}_6\text{H}_5-\text{CH}_2\text{CHCO}_2\text{H}$$

(with OH substituent)

2-hydroxy-3-phenylpropanoic acid

starting material: $\text{C}_6\text{H}_5-\text{CH}_2\text{CHCO}_2\text{H}$ with NH_2

12. N terminal glycine. The dipeptides must be leucylleucine and glycylvaline. Tripeptide 2 can only be glycylglycylleucine. Thus, there must be a tetrapeptide: glycylglycylleucylleucine. To have the required dipeptide glycylvaline, tripeptide 1 must be leucyl-serylglycine. Thus, tripeptide 3 becomes serylglycylvaline.

$$\text{H}_2\text{NCH}_2\overset{\text{O}}{\overset{\|}{\text{C}}}-\text{NHCH}_2\overset{\text{O}}{\overset{\|}{\text{C}}}-\text{NHCH}\overset{\text{O}}{\overset{\|}{\text{C}}}-\text{NHCH}\overset{\text{O}}{\overset{\|}{\text{C}}}-\text{NHCH}\overset{\text{O}}{\overset{\|}{\text{C}}}-\text{NHCH}_2\overset{\text{O}}{\overset{\|}{\text{C}}}-\text{NHCH}\overset{\text{O}}{\overset{\|}{\text{C}}}\text{OH}$$

with side chains:
CH_2 / CH_2 / CH_2OH / $\text{CH(CH}_3)_2$
$(\text{CH}_3)_2\text{CH}$ / $\text{CH(CH}_3)_2$

|←——— 2 ———→|←——————— 1 ———————→|
  |←——— 4 ———→| |←——— 3 ———
    |←——— 5 ———

13. 1.
$$\text{C}_6\text{H}_5\text{CH}_2\text{O}_2\text{CCl} + \text{H}_2\text{NCHCO}_2\text{H} \longrightarrow$$

(with CH_2 / $\text{CH(CH}_3)_2$ side chain)

$$\text{C}_6\text{H}_5\text{CH}_2\text{O}_2\text{CNHCHCO}_2\text{H} \xrightarrow{\text{SOCl}_2}$$

(with CH_2 / $\text{CH(CH}_3)_2$ side chain)

$$\text{C}_6\text{H}_5\text{CH}_2\text{O}_2\text{CNHCHCOCl} \xrightarrow[\text{CH}_2\text{OH}]{\text{H}_2\text{NCHCO}_2\text{H}}$$

(with CH_2 / $\text{CH(CH}_3)_2$ side chain)

$$\text{CH}_2\text{O}_2\text{CNHCHCNHCHCO}_2\text{H} \xrightarrow{\text{SOCl}_2} \xrightarrow{\text{H}_2\text{NCH}_2\text{CO}_2\text{H}}$$

$$\xrightarrow[\text{Pd}]{\text{H}_2} \text{ tripeptide } 1$$

CHAPTER 11

3.

4. $\text{HO}_2\text{CCH}_2\text{CH}_2\text{CNH}\!-\!\bigcirc\!-\!\text{SO}_2\text{NH}\!-\!\big\langle\text{thiazole}\big\rangle$

$$\text{H}_2\text{CH}_2\text{CH}_2\text{CH}_2 \xrightarrow{\text{[O]}} \text{HO}_2\text{CCH}_2\text{CH}_2\text{CO}_2\text{H}$$

$$\xrightarrow{\text{P}_2\text{O}_5} \text{HO}_2\text{CCH}_2\text{CH}_2\text{CNH}\!-\!\bigcirc$$

$$\downarrow \text{ClSO}_3\text{H}$$

$$\xrightarrow[\text{H}_2\text{SO}_4]{\text{HNO}_3} \xrightarrow{\text{[H]}}$$

$$\text{HO}_2\text{CCH}_2\text{CH}_2\text{CNH}\!-\!\bigcirc\!-\!\text{SO}_2\text{Cl}$$

$$\searrow \overset{\text{NH}_2}{\underset{\text{thiazole}}{}}$$

$$\text{HO}_2\text{CCH}_2\text{CH}_2\text{CNH}\!-\!\bigcirc\!-\!\text{SO}_2\text{NH}\!-\!\big\langle\text{thiazole}\big\rangle$$

5.

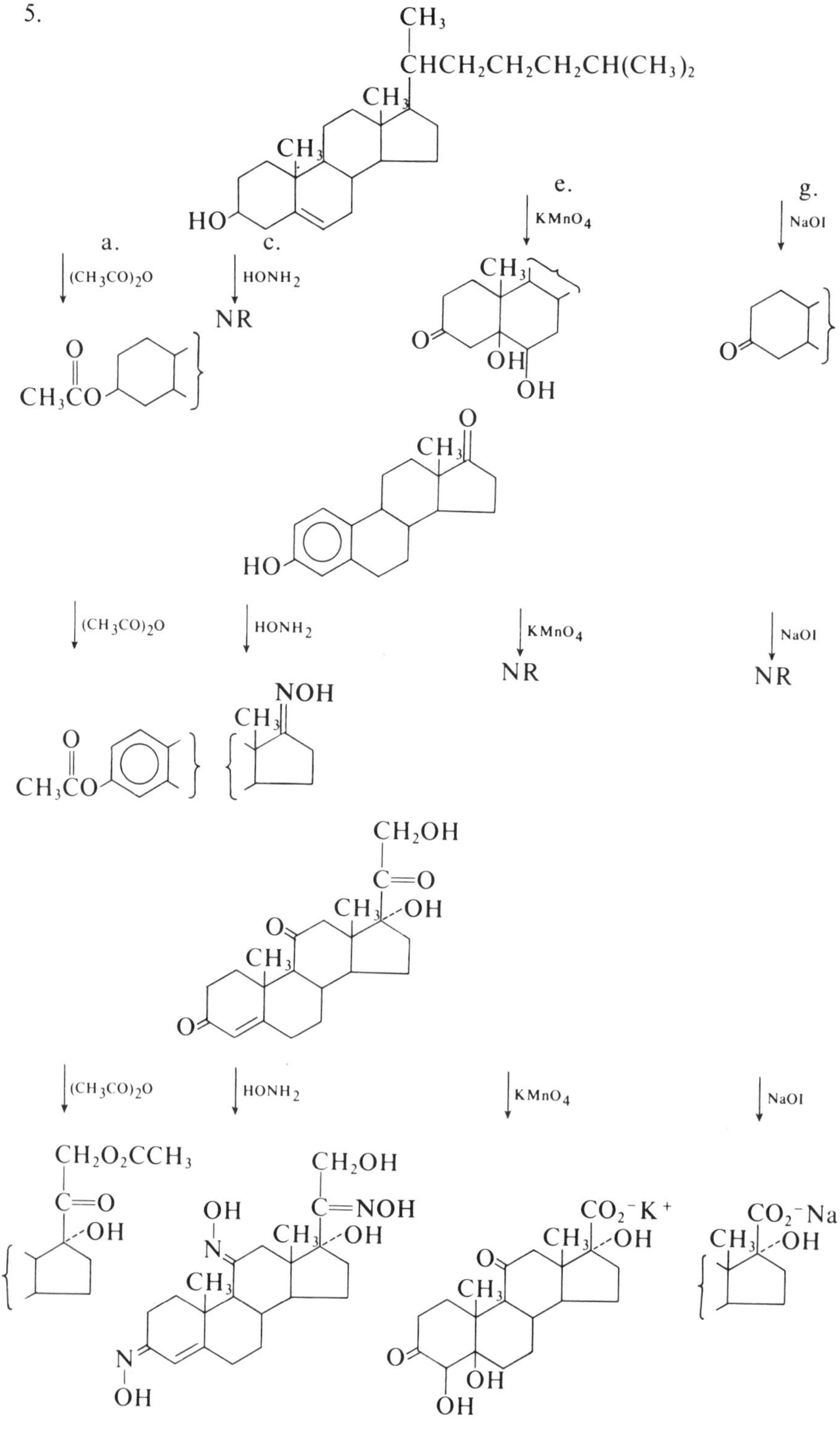

CH_3

$CHCH_2CH_2CH_2CH(CH_3)_2$

CH_3

CH_3

CH_3

HO

a.

c.

e.

g.

$(CH_3CO)_2O$

HONH$_2$

KMnO$_4$

NaOI

NR

O

CH_3CO

O

O

OH

OH

O

CH_3

OH

OH

CH_3

O

HO

$(CH_3CO)_2O$

HONH$_2$

KMnO$_4$

NaOI

NR

NR

O

CH_3CO

O

NOH

CH_3

CH_2OH

$C=O$

CH_3 OH

O

CH_3

O

$(CH_3CO)_2O$

HONH$_2$

KMnO$_4$

NaOI

$CH_2O_2CCH_3$

$C=O$

OH

CH_2OH

$C=NOH$

OH

CH_3 OH

OH

N

CH_3

N

OH

$CO_2^-K^+$

CH_3 OH

O

CH_3

O

OH

OH

CO_2^-Na

CH_3 OH

7.

$$\underset{\underset{\displaystyle CO_2C_2H_5}{|}}{\overset{\overset{\displaystyle CO_2C_2H_5}{|}}{CH^-Na^+}} \quad + \; BrCH_2CH_2CH_2Br \;\rightarrow$$

$$\underset{\underset{\displaystyle CO_2C_2H_5}{|}}{\overset{\overset{\displaystyle CO_2C_2H_5}{|}}{CHCH_2CH_2CH_2Br}} \quad \xrightarrow{Br_2}$$

$$\underset{\underset{\displaystyle CO_2C_2H_5}{|}}{\overset{\overset{\displaystyle CO_2C_2H_5}{|}}{BrCCH_2CH_2CH_2Br}} \quad \xrightarrow{CH_3NH_2} \quad \text{(pyrrolidine ring)} \; \begin{matrix} CH_3 \\ \diagdown \\ N \end{matrix} \begin{matrix} CO_2C_2H_5 \\ \diagup \\ CO_2C_2H_5 \end{matrix}$$

$$\downarrow \begin{array}{l} \text{(1) OH}^- \\ \text{(2) H}^+ \\ \text{(3) heat} \end{array}$$

$$\begin{matrix} CH_3 \\ \diagdown \\ N \end{matrix} \diagup CO_2H$$

hygrinic acid

CHAPTER 12

1.

$$(CH_3)_3\overset{+}{N}-CH=CH_2 \quad \xrightarrow{H^+} \quad \begin{matrix} (CH_3)_3\overset{+}{N}-\overset{+}{C}HCH_3 \\ \text{or} \\ (CH_3)_3\overset{+}{N}-CH_2CH_2^+ \end{matrix} \quad \xrightarrow{I^-}$$

$$\underset{\underset{\displaystyle I}{|}}{(CH_3)_3N^+CHCH_3} \qquad \text{or} \qquad (CH_3)_3N^+CH_2CH_2I$$

Markownikoff   anti-Markownikoff

The carbonium ion intermediate with the positive charges farthest apart should be the more favorable, which leads to the anti-Markownikoff product.

2.

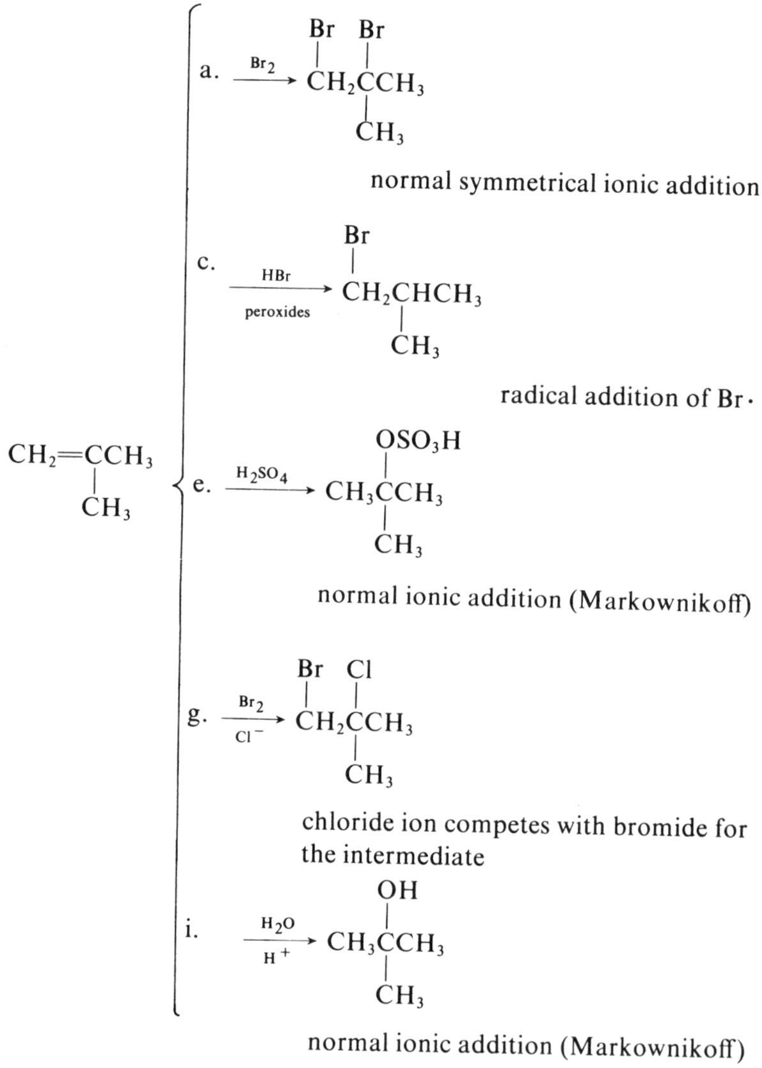

a. $\xrightarrow{Br_2}$ $CH_2\overset{\overset{\displaystyle Br}{|}}{\underset{\underset{\displaystyle CH_3}{|}}{C}}\overset{\displaystyle Br}{CH_3}$

normal symmetrical ionic addition

c. $\xrightarrow[\text{peroxides}]{\text{HBr}}$ $CH_2CH\overset{\overset{\displaystyle Br}{|}}{\underset{\underset{\displaystyle CH_3}{|}}{CH_3}}$

radical addition of Br·

$CH_2{=}\overset{\overset{\displaystyle }{}}{\underset{\underset{\displaystyle CH_3}{|}}{C}}CH_3$

e. $\xrightarrow{H_2SO_4}$ $CH_3\overset{\overset{\displaystyle OSO_3H}{|}}{\underset{\underset{\displaystyle CH_3}{|}}{C}}CH_3$

normal ionic addition (Markownikoff)

g. $\xrightarrow[\text{Cl}^-]{Br_2}$ $CH_2\overset{\overset{\displaystyle Br}{|}}{\underset{\underset{\displaystyle CH_3}{|}}{C}}\overset{\displaystyle Cl}{CH_3}$

chloride ion competes with bromide for the intermediate

i. $\xrightarrow[\text{H}^+]{H_2O}$ $CH_3\overset{\overset{\displaystyle OH}{|}}{\underset{\underset{\displaystyle CH_3}{|}}{C}}CH_3$

normal ionic addition (Markownikoff)

6.

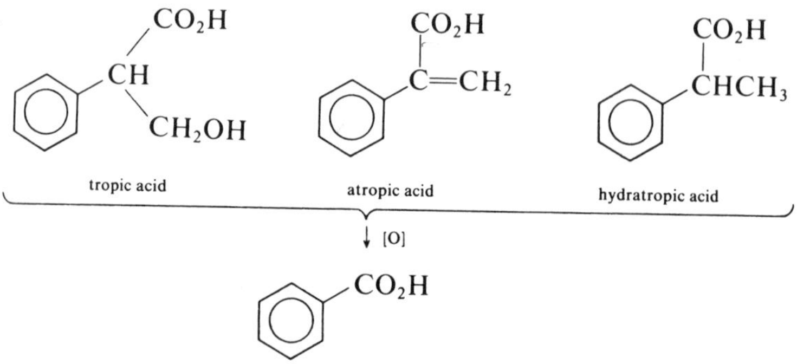

tropic acid

atropic acid

hydratropic acid

$\downarrow$ [O]

CO_2H

continuously conjugated ring and showing special stability by virtue of resonance.

Asymmetric induction	The effect the stereochemistry of a molecule has on the introduction of a new optically active center.
Atomic number	The position an atom occupies in the periodic system; it is equal to the numbers of protons and electrons for a neutral atom.
Atomic orbital	The region of space where an electron is most likely to be found.
Brønsted acidity	The theory that considers acids as protons.
Carbanion	A reactive intermediate that contains a carbon atom bearing a negative charge.
Carbonium ion	A reactive intermediate that contains a carbon atom bearing a positive charge.
Catalyst	A material that influences a reaction by altering the activation energy; usually indicates the positive effect of promoting the reaction.
Chemical shift	The position of nmr absorptions, relative to a standard, indicating the type of proton involved.
Composition	The number and kind of atoms present in a molecule, i.e., the molecular formula.
Condensation	A two-step reaction in which an initial addition is followed by the elimination of some small molecule such as water.

Configuration	The spatial arrangement of atoms in an optically active molecule.
Conformation	The spatial arrangement of atoms involved in σ bonding.
Conjugate acid or base	Compounds related by the addition or removal of a proton.
Conjugation	A system of at least four atoms whose Lewis structures possess alternating double and single bonds.
Constitution	The sequence of atoms in a molecule, i.e., the structural formula.
Coordinate covalence	A covalent bond involving two electrons donated by a single atom.
Covalence	Bonding resulting from the sharing of two electrons, one supplied by each of the atoms.
Delocalization	The ability of a system (usually conjugated) to spread electrons over a larger number of atoms.
Denaturation	The irreversible loss of properties often suffered by proteins when subjected to nonphysiological conditions.
Derivative	A molecule of known structure prepared from an unknown compound as an aid in identification.
Diastereomer	Non-mirror image stereoisomers.
Electronegativity	The affinity an atom has for electrons.
Electrophile	An electron-poor species that will react at a center of high electron density.
Elimination	A reaction involving the loss of a collection of atoms from two ad-

	jacent atoms and leading to unsaturation.
Emulsion	A fine dispersion of two immiscible liquids that shows little tendency toward recombination of the dispersed phase.
Enantiomers	Two optically active materials of opposite configuration, i.e., an object-mirror image pair.
Endothermic	A reacting system that absorbs heat from its surroundings.
Epimers	Diastereomers which differ in configuration at only one carbon atom; in carbohydrates it is taken as C-2.
Equilibrium	A system showing no net change in composition because the formation of products and their reversion to starting material are proceeding at the same rate.
Equivalent weight	The amount of a substance that will undergo a chemical change with some specified amount of a standard material; usually refers to 1.008 g or 1 mole of protons.
Exothermic	A reacting system that gives off heat to its surroundings.
Fragmentation pattern	A plot of intensity versus the mass-to-charge ratio of ions formed in a mass spectrometer, i.e., a mass spectrum.
Functional group	A collection of atoms that shows a characteristic set of chemical properties in a large number of related compounds.
Geometric stereoisomers	Diastereomers that result from hindered rotation of bonds such as alkenes and ring compounds.

Glycolysis	The enzymatic breakdown of glucose or other carbohydrates.
Homologs	Compounds having the same functional group(s) and differing from each other by one or more methylene groups.
Hybridization	The process of combining orbitals to make more efficient use of their properties.
Hydrogen bond	The interaction of a hydrogen atom attached to an electronegative atom with an electron rich atom in the same or another molecule.
Hydrophilic	A substance that is attracted to water.
Hydrophobic	A substance that is repelled by water.
Inductive effect	The transmission of charge in a molecule or through space by virtue of the electronegativity of atoms.
Intermediate	An arrangement of atoms found at a potential energy minimum between reactants and products.
In vivo-in vitro	Terms used to describe processes taking place in a living organism or outside of it respectively.
Ionic bond	An extreme case of the polar covalent bond where the difference in electronegativity of the atoms is so great one of them has lost control of its donated electron to the other.
Isomers	Compounds with the same molecular formula that differ in the spatial arrangement of the atoms.

LCAO	An approximate method of forming a molecular orbital where the atomic orbitals are simply added together.
Lewis acid and base	A theory that describes an acid as having an empty orbital available for bonding and a base as having an unshared pair of electrons.
Lewis structure	A representation of bonding that uses the atomic symbol as the nucleus and all nonvalence electrons. The valence electrons (and bonds) are shown as small marks such as dots or asterisks.
Mass action law	The principle that the rate of a chemical reaction is directly proportional to the concentration of the reactants.
Mechanism	A description of the path by which reactants become products.
Metabolism	The sum of the chemical processes involved in maintaining a living organism.
Molecular ion	That fragment in a mass spectrum where the substance being examined has lost 1 electron.
Molecular orbital	A combination of atomic orbitals where the two electrons are associated with both atoms involved in the bond formed.
Mutarotation	The process of converting either anomer of a saccharide to an equilibrium mixture through the open chain form.
Nucleophile	An electron rich species that will react at a center of low electron density.

Overlap	The interaction of orbitals combining to form a covalent bond.
Oxidation	The loss of electrons and the increase in oxidation number.
Physiological conditions	The condition of temperature, pH, ionic strength, etc., found in living tissue.
Pi bond	The overlap of two p electrons.
Plane-polarized light	Visible radiation with the vibration restricted to a single plane.
Polar covalence	A covalent bond with unequal sharing of the electrons.
Polarization	The shift of electrons caused by some external center of high or low electron density.
Pyrolysis	Strong heating resulting in the thermal cleavage of bonds.
Quantization	The principle that the electronic energy levels of atoms and molecules can have only certain specific values.
Racemate	A mixture of equal numbers of enantiomers.
Radical	A reactive intermediate having an unpaired electron.
Reaction coordinate	The potential energy path taken by a reactant being converted to product.
Reagent	One of the reactants; usually taken as material not under direct study.
Rearrangement	A fundamental change in the structural formula leading to an isomeric arrangement.
Reduction	The gain of electrons and the decrease in oxidation number.

Resolution	The process of separating enantiomers.
Resonance	The ability of certain molecules, ions, or radicals to be represented by more than one Lewis structure.
Resonance effect	The transmission of charge through a conjugated system, especially an aromatic one.
Resonance energy	The magnitude of enhanced stability of a system over an analogous nonresonating system.
Resonance frequency	The energy where absorption takes place in the various forms of spectroscopy.
Resonance hybrid	The "true" structure of a substance that shows resonance.
Sigma bond	A covalent bond that contains some amount of s character.
Substitution	A reaction involving some reactive species replacing a group or atom originally bonded to the substrate.
Substrate	A reactant; usually taken as the species under study.
System—open and closed	The total material and energy under investigation that may or may not be gaining and/or losing these factors to its surroundings.
Tautomers	Compounds that are markedly different structurally, but are in equilibrium with each other.
Transannular interaction	The effect substituents on opposite sides of a ring have on one another because of the geometry of the cyclic system.
Transition state	A potential energy maximum along the path between reactant and product.

Zwitterion A dipolar ion resulting from the presence of an acidic and a basic group in the same molecule.

Index

SUMMARY OF ORGANIC NOMENCLATURE

Functional Group	Type of Compound	IUPAC	
		Suffix	Prefix
R —N R′	tertiary amine	-amine	amino-
R—OH	alcohol	-ol	hydroxy-
Ar—OH	phenol	-phenol	—
—O—	ether	—	alkoxy- or aryloxy
—NO₂	nitro compound	—	nitro-
—C—C— *	alkane (saturated hydrocarbons)	-ane	—
C=C	alkene (olefins)	-ene	—
—C≡C—	alkyne (acetylenes)	-yne	—
(CH₂)ₙ *	cyclic hydrocarbon (saturated)	-ane	cyclo-
—X F Cl Br I	halide	— — — — —	fluoro- chloro- bromo- iodo-

*Not a functional group, but included for completeness.